Elements
of
Cartography

Elements

of

Cartography

ARTHUR H. ROBINSON

Professor of Geography
University of Wisconsin

John Wiley & Sons, Inc.   *Chapman & Hall, Ltd.*
NEW YORK   LONDON

Original illustrations drawn by

JAMES J. FLANNERY

Lecturer in Geography
Wharton School
University of Pennsylvania

SECOND PRINTING, JANUARY, 1958

Library of Congress Catalog Card Number: 52–14188

Preface

Cartography, according to the late Max Eckert, the great German cartographer, is a mixture of science and art. It is concerned on the one hand with problems of exactitude susceptible of precise treatment and varying according to the laws of mathematics and geometry. On the other hand a map is made to be looked at, and in this respect it is one of the visual arts. Add to these aspects the fact that no cartographer can intelligently represent earth relationships unless he "knows whereof he speaks" geographically, and it becomes apparent that a cartographer must combine in some fashion the abilities of the geographer, the mathematician, and the artist. Of these talents, the most important is that of the geographer, for out of the number of decisions a cartographer must make when drawing a map, the vast majority are of a geographical nature.

Training as a geographer will not alone, as some have maintained, produce a cartographer. One must also learn to present his geographical knowledge so that it will be intelligible to others. For this he must learn cartographic symbolism, draw upon the graphic arts for principles of presentation, and look to mathematics for methods and for principles of accuracy. Except for the utilization of the more advanced techniques and concepts, the command of mathematics and graphic arts necessary to the training of the geographical cartographer is relatively limited. It is perfectly possible (as has been demonstrated repeatedly) to learn the principles of the proper employment of projections or mathematically based symbols with little or no mathematical background; and for most black and white and flat color maps the cartographer need only become familiar with the basic elements of visual presentation.

The preparation of a textbook in the field of cartography is difficult because there have been few previous attempts in any way comparable; consequently one does not have a wealth of pedagogical procedures and ideas from which to select. Part of the reason for this lack lies in the general disinterest in cartography in colleges and universities in the United States until comparatively recently. Fortunately the situation has changed. Cartography as a profession and as an academic subject has been gaining ground for several decades, and World War II sent interest in it to an all-time high. This interest, which is steadily increasing, has resulted both in many new techniques and in a better understanding of the place of cartography in the academic curriculum.

Much of the cartography taught in the United States is appropriately done in geography departments. Their concern with the making of maps is generally, although not entirely, for those of smaller scales. Such large-scale geographic field mapping as is undertaken is more a research or inventory technique than it is cartography and should be separately taught. Geography having taken unto itself the responsibility for a large share of cartography has thereby assumed the further duty of providing instruction for the interested student in other fields. These students, like many geography majors, are commonly less concerned with becoming practicing cartographers than they are with learning how maps are made and how to use properly and intelligently the maps they see in books, periodicals, and atlases.

This book is, then, primarily designed as a textbook for a first course in cartography for graduate and undergraduate students majoring in geography or allied social and natural sciences. The approach is toward cartography as an intellectual art and science rather than as a subject primarily consisting of drafting and drawing procedures. Cartography is a broad profession and has many facets that are interesting, to say the least. It has been a difficult task indeed to decide what not to include in a textbook of this kind. Every rubric in the field from projections to terrain representation has manifold old and new concepts, materials, procedures, and applications ranging, for example, from Murdoch's conics to the flat polar quartic authalic projection and from the appearance of topography on a radar scope to relief models made of plastic. I have tried to encompass the items of importance but have made no attempt to mention or cite all the developments past or present. Such an effort would have produced an encyclopedia, not a textbook. The student desirous of ranging afield can do so with the aid of the Bibliography. The coverage of the book has, therefore, been limited by those elements that can appropriately be investigated in a survey course, leaving for later courses the more advanced aspects of theory and technique.

A definite attempt has been made to restrict the textual presentation of the various elements to a minimum in order to promote the indispensable classroom and laboratory discussion. It is expected that the instructor will supplement the text with lectures fitted to his particular group of students and the type of course he wishes to teach. Specific instruction on varieties of methods and media for drafting and the more complex techniques, e.g., land-form drawing, have been held to a minimum, for they can better be demonstrated and discussed in the freedom of the classroom or laboratory than on the pages of a book.

It is a pleasure to make acknowledgments in an undertaking such as this. I should particularly like to acknowledge my debt to Professor Vernor C. Finch, of the University of Wisconsin, in whose class I first became interested in cartography as an art and science, and learned that there was something more to it than mere manual dexterity. Professor Finch's cartographic skill, his analytical attitude toward this and other subjects, and his subsequent personal encouragement are largely responsible for my having initially chosen to work in the field of cartography. Likewise, I am greatly indebted to Professor Guy-Harold Smith, of the Ohio State University, who, in addition to his many professional encouragements, has read the entire manuscript and has made many valuable suggestions and criticisms. My debt to such cartographic stalwarts as M. Eckert, M. A. Tissot, K. Zöppritz, E. Raisz, J. K. Wright, O. S. Adams, and others will be readily recognized by the professional reader. A number of persons read all, or portions, of the manuscript and made useful suggestions. Professor James A. Barnes, of the University of Georgia, has been especially helpful with respect to the chapter on projections. Many of my students have, perhaps unwittingly, contributed heavily toward this undertaking, for they have constituted an invaluable sounding board for considerable experimentation in methods of approach and content.

The task of illustration has been made a pleasure for a number of reasons. First, Professor James J. Flannery, of the University of Pennsylvania, interpreted my ideas with uncommon dispatch and skill and contributed many suggestions for improvement. Much assistance in making illustrations available has been rendered by Richard Edes Harrison, Dr. Carl Mapes of Rand McNally and Company, Myron T. Monsen of Monsen-Chicago Incorporated, and others too numerous to mention. Permission to reproduce illustrations in books, periodicals, and catalogues has been cordially forthcoming without exception, and the sources are noted in the appropriate legends. The American Geographical Society of New York and Mrs. Wilma Fairchild, the editor of *The Geographical Review*, have been especially helpful. My wife, in addition to providing indispensable encouragement, read much of the manuscript in draft, and all of it in final form, and made many worthwhile editorial proposals.

ARTHUR H. ROBINSON

Madison, Wisconsin
February, 1953

Contents

1

The Art and Science of Cartography

1 Maps, Indispensable Tools

Man is so small and he is tied so closely to his earth habitat that he must employ, among other techniques, that of cartography in order to see the broader spatial relationships that exist in his complex world. The cartographic technique enables him to rise, so to speak, above his immediate range of vision and contemplate the salient features of larger areas. A large-scale map of a small region, depicting its land forms, drainage, settlement patterns, roads, geology, or a host of other geographic and economic distributions, provides him with the knowledge of the relationships necessary to carry on his works intelligently. The building of a road, a house, a flood-control system, or almost any other constructive endeavor requires prior mapping. At a smaller scale, maps of soil erosion, land use, population character, climates, income, and so on, are indispensable to understanding the problems and potentialities of an area. At the smallest scale, maps of the whole earth indicate generalizations and relationships of broad earth patterns with which we may intelligently consider the course of events past, present, and future.

To attempt to catalog with precision the infinite number of kinds and uses of maps is an impossible task. Anything that man can observe, tangible or otherwise, can be mapped in its two- or three-dimensional distribution on the earth. The uses of maps may vary from that of the historian plotting and analyzing the routes of Marco Polo or Alexander in order to evaluate their cultural influences to the engineer analyzing the drainage characteristics of a portion of a city to determine the run-off potential in order to supply adequate storm sewers. The scales may vary from a page-size map of the world presenting airline routes focusing on Chicago to a foot-square insurance map of a city block including the building in which the airlines map was made. The most meaningful listing of varieties of maps is one based on utility, and many such catalogs have been attempted. They include the standard divisions such as topographic maps, nautical charts, economic maps, historical maps, and other broad use categories. But they all fail to impress on the reader that all maps are related, being of the earth; and that uses, scales, varieties, and sizes all shade, imperceptibly, one into another.

Truly, so far as modern maps of the earth are concerned, the "sky is the limit."

2 The Beginnings of Cartography

In ancient times the limits of cartography were apparently very narrow. Islanders

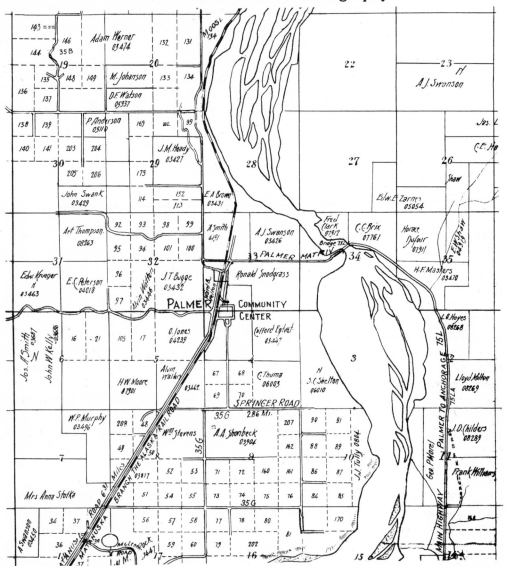

FIG. 1. Portion of a cadastral map showing property lines.

of the Southern seas are said to have constructed, at an early date, charts of reeds and sticks to record the relative positions of islands. Perhaps the oldest authentic map which survives is a record of some land holdings in Babylon. Certainly, the valley of the Nile was mapped at an early time in order to record property lines. Aside from the islanders' maps, and others like them, it is probable that the earliest maps were records of land ownership. That same kind of map still survives as one important use category of cartography. Today they are called cadastral maps, and they record land holdings the same way they did several thousand years ago. (See Fig. 1.) One of the principal uses of cadastral maps is to assess taxes, which may

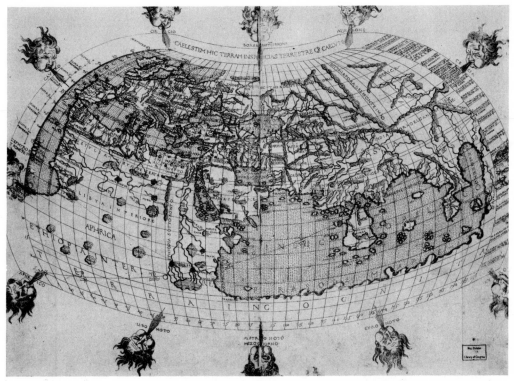

FIG. 2. One of "Ptolemy's" maps. His written works were "rediscovered" during the fifteenth century, but his maps had to be reconstructed from his directions. His world map was better than any other, even in the fifteenth century, a thousand years after its original construction. From the Library of Congress collection.

account for the fact that they have always been with us.

Not for some time after the birth of the local cadastral map did other kinds of maps develop. Maps of larger areas depended upon the collections of travelers' tales together with some rational thinking about the area beyond one's immediate surroundings. The spherical shape of the earth, close estimates of its size, and devices for plotting position on the spherical surface had all been reasoned into being by the time of Christ. The scholar Claudius Ptolemy gathered these and other ideas together and in the second century A.D. made a very respectable series of maps (see Fig. 2). He concerned himself with the problem of presenting the spherical surface of the earth on a flat piece of paper and recognized the inevitability of deformation in the process. Ptolemy, who lived and worked in Alexandria, Egypt, was probably the earliest real counterpart of the modern-day cartographer. Rather than surveying in the field he gathered his materials from divers sources, and leaned heavily on the excellent library facilities of Alexandria. In general he did what the modern cartographer does. Ptolemy was a *compiler* of small-scale maps of large areas, and he left to the *surveyor* the job of preparing large-scale maps of small areas.

After Ptolemy, cartography gradually declined. A thousand years later this art and science had reverted to the status of

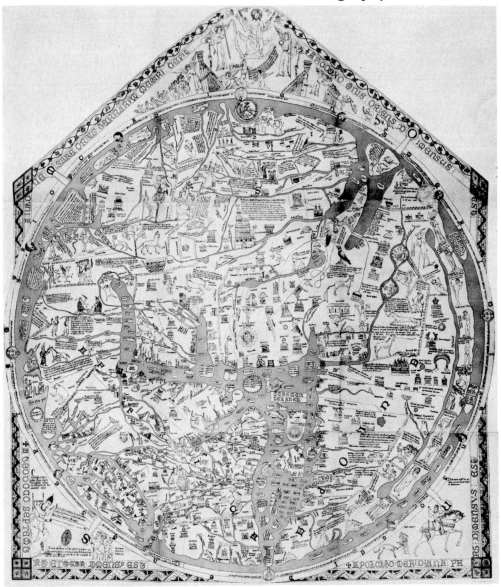

FIG. 3. The Hereford world map. This map made in the thirteenth century illustrates the degree to which cartography had degenerated from the time of Ptolemy, a thousand years earlier. The map is oriented with east at the top and Jerusalem at the center. From the Library of Congress collection.

fancy and imagination (see Fig. 3). Mythical kings and kingdoms, beasts, and places on a flat earth replaced the careful cartographic determinations of the Greek and early Roman periods. There was, however, one bright cartographic light in the comparative darkness of the period, viz., the sailing charts prepared to accompany the sailing directions, or *peripli*, which apparently existed in considerable numbers.

These charts, called *portolani* or harbor-finding charts, were the products of the experience of a large amount of navigation and coastwise sailing in the Mediterranean and adjacent areas. They were remarkably accurate in their outlines and shapes of bounding coasts of the seas, but unfortunately their accuracy did not seem to penetrate to maps of the land until toward the end of the Dark Ages. Although many of them must have been made, none earlier than the fourteenth century has survived. Undoubtedly they were jealously guarded by their owners, which may account for their rarity.

With the discovery and copying of Ptolemy's writings and maps, after they had lain dormant for a thousand years, a new interest in cartography developed along with the general rebirth of culture in western Europe. The Age of Discovery, the monumental achievements of Columbus, Magellan, and others, kindled such an interest that map publishing soon became a lucrative calling, and by the sixteenth century the profession was generally in good standing and well supported, albeit its products were still far from being first-class examples of objective scientific thought. One of the circumstances that contributed greatly to the rapid advance of cartography was the invention, in Europe, of printing, which made possible the reproduction of maps in numerous copies. Previously, each map had had to be laboriously hand drawn. Great map-publishing houses such as Mercator, Blaeu, Hondius, and others in Holland and France rose and flourished.

Their maps were still little more than reference maps containing hardly anything other than coastlines, rivers, cities, and occasional crude indications of mountains. Fancy and intricate craftsmanship was popular, and the maps were richly embellished with scrolls, compass roses, and drawings of men, animals, and ships. Except for religious, and some navigational data, the mapping of any geographic information beyond what we call, today, base data was unknown. The mapping of other distributions had to wait for more accurate internal surveys and especially for the inquiring minds who would want such maps.

3 The Early Modern Period of Cartography

The dawning of the eighteenth century saw the beginnings of a new and fresh attitude among all thinkers and investigators, including the cartographers. For the first time since the ending of the Greek era, accuracy and the scientific method became fashionable. This attitude, replacing the dogmatic and unscientific attitude which was more or less dominant during the long Dark Ages, made itself evident in a number of ways. Feverish activity was expended on the problem of the measurement of the earth; the degrees of latitude were recalculated; Harrison's chronometer for longitude determination was perfected in England in 1765; and there were many other evidences of curiosity about the earth. But perhaps the most notable and optimistic cartographic trend was the realization by many that their fund of knowledge about the land behind the coastlines was quite erroneous. Even the administrators and rulers of countries, particularly in Europe, became aware that it was impossible to govern (or fight wars) without adequate maps of the land.

This led to the establishment of the great national topographic surveys of Europe, such as France in 1817 and England in 1791, and the relatively rapid production thereafter, for the first time, of the topographic kind of map. The problem of representing land forms arose, and, almost as quickly, devices such as the hachure and contour were developed. By the last half of the nineteenth century a large portion of Europe had been covered by these maps. Such maps were still, however, expensive to make and did not have a wide distribution. But they were the foundation upon which all future cartography of the land was to be based. It was to be expected that, as topographic maps became available, compilations of smaller-scale maps of diverse kinds would grow from them. Such was the case.

Several factors influenced the growth of the compiled map during the nineteenth century. In addition to the one mentioned above, a new reproduction process, lithography, was developed. It made possible, for the first time, the relatively easy and inexpensive duplication of drawings. Far more important than any technical advance, however, was the branching out of science into a number of separate fields, in contrast to its previous state which was a kind of all-inclusive complex of physical science, philosophy, and general geography. To be sure, the more exact sciences such as physics, chemistry, mathematics, and astronomy had progressed far; but the physical scientists who were preoccupied with one aspect of the earth, such as the geologist, meteorologist, and biologist, as well as the host of investigators whom we now call by the general term "social scientist" were just getting under way. Especially did they need maps; and in general their needs were for the smaller-scale maps, the compiled maps, of the land areas.

By the beginning of the twentieth century this search for knowledge about the earth had led to remarkable strides in cartography. Many investigations had been made into projection problems; the colored lithographic map was fairly common; a serious proposal to map the earth at the comparatively large scale of 1:1,000,000 had been made; and, of particular impor-

tance, some great map-publishing houses such as Bartholomew in Great Britain and Justus Perthes in Germany had come into being. The discipline most concerned with cartography, geography, was beginning a rapid growth. The way was open for the small-scale, compiled map for use as an investigative and teaching tool.

4   Twentieth Century Cartography

During the past fifty years or so, cartography and maps have advanced more technically and have become more widely used than at any other period. It is probably correct to say that the number of maps made in the last half century is greater than the production during all previous time, even if we do not count the millions made for military purposes. Almost everyone in the United States has handled numerous maps; maps are frequently in the newspapers; atlases have enjoyed a wide sale; and a comforting proportion of the population now knows the meaning of the words "cartography" and "cartographic." The profession is again attaining a position comparable to that which it held during the period of Flemish and French dominance in the sixteenth and seventeenth centuries. Its position is on somewhat sounder ground now for it has a more universal appeal.

Several factors have combined to promote this phenomenal growth. One of the most important is the fact that two world wars have occurred. Both wars have required vast numbers of maps for military purposes. Particularly the second world war with its requirements of rapid movement and air activity made necessary literally millions of maps. War-time travels and military activities all over the globe created a demand for information from the general public which was supplied by a flood of small atlases, separate maps, and newspaper and magazine maps. War clearly has been a great influence in the course of cartographic history, and the last war was probably the most influential. Since 1940 several maps of the entire world have been made at a scale of 16 miles to 1 inch. The far-flung theaters of activity, new routes, new relationships, and the necessity for world-wide understanding created feverish activity in all phases of cartography.

That so much mapping activity was actually possible was the result of a number of factors that entered the cartographic scene early in the present century or late in the last.

Although lithography was much cheaper and easier than engraving as a process for reproducing maps, it was still highly technical and required considerable skill. Consequently, the invention of photography and its union with the lithographic process late in the nineteenth century provided, at last, an easy and relatively inexpensive means of reproducing an original drawing on any substance. From then on advances in the photo-lithographic and photo-engraving fields have been rapid and continuous. Today, although costs are considerable, the high-speed, multiple-color presses are capable of handling almost any kind of cartographic problem. Consequently, reproduction is no longer the fundamental problem to the cartographer that it once was.

Of equal significance to modern cartography is the development of the airplane. It has operated as a catalyst in bringing about the demand for more mapping, and at the same time the airplane has made it possible. The need for smaller-scale coverage of larger areas, such as the aeronautical chart, promoted larger-scale mapping of the unknown areas. Furthermore the earth seen from the vantage point of an airplane in flight is like a map, and those who fly above the earth develop an interest in maps.

The increasing complexity of modern life with its attendant pressures and contentions for available resources has made necessary increasingly detailed studies of land utilization, soil characteristics, disease migrations, population and settlement distributions, and numberless other social and economic factors. The geographer, preeminently, as well as the historian, economist, agriculturalist, and others of the social and applied physical science fields, has found the map a useful and often indispensable aid to his research and its presentation.

The map is a promoter of business, and it is seen in increasing numbers in advertising; and the demand for market and resource information encourages distribution mapping for commercial purposes. The familiar and excellent road map, standard equipment of any driver in the United States, is prepared and distributed free in such quantities that every year each adult in this country could have his own personal copy.

The quantity of maps and mapping and the diversity of cartographic subject matter is indeed staggering. As society becomes even more complicated, it is to be expected that the demand in future years will increase. Certainly there are numerous subjects and areas of which we do not have adequate or, in many cases, any maps. The new processes and techniques of making maps, together with the wealth of compilation material from air photography, census activity, and other outgrowths of modern organized society, make the field of cartography a broad and always interesting endeavor.

5 Present Divisions of Cartography

As must be apparent from the preceding, cartography has in recent years developed rapidly and has branched out, as it were, into a number of somewhat separate kinds of activity. It is a perfectly natural indication of growth, for as each science or art has developed it has separated into various specialized divisions.

The entire field of map making is usually thought of as consisting of two distinct phases. The first is concerned with the detailed large-scale topographic mapping of the land or charting of the sea. The remaining large proportion of cartographic activity is less clearly defined, being usually thought of merely as smaller-scale, special cartography, or simply as *not* the first mentioned. Within each of these two broad categories there is also considerable specialization such as may occur among the survey, drafting, and reproduction phases of making a topographic map. All divisions and activities shade one into another, and it is to be expected that sharp compartmentalization rarely occurs.

Notwithstanding the obvious overlapping there is no doubt that large numbers of cartographers are concerned with smaller-scale map making and are generally quite separate from those who do survey, topographic mapping, and nautical charting. Although not strictly exclusive, the one group makes maps from field or air survey and is concerned with such things as the shape of the earth, height of sea level, land elevations, and exact and detailed locational information. Generally speaking, this group, which includes the great national survey organizations, national land offices, and most military mapping organizations, makes the basic maps from which the other group starts.

The second category of cartographers does not usually make maps from surveys but, using the detailed maps, compiles from them the basic data required and then proceeds to add relationships, generalizations, and a host of other kinds of material. To this group belong the geographers, historians, economists, and many others of the social and physical sciences who are seeking to understand and interpret the social and physical complex on the earth's surface. The subject matter and the base material is unlimited. The climatic map, the synoptic chart, the agricultural map, the traffic-flow map, the political map, and many others all are products that belong to this second group.

6 The Map Data

As has been pointed out, almost any kind of information is mappable. From this array of possibilities it may be questioned whether any valid generalization can be made concerning the kinds of information with which a cartographer deals. Although there are no limits to the possibilities, in practice the map maker finds that the entire gamut is rarely approached and that most of his concern is with recurring kinds of information.

By its very nature any map is the presentation of spatial relationships. Therefore the cartographer's first problem is to transform the surface of the sphere which curves away in every direction from every point (called the allside curved surface) into a surface that does not curve in any direction at any point (a plane). Such a radical transformation introduces some unavoidable changes in the directions, distances, areas, and shapes from the way they appear on the spherical surface. A system of transformation from the spherical to the plane surface is called a projection, and the choice, utilization, and construction of map projections is of perennial concern to the cartographer. Properly approached, the study of projections becomes a fascinating endeavor for it involves, in a sense, the weighing and balancing of the assets and liabilities of a surprisingly large number of possibilities. The theoretical and actual derivation of many systems of projection are undertakings that require considerable mathematical competence, as would be expected. Their utilization and very often their construction requires, however, little more than arithmetic, some very elementary geometry, and, most necessary, some clear thinking.

Of equally universal concern is what is usually called "base data." This ordinarily consists of coastlines, rivers, boundaries, and occasionally settlements, roads, or other outstanding features. On this base are plotted the materials that prompted the making of the map. Of course, some small-scale maps such as general atlas maps are primarily detailed base or reference maps alone, and consequently they seldom emphasize or portray any special information. The base data serve the very important function of providing orientation and background for the other information being presented. It is useless to provide considerable detail in the mapping of a distribution, such as vegetation, if the reader has no base data with which to correlate it visually. The base information, of course, varies from one map to the next and must be selected especially for the purpose at hand. This selection, together with the compilation and representation of the particular base information desired, constitutes the second major portion of the cartographer's concern with map data.

The third kind of map material with which the cartographer works is that which prompted the making of the map. As noted earlier, it can consist of almost anything from election returns to soil constituents. Upon a clear understanding of its significance and of the possible inferences that may be derived from the readers' viewing it depend the selection and employment of the base materials and the projection. Usually, substantive material may be modified or presented in numerous ways. Only the cartographer who is familiar with his subject matter, and who at the same time allows his imagination to roam widely, will be able to determine the most desirable form and manner by which to serve this, the main, course.

7 The Techniques of Cartography

The means whereby the map data are graphically portrayed, or, in other words, the techniques and media of representation, make a considerable list. In the early days of cartography there was little choice of ways and means of presenting data or of the media with which to work. The methods of producing inks and colors and the techniques of draftsmanship were known only to a few, and they were sufficiently difficult so that great skill was necessary to produce an acceptable map. Today the cartographer is fortunate indeed, for, as in most other mechanical and technical fields, great advances have been made toward the perfection of devices, papers, and other aids to map making. In addition drafting has become a kind of standard technique in a number of activities, and manual skill in drawing is widespread.

The actual drawing is only a portion of the technical effort that goes into the making of a map. That part of the effort might be referred to as the mechanical phase of the technique. Considerably more important is the skill with which the cartographer devises ways and means of organizing the data and of fitting the data to the media, and the general manipulation of the various substantive elements of the map in order to have the result equal the expectations. Unfortunately, these two aspects are often confused to the end that we mistakenly assume that a "nicely drawn" map is a good map. Likewise, a skillfully planned map may be depreciated because of poor drafting. Both good planning and good execution are, of course, indispensable to excellent cartography, but they are quite different in regard to the training and skills required.

Drafting is an honorable calling, and a good, versatile cartographic draftsman is rare enough to command great respect. He is fully familiar with all the tools and with the use of the various media such as lettering, screens, and different kinds of papers. He is a good freehand letterer and is capable of using all the various pens, brushes, inks, and paints. There is no other trade quite comparable to that of cartographic drafting. The judgment and skills required make it always interesting, and there is considerable creative pleasure in completing a well-drawn map. On the other hand, the act of drafting a map is no more cartography than typing is authorship. The analogy is not strictly correct for the draftsman, if good, is usually given some latitude in the execution of the cartographer's desires.

It is important to understand the above relation between drafting and cartography. There has been and still is a tendency to think of the two as synonymous. Many draftsmen think of themselves as cartographers, and many cartographers, who are themselves good draftsmen, feel that drafting ability is indispensable to the cartographer. There is no question that drafting is a desirable and useful ability, but it is by no means indispensable. A lack of manual skill need deter no one from entering the field of cartography, and particularly it should not deter the geographer and other physical and social scientists from learning the principles of graphic expression. Since learning by doing is one of the better ways of gaining a well-founded understanding of any endeavor it is to be expected that one who would learn cartography should also learn the elements of drafting. If he finds that he is deficient in the manual skills he should in no way be discouraged. Trying the techniques and

studying their difficulties and possibilities will better prepare him to direct a more skillful draftsman.

There are some drafting procedures that are better done by the cartographer if he is to work with certain kinds of maps. For example, the drawing of terrain as in a physiographic diagram must, except in unusual cases, be done by the cartographer who is planning and executing as he proceeds. The dotting of a dot map, which requires relatively little drafting skill but considerable geographic understanding, cannot be done by directing a draftsman, except in extraordinary circumstances. Similarly, the brushing on of colors in gradation with a wet brush or an airbrush must be done by the cartographer in most circumstances, not by the draftsman.

Probably as valid a reason as any for the would-be cartographer to learn at least the elements of drafting is that, in many cases, the research investigator must lay out preliminary plans for maps, and his job is much easier if he knows the limitations and possibilities of the drafting technique. Also, frequently the teacher or researcher must do his own elementary map drawing for slides and for professional papers because a competent draftsman is either unavailable or too expensive. In any case, the manual skills required for simple drafting are capable of attainment by most everyone. The rare person who cannot learn to use the ruling pen, triangle, and T-square need not be discouraged, for the art and science of cartography is based primarily on intellectual and visual skills, not on manual skills.

8   The Science of Cartography

The skills or techniques of the cartographer are based upon the findings of many scientists. These skills generally fall into two categories, intellectual or visual, depending upon whether their main function is to stimulate the reason or the visual sense of the map reader.

In the first category we find such cartographic activities as generalization or small-scale simplification. This is one of the most difficult of the cartographer's tasks, for, as was pointed out by one of the great German cartographers, "only a master of the subject can generalize well." This is one of the ways wherein cartography differs from drafting. If we are to draw a small-scale coastline we must know the characteristics of that coastline or at least the characteristics of that type of coastline. Similarly, if we are to generalize a river we must know if it is a dry-land or a humid-land stream, something of its meanderings, its volume, and other important factors which might make it distinctive from or in character with others of its nature. The selection of the important and the subordination or elimination of the nonessential factors of the map data require that the map maker be well trained in each of the fields in which he essays to prepare maps. He must apply logic in his approach to projections, generalizations, line characterizations, and so on, and in this respect he is a kind of practical scientist much like an engineer. He must study the characteristics of his building materials and know the ways and means of fitting them together so that the end product will convey the correct intellectual meaning to the reader.

Of equal, and sometimes greater, importance are the visual relationships inherent in this form of expression. People, or map readers, think and react in certain ways to visual stimuli. With knowledge of the laws governing these reactions the cartographer can design his product to fit these habits. A great many principles of visual design have been established in recent years, and the cartographer cannot afford to ignore these findings. The selection of dot size for representing statistics and the colors and tones to be used in representing gradations of amount are examples of questions to be answered by the characteristics of visibility as applied to symbols and constitute problems of visual logic.

The cartographer is scientific in other ways. One of the largest categories of information with which he works is that contained in other maps, and since he can hardly have first-hand familiarity with all places in the world he must be able to evaluate his source materials. This means that he must be familiar with the state of topographic mapping and its geodetic foundations. To supplement his map information he needs to be able to evaluate and rectify census data, air photographs, documentary materials, and a host of other kinds of sources.

Cartography is neither an experimental science in the sense that chemistry or physics are nor is it searching for truth in the manner of the social sciences. Nevertheless, it employs the scientific method in the form of reason and logic in constructing its products. Its principles are derived through the analysis of scientific data. It has its foundations in the sciences of geodesy, geography, and psychology. In the sense that it is based on sound principles and seeks to accomplish its ends by way of intellectual and visual logic it is scientific in nature.

9 The Principles of Cartography

Any scientific activity must be founded on principles of procedure derived from fundamental concepts and laws. These laws may be either more precisely demonstrable, as in physics, or less precisely based on empirical data and inductive reasoning. The principles of cartography are built from both kinds of concepts.

On the one hand there have been many investigations by psychologists and others in the field of optics. We know, for example, what colors are seen first, how many shades of gray can be detected, what sizes of lettering are legible, and many other precise reactions of the eye to visual stimuli. Since a map is, quite obviously, a visual stimulus intended to portray an intellectual thought it is, of course, necessary to base the selection and utilization of the lines, colors, letters, and other map parts on principles derived from these precise determinations.

On the other hand investigators of the intellectual responses to visual stimuli provide us with a more or less precise understanding of how peoples' minds react to visual stimuli. Through experiment, study of fundamental design, and recording of reactions to such standardized and widespread phenomena as advertising, these researchers have been able to compile a number of principles of design. For example, it is known what kind of rectangle is best, what kinds of layout or lettering can be employed (or avoided) in order to suggest (or not to suggest) such intangibles as stability, power, movement, and so on. There are widespread preferences as to colors, shapes, and designs that must be utilized to make more effective a presentation. The number of cartographic principles based on research and analysis in optics and psychology is surprising.

In addition to the well-founded physical and intellectual principles there are a great many conventions and traditions in cartography which have almost the stature of principles. Cartography is an ancient art and science, and it is to be expected that over the centuries these traditional procedures would become almost standard practice. Many of them have been changed and modified by long-continued use until they have, through the process of trial and error, become "good practice." Many forms of symbolism such as that for political boundaries and cities, or such practices as north orientation, carry as much authority, in many circumstances, as do more objectively based principles. However, it is to be expected in such a conventionalized profession as cartography that many conventions, especially those of recent vintage, are hardly of sound foundation. These must be carefully analyzed before being used in the light of known principles in order that the purposes of presentation will not be violated by the methods employed. A good example of this kind of "new" convention is the use of the color progression of the spectrum for altitude tints on colored relief maps. Originally, some fifty or seventy-five years ago it was thought logical to parallel increasing altitude above sea level with increasing wave length of light. But more recent researches have shown that elements other than wave length are of more significance in vision. Consequently, the convention does not fit the known principles. There are other examples of modern or new conventions that have developed in the recent history of cartography but which have not had the benefit of the judgment of time.

In general, however, the basic principles of optics and vision as applied to cartography are known, and the cartographer, with these guides, may proceed without much doubt.

10 Art in Cartography

The question is frequently raised as to whether cartography is a legitimate branch of art and what function an artistic talent plays in the making of a map. Prior to the last century the question never arose for cartography was very definitely an art. This is evident when one views the products of the earlier cartographers who embellished their maps with all sorts of imaginative things, together with fancy scroll work, ornate lettering, and intricate compass roses. Special coloring methods and ingredients were carefully guarded secrets. Even as late as a hundred years ago the coloring of maps in one of Germany's greatest map houses was done by the society ladies of the town. Throughout the history of cartography, great emphasis has been laid on fine pen and brush skill, and the aim has been to make something good to look at and perhaps even to hang on a wall as a decoration.

Today a great many people still think of cartography as being an artistic calling, and it is likely that a considerable number of otherwise intelligent students shy away from it for fear they are "not artistic." Good judgment, based on principles, is the major requirement of design in cartography; and such judgment may be easily acquired by training.

Most maps are functional in that they are designed, like a bridge or a house, for a purpose. Their primary purpose is to "get across" a concept or relationship; it is not to serve as adornment for an office wall. As a matter of fact, if a map is made too much of a work of art, it is very likely that the viewer will be stimulated first by its beauty and will fail to see the concept. Probably one of the cartographer's major concerns is to refrain from making the map ugly, and in this respect he is definitely an artist, albeit in a somewhat negative sense.

Although the question of whether cartography is an art will always be debated with vigor, there is no question that it is a creative kind of endeavor which repays the effort by the satisfaction that comes from producing something that has never been done before. Every map is a different problem requiring a new solution in the field of design. It requires a good command of the principles of presentation to build a map anew each time. In this it is like creative writing that requires new combinations of technique and media. In this respect cartography is certainly a creative art.

2

The Earth and the System of Coordinates

11 The Shape of the Earth

The earth is in reality a complex geometric form. The massive plastic earth ball, spinning through space, is beset by tremendous forces, and it assumes a form which makes large-scale precision mapping of its surface a difficult undertaking. On the other hand, for the small-scale mapping of large regions (extensive area on a small sheet) most of these complications need hardly concern us at all.

Man's first ideas of the earth around him included little beyond that which he could see; consequently it appeared flat. The earliest world maps apparently represented it so, and the idea of sphericity was not generated until the philosophers of the pre-Christian, Greek era applied reason to the problem. By the time of Ptolemy (second century A.D.) the earth was recognized as being a sphere. Although the idea of sphericity did not altogether die out during the Dark Ages it languished, to say the least, and the notion of a flat surface again prevailed. With the reissuance of Ptolemy's *Geographia* and the subsequent Age of Discovery following the fifteenth century the representation of the earth reverted to the sphere. In the late seventeenth century the idea of oblateness because of rotation was advanced by Newton and eagerly pursued. During the last century or so several determinations of the amount of bulging and flattening have been made, and there are several oblate spheroids recognized. Recent geodetic investigation has shown, however, that the earth is not precisely an oblate spheroid but is somewhat irregular in form. The precise shape, called the geoid, is not yet known.

The largest of the earth's deformations from a true sphere must occasionally be acknowledged even in small-scale mapping, which is our primary concern. On account of its spinning on an axis the earth ball is bulged somewhat in the area midway between the poles and consequently flattened a bit in the polar regions. The actual amount of flattening is of the order of some 26 miles difference between the polar and equatorial diameters, the equatorial, of course, being larger.

Because of the bulging and flattening, a line around the earth that passes through the poles and bisects the earth will not be a circle but will be, to exaggerate a bit, oval in shape. The flatter portion will be in the polar regions and the more rapid curvature will be in the equatorial areas. Since a considerable amount of navigation is based upon observations aimed at finding the angle between the horizon and some celestial body it is apparent that complications result from this departure from a true sphere. Consequently, whenever maps are being prepared for navigation or for plotting exact courses and distances from one place to another, it is necessary to take into account this flattening and bulging.

In most other cases of small-scale mapping it may safely be ignored.

12 The Size of the Earth

Since ancient times man has been attempting to arrive at exact measurements of the planet on which he lives. Near the beginning of the Christian era several calculations of the size of the earth were made that apparently came quite close to the figures we now accept, but their closeness was the result of fortunate compensation of errors rather than precision. These early estimates were reported by Ptolemy, who, recognizing the observational errors, accepted "corrected" values which reduced the earth's circumference by nearly a fourth. Unfortunately or fortunately depending upon one's viewpoint, Ptolemy's convictions were generally accepted. If Columbus had known the true size of the earth he probably would not have dared set sail to find the orient by going west. Because of Ptolemy's acceptance, in the second century A.D., of the reduced value the native of America is called an Indian instead of an American, as he should be!

In recent times the dimensions of the earth have been calculated and with relatively great precision. International standardization has been proposed but not accepted as yet. The following values are those generally used in the United States and are those of the Clarke spheroid of 1866:

Equatorial radius	6 378 206.4 meters
Polar semi-axis	6 356 583.8 meters
Radius of sphere of equal area	6 370 997.2 meters
Area of earth (approx.)	510 900 000 sq. km.
Equatorial circumference	40 057 km.

13 The Earth Grid

In order to locate points on any surface we must have concepts of direction and distance. Primitive man probably developed these concepts in relation to the rising and setting sun and the necessity for travel. All locations are relative, and therefore they must be established in relation to some reference or starting point. If such a point is determined every other point on the surface can be located in terms of direction and distance from this point.

On a limitless plane surface or on a spherical surface, there is no natural reference point; i.e., every point is the same as every other point except for relative location. In mathematics a system of location on a plane surface is developed by establishing a convenient "point of origin" at the intersection of a horizontal axis and a vertical axis and then dividing the plane into a rectangular grid by additional horizontal and vertical lines, usually equally spaced. Then any point is located by its distance above or below the horizontal axis and its distance, on either side, from the vertical axis. In order to locate ourselves on the surface of the earth a similar coordinate system, called the earth grid, is used; but this surface is an "allside" curved one (i.e., it curves away in every direction from every point), and the use of straight lines is impossible. On the earth, however, we are fortunate in having two convenient reference points established by nature; they are the poles or points where the axis of rotation meets the spherical surface. Furthermore, on the surface of the sphere we can conveniently measure distance in degrees of arc.

14 Latitude

The ancients appreciated this problem, and as long ago as Greek times a system of locating oneself between the two poles was devised. A line joining the **two poles** on the earth's surface is a half-circle containing 180°. When one stands anywhere on this line his horizon seems to him to bound a flat (or nearly flat) circular plane. If one can imagine himself being out in space and looking at this little horizon plane he will see that the plane is tangent to the circle, and that if he were to shift it north or south along the line it would

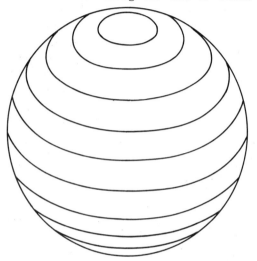

FIG. 4. Parallels on the earth.

change orientation but would always be tangent. Now, if we assume that the sun is directly overhead at a point on the equator the direction of the sun will make an angle of 90° with the horizon disc on the equator. At that same moment the sun would be cut in half by the horizon if the disc were at either pole; i.e., the sun's angle with the disc would be 0°. The relationship is complementary. If the angle of the sun's direction and the horizon disc varies from 90° to 0° each way from the midpoint between the poles it is only necessary to observe the angle made by the sun and the horizon to calculate how far north or south of the midpoint one's position is.

The foregoing simplifies the problem somewhat for the sun is overhead at the midpoint only twice a year; furthermore,

observations must, of course, be made at noon, and sometimes it's cloudy, but the essential facts can be easily determined. Stars can be used the same way, but the fundamental fact remains that position north-south can be determined by measuring the angle between the horizon and a celestial body.

To utilize this relationship in a spherical coordinate system was natural, even for the ancients. They imagined a series of circles around the earth parallel to one another. The one dividing the earth in half, equidistant between the poles, was named, as might be expected, the equator. The series north of the equator was called north latitude. Similarly, the series south from the equator was called south latitude. To determine which circle one was on and hence his distance north or south of the equator required only the observation of the angle between the horizon and some known celestial body such as the sun, Polaris, or some other star.

No change has been made in the system since it was first devised nearly twenty-five hundred years ago.

15 The Length of a Degree of Latitude

In the generally accepted system of measuring angles, a circle contains 360°; a half-circle, 180°. Consequently, there are 180° of latitude from pole to pole. The quadrant of the circle from the equator to each pole is divided into 90°, and the numbering starts from 0° at the equator and goes to 90° at each pole. Latitude is always designated as north or south.

On a perfect sphere each degree of latitude would be the same length, but the earth is not a perfect sphere. Rather, as we have seen, it is bulged at the equator and flattened near the poles. Since the bulging makes the surface curve faster near the equator one does not need to travel so far in order to observe a change of 1° between the horizon and a celestial body. Conversely, one must travel farther near the poles where the surface does not curve so much. Consequently, the degrees of latitude are not the same length in earth distance but vary from a little less than 69 statute miles (68.7) near the equator to a little more than 69 (69.4) near the poles. It is apparent that this difference of less than 1 mile in 69 is of little significance in small-scale maps but it may become important on large maps of small areas. Table 1

TABLE 1. LENGTHS OF DEGREES OF THE MERIDIAN.

Lat.	Stat. mi.	Km.
0–1°	68.703	110.567
9–10°	68.722	110.598
19–20°	68.781	110.692
29–30°	68.873	110.840
39–40°	68.986	111.023
49–50°	69.108	111.220
59–60°	69.224	111.406
69–70°	69.320	111.560
79–80°	69.383	111.661
89–90°	69.407	111.699

provides, in abbreviated form, the length of the degrees of the meridian. A more complete table is included in Appendix C.

For ordinary small-scale use it is well to keep in mind the fundamental fact that degrees of latitude or parallels (as the latitude lines are called) are very nearly the same distance apart from pole to pole.

16 Longitude

The latitude phase of the coordinate system establishes position north or south of the equator, but it cannot, of course, do more than that. If one is, for example, on the 45th parallel north he may in fact be anywhere on that parallel, which is a circle extending all the way around the earth halfway between the equator and the north pole. In a sense, the ordinate of the coordinate systems is established, but an abscissa is also necessary to establish position along the parallel. This is done by another

set of lines, meridians, arranged at right angles to the parallels.

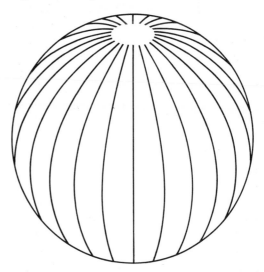

FIG. 5. Meridians on the earth.

All parallels, including the equator, are circles; and since each circle is divided in 360° it is possible to arrange a series of

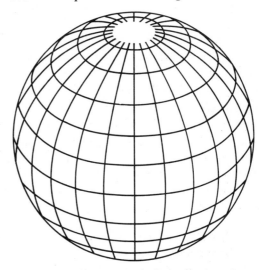

FIG. 6. The earth's spherical coordinate system.

lines through the corresponding divisions of each parallel. Each of these lines (meridians) will then extend due north-south and they will be equally spaced east-west on any parallel. They will cross the parallels at right angles and thus give us a coordinate system which is like the lines on cross-section paper except that in this case the system lies on a spherical surface rather than the plane surface of paper.

If one chooses a meridian from which to start numbering he may then establish his position as so many degrees east or west of that line. If he were 180° from it he would be halfway around the earth from the starting line. We have already seen that it is not difficult to find one's latitude, but although longitude is actually a simpler system than latitude it turns out to be very much more difficult to determine.

The earth rotates once on its axis in 24 hours. Therefore, since there are 360° in a circle the earth will rotate 15° in 1 hour. All that is necessary, then, is to know the difference in local sun time between two places, and the longitude difference will be a matter of arithmetic. This also was reasoned out by the ancients, but since they had no way of telling the time of day at two places simultaneously they were unable to figure longitude accurately. As a matter of fact it wasn't until a few hundred years ago that clocks (called chronometers) were made accurate enough so that it was possible to determine longitude with any degree of precision, by carrying one along showing the time of the starting place. Today this is accomplished not only by using chronometers, but by means of radio time signals broadcast at regular intervals.

17 The Length of a Degree of Longitude

The length of a degree of longitude on the equator is very nearly the same as a degree of latitude. But the meridians converge and pass through the poles, and, thus, everywhere except near the equator a degree of longitude will be shorter than one of latitude. The geometrical relation between the two lengths anywhere is

Length of a degree of longitude

= Cosine of the latitude ×

Length of a degree of latitude

A table of cosines (see Appendix A) will show that

$$\cos 0° = 1.0$$
$$\cos 60° = .50$$
$$\cos 90° = 0.0$$

Thus at 60° north and south latitude the distance between the meridians is half the distance between the parallels. This relationship is helpful in judging the quality of representation of the earth grid on maps, as we shall see later. Table 2 is included

TABLE 2. LENGTHS OF DEGREES OF THE PARALLELS.

Lat.	Stat. mi.	Km.
0°	69.172	111.321
5°	68.911	110.900
10°	68.129	109.641
15°	66.830	107.553
20°	65.026	104.649
25°	62.729	100.952
30°	59.956	96.448
35°	56.725	91.290
40°	53.063	85.396
45°	48.995	78.849
50°	44.552	71.698
55°	39.766	63.996
60°	34.674	55.802
65°	29.315	47.177
70°	23.729	38.188
75°	17.960	28.903
80°	12.051	19.394
85°	6.049	9.735
90°	0	0

here as an illustration of the decreasing length of a degree of longitude from the equator toward the pole. A more complete table is included in Appendix C.

18 The Prime Meridian

Unlike the parallels, which have different lengths and bear different relationships to the celestial bodies, the meridians are all alike. Consequently, the choice of the one from which to start the numbering has been, as might be expected, a problem of international consequence. Each country, with characteristic national ambition, wished to have 0° longitude within its borders or as the meridian of its capital. For many years each nation published its own maps and charts with longitude reckoned from its own meridian of origin. This, of course, made for much confusion when referring to coordinate positions while using maps of different countries.

During the last century many nations began to accept the meridian of the observatory at Greenwich near London, England, as 0°, and in 1884 it was agreed upon at an international conference. Today this is almost universally accepted as the prime meridian. Since longitude is reckoned as either east or west from Greenwich (to 180°), the prime meridian is somewhat troublesome because it divides both Europe and Africa into east and west longitude. The choice of the meridian of Greenwich as the prime meridian establishes the "point of origin" of the earth's coordinate system in the Gulf of Guinea. The opposite of the prime meridian, the 180° meridian, is more fortunately located, for its position in the Pacific provides a convenient international date line, requiring only a few departures.

19 The Great Circle

The shortest distance between two points is a straight line; however, on the earth it is obviously impractical to follow this straight line through the solid portion of the planet. The shortest distance between two points on a sphere is the arc along the surface directly above the straight line. This arc is formed by the intersection of the spherical surface with the plane passing through the two points and the center of the earth. The circle established by the intersection of this plane with the surface, if extended, divides the earth equally into hemispheres and is termed a *great circle*. Each meridian is an arc of a great circle, and if joined with its opposite (e.g., 0°–180°, 90°E–90°W) it constitutes a great circle. The equator is a great circle, but all other parallels are "small circles" since they do not bisect the earth.

Great circles bear a number of geometrical relationships with the spherical earth that are of considerable significance in cartography and map use:

1. Any great circle always bisects any other great circle.

2. An arc of a great circle is the shortest distance between two points on the spherical earth.

3. The plane in which any great circle lies always bisects the earth and hence always includes the center of the earth.

Because a great circle is the shortest distance between two points on a spherical surface, air and sea travel, in so far as is possible or desirable, move along such routes. Radio waves and certain other electronic impulses tend to travel along great circles. For this reason many maps must be made on which great circles are shown to best advantage.

20 Distance Measurement

Distances on the earth's surface are always reckoned along arcs of great circles unless otherwise qualified. Because no map, except one on a globe, can represent the distances between all points correctly it is frequently necessary to refer to a globe, to a table of distances, or to calculate the length of the great-circle arc between two places. A piece of string or the edge of a piece of paper can be employed to establish the great circle on a globe. If the scale of the globe is not readily available, the string or paper may be transferred to a meridian and its length in degrees of latitude ascertained. Since all degrees of latitude are nearly equal and approximately 69 miles, the length of the arc in miles may be determined.

There are, of course, many units of distance measurement used in cartography. For foreign maps not using the English or the metric system it is necessary to refer to glossaries or some other source having the information needed for conversion. The common English and metric units are given below together with some other units occasionally used in cartography.

	Feet	*Meters*
Statute mile	5 280	1 609.34
Nautical mile (U.S.)	6 080.20	1 853.24
Kilometer	3 280.83	1 000.00
Foot	—	0.3048
Meter	3.2808	—

21　The Compass Rose

The points of the compass, collectively called the compass rose, were formerly standard items on most maps, and they were usually embellished and made quite ornate. Today the compass points appear less frequently except that, of course, they are included on all charts for navigational purposes. Nevertheless, the compass points and their relation to the earth grid and to earth directions are important concepts in cartography.

The familiar compass is well known to everyone. Its cardinal directions at 90° to one another are the result of the geometric relations of the earth grid. Parallels and meridians are perpendicular to one another everywhere on the earth. Meridians establish the north-south direction, and parallels, the east-west; but the meridians converge to a point at each pole whereas the parallels in each hemisphere simply become smaller and smaller circles until the 90° "parallel" is one point, the pole. Conse-

quently, north, east, south, and west are never the same actual directions at any two points. This does not appear to create much of a problem when we look at a globe map, but if we transfer the parallels and meridians to a plane surface we find that, just as it is impossible for any map to show all the distances correctly, so also is it impossible to duplicate everywhere the orientation of the compass rose as it appears on the globe.

22　The Azimuth

As we have seen, the directions on the earth, established by the earth grid, constantly change if one moves across the face of the sphere. Only on a meridian or on the equator does direction remain constant along a great circle; but since arcs of a great circle represent the shortest distances between any two points on that great circle, it is convenient to be able to designate the "direction" the great circle has at any starting point toward a destination. This direction is reckoned by observing the angle the great circle makes with the meridian of the starting point. The angle is usually designated as a certain number of degrees from north reading clockwise (0° to 360°).

In these days of radio waves and air transport the direction and route of travel along great circles are of major importance. Hence many maps are constructed so that directional relations are maintained as far as possible.

23　The Loxodrome

A great circle, being the shortest route between points on the sphere, is the most economical route to follow when traveling on the earth. But it is practically impossible to do this, except when travel is along a meridian or along the equator. The difficulty arises from the fact that, except for those particular great circles, directions

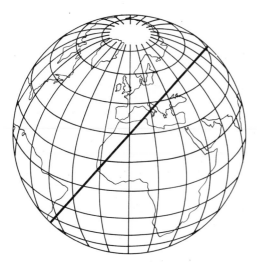 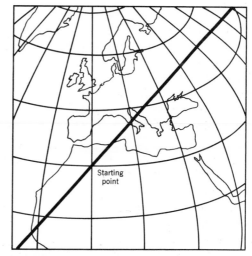

Fig. 7. How azimuth (direction) is read. The drawings show a great circle on the earth grid. The drawing on the right is an enlarged view of the center section of the drawing on the left. The azimuth, from the starting point, of any place along the great circle to the northeast is the angle between the meridian and the great circle, reckoned clockwise from the meridian. Note that the great circle cuts each meridian at a different angle.

constantly change along all other great-circle routes. This is illustrated in Fig. 7. Because travel along a definite route must be directed in some manner, such as by the compass, it is not only inconvenient but impracticable to try to change course at, so to speak, each step.

The line of constant compass direction is called a loxodrome. Meridians and the equator are loxodromes as well as great circles, but all other lines of constant compass direction are not great circles. As a matter of fact loxodromes are complicated curves, and if one were to travel along a loxodrome (other than the meridians or the equator) he would spiral toward the pole but in theory never reach it.

In order to approximate as closely as possible the great circle, movement is directed along a line of constant compass direction "inside" the great circle, e.g., northeast, leaving the great circle and then coming back to it, and then taking another constant compass direction for a short distance, and so on. This procedure is similar

to following the inside of the circumference of a circle by a series of short straight-line chords. It is not the same, of course, since the great circle is the straight line, if viewed from above as it should be, and the short (rhumb) lines of constant compass direction are curved lines and are actually longer routes.

24   Direction and Orientation

As may be seen from the preceding, the representation of directions on maps is no simple matter. Consequently, the determination of directions from maps should be done with caution, even from those maps that have been constructed especially for the purpose.

Many conventions exist in cartography, and one of the stronger is that of orientation or the way the directions on the mapped earth segment are arranged on the sheet. Naturally, on a spherical surface there is no up or down along the surface. But a sheet when looked at or held in the hand has a top and a bottom. The top seems to be the direction in which the reader is looking. Originally, when maps were made of the as yet unknown earth it was common for the medieval European cartographer to place the "more important" area at the top or in the center. Because of the significance that paradise and the place of origin of Christianity had in men's minds during that period, it was the practice to place the east or the orient (paradise) at the top and Jerusalem at the center. Hence the term "orientation." Other orientations were common in other areas.

Several centuries ago the convention of placing north at the top became the practice and has become so strongly established that we think of "up north" and "down south"; upper Michigan and lower California are examples of the unconscious adjustment to this convention. Needless to say, save for the convention, there is no reason why a map cannot be oriented any way the cartographer pleases. Since we think of the top of a sheet as "away" from us it is apparent that orienting the maps in the direction of interest or movement, if any, may well promote the purpose of the map.

25   Areas on the Earth

As the spherical earth complicates the determination and representation of distances and directions, the allside curved surface likewise makes difficult the reckoning and representing of areas. To arrive at the area of a segment of the surface of a sphere is not difficult, but the earth is not a sphere. Because it is not a sphere, and for various other reasons that were suggested earlier, the establishment of exact position is difficult. If positions are doubtful then the shape of the spherical segment is in doubt and thus the area of it is open to question. Besides, most of the areas in which one would be interested, aside from small land holdings, are extremely irregular, for instance, continents, countries and such with complex boundaries or coastlines. Consequently, the only way to measure such areas is to map them first and then calculate in some manner the area enclosed. Of course, such a map must be one in which the earth grid has been arranged on the plane surface so that areas are correctly represented as to size anywhere within the map.

26   The Measurement of Areas

The area of the irregular shape can be determined in several ways. One simple but not particularly precise manner is to lay cross-section paper over the region and count the number of squares and part-squares enclosed by the boundary. The other and more precise manner is to employ a polar planimeter. This instrument

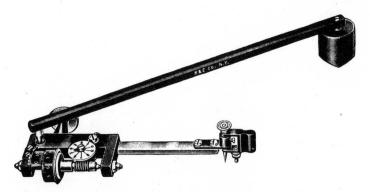

FIG. 8.   A polar planimeter.   Courtesy Keuffel and Esser Company, Hoboken, N. J.

requires merely tracing the outline of the area with a pointer and the result is read directly in square units from a dial. Some planimeters are capable of being set several ways so that the total area may be determined in square miles, centimeters, miles, acres, or in whatever units the operator may wish.

Occasionally it is necessary to determine the area of a region from a map that does not have a proper scale, or, more often, the result is desired in some unit requiring a knowledge of square values from the map. Although this can usually be figured from the scale (if the scale is expressed properly), it is frequently desirable to determine the relationship with the planimeter by measuring a known area on the map. This has the advantages of rectifying the usual paper distortion of the map (which would make the scale erroneous) and of making certain the relation between the measured units and areas on the earth. Table 19, Appendix C, shows the area bounded by 1° longitude and 1° latitude for latitudes from the equator to the pole.

27 The Map Scale

Since maps must necessarily be smaller than the areas mapped, their use requires that the ratio or proportion between the one and the other be expressed on the map. This is called the map scale and should be the first thing the map user reads. The scale is commonly expressed as a *distance on the map to distance on the earth* ratio with the distance on the map always expressed as unity. The map scale may be expressed in the following ways:

1. As a simple fraction or ratio. This may be shown either as 1:1,000,000 or $\frac{1}{1,000,000}$. The former is preferred. This means that 1 inch or 1 foot or 1 centimeter on the map represents 1,000,000 inches, feet, or centimeters on the earth's surface. It is usually referred to as the representative fraction, or "RF" for short. The unit of distance on both sides of the ratio must be in the same units.

2. As a statement of map distance in relation to earth distance. For example, the ratio 1:1,000,000 works out to be approximately 1 inch to about 16 miles. Many map series are commonly referred to by this type of scale, e.g., 1-inch or 6-inch maps of the British Ordinance Survey (1 inch to 1 mile, 6 inches to 1 mile).

3. As a graphic representation or bar scale. This is simply a line on the map

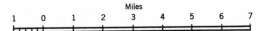

Fig. 9. A graphic or bar scale. They may be made in simple fashion, as above, or they may be made in more complex form such as those shown in Fig. 109.

which is subdivided to show the length of a unit of earth distance. One end of the bar scale is usually subdivided further in order that the map reader may measure distances more precisely.

4. As an area scale instead of a distance scale. When the earth grid is constructed so that all area proportions on the earth are correctly represented, the stated scale is one in which 1 unit of area (square inches, square centimeters) is proportional to a particular number of the same square units on the earth. This may be expressed, for example, either as 1:1,000,000^2 or as 1 to the square of 1,000,000. Usually, however, the fact that the number is squared is assumed and not shown.

28 Determining the Scale of a Map

Sometimes maps are made that do not include a scale. This is poor practice, to say the least, but nevertheless it occurs. More often it is necessary to determine the scale for a particular part of the map, for, as was emphasized previously, the distance scale can never be the same all over a flat map. Determination of the map scale may be accomplished by measuring the map distance between two points that are a known earth distance apart and then computing the scale or making a bar scale. Certain known distances of the earth grid are easy to use, such as the distance between parallels (average of 69 miles) or the distance between meridians (see Table 17, Appendix C). Care should be exercised that the measurement is taken in the direction the scale is to be used, for frequently the distance scale of the map will not be the same in all directions from a point.

If the area scale is desired, a known area on the earth (see Table 19, Appendix C) may be measured on the map with a planimeter and the proportion thus determined. It should be remembered that area scales are conventionally expressed as the square root of the number of units on the right of the ratio. Thus if the measurement shows that 1 square unit on the map represents 25,000,000,000,000 of the same units on the earth it would not be recorded that way, but as $1:5,000,000^2$ or merely by the square root, $1:5,000,000$, which approximates the linear scale.

29 Transforming the Map Scale

Frequently the cartographer is called upon to change the size of a map, that is, to reduce or enlarge it. The mechanical means of accomplishing this will be dealt with in a later chapter, but the problem of determining how to change it in terms of scale is similar to the problem of transforming one type of scale to another. If the cartographer can develop a facility with scale transformation he will experience no difficulty in enlarging or reducing maps.

The essential information necessary for transforming linear scales is that 1 mile (statute) = 63,360 inches. With this in-

formation one can change each of the linear scales (RF, graphic, inch to mile) previously described to the others. Examples follow.

If the RF of the map is shown as 1:75,000

Example 1. The inch/mile scale will be

(1) 1 inch (map) represents 75,000 inches (earth), and

(2) $\dfrac{75,000}{63,360} = 1.183$; therefore

(3) 1 inch represents 1.183 miles.

Example 2. To construct the graphic scale a proportion is established as

(1) 1.183 miles/1 inch = 10 miles/x inches; since

(2) $1.183x = 10$, then

(3) $x = 8.45$, and

(4) 8.45 inches represents 10 miles, which may be easily plotted and subdivided.

If the graphic scale shows by measurement that 1 inch represents 35 miles

Example 3. The RF may be determined

(1) 1 inch represents 35 $\times$ 63,360 inches, or

(2) 1 inch to 2,217,600 inches; and therefore

(3) RF = 1:2,217,600.

The number of miles to the inch may be read directly from the graphic scale.

If the inch/mile scale is stated as 1 inch to 26 miles the graphic scale may be constructed as in Example 2 above. The RF may be determined as in Example 3.

The changing of the scale of a map which has an area scale is accomplished by converting the known area scale and the desired area scale to a linear proportion.

3

The Employment of Map Projections

30 The Map Projection

Ever since the Greek philosophers reasoned that the earth must be a sphere the problem of how to represent the earth's spherical surface as a flat map has been of paramount interest in cartography. The problem arises from the indisputable fact that it is geometrically impossible to transfer the relationships existing on a spherical surface to a plane surface without modifying them in some manner. But it is also a fact that there are innumerable possibilities of systematic transformation that can retain, on the plane, one or several of the spherical relationships. The essential problem of the cartographer, then, is the analysis of the geometrical requirements of the proposed map and the selection of the system or method of transformation which will best or most nearly meet them.

The easiest way to visualize the process of changing from the spherical surface to the plane surface is to think of it in terms of the earth grid. The actual process of transformation is called projection, and the term "projection" stems from the fact that many means of transformation can be accomplished by "projecting," with lines or shadows, the graticule from the sphere to a plane surface. It is similar to the manner in which an artist or draftsman can construct a scale drawing of a building as seen from a particular point of view. As a matter of fact there is considerable similarity between architectural projection and some kinds of map projection. Properly done, an architectural "elevation" of a building is systematically done in perspective so that every aspect of the building appears correct *from that viewpoint*. If one attempted to measure one of the foreshortened sides without knowing the system of projection, the result would probably be erroneous. Similarly the cartographer "projects" his spherical coordinate system to a plane surface in a *systematic* manner, and if the map user attempts to obtain some relationship from the projection without knowing the system, his result will likewise probably be erroneous.

Actual geometric projection of the grid from the sphere to the plane includes only a few of the possibilities. There are a larger number of possibilities for the retention of significant earth relationships that can be determined mathematically. These are also called projections, and no purpose would be served by attempting to distinguish between geometric and mathematical projections.

They are all systematic representations of the earth grid on a plane surface, and each has, for some map use, specific assets and liabilities.

31 The History of Map Projections

The earliest thought of projections of the spherical earth on a plane surface probably occurred no earlier than several centuries B.C., but in the few hundred years following the realization that the earth is a sphere several solutions to the projection problem were presented. Probably one of the first projections was a simple representation of the grid as a series of rectangles, and today we still occasionally use the same kind of projection. By the end of the Greek era enough had become known about the earth, and the problem of projection was so well understood, that the great Claudius Ptolemy in his monumental work on geography was able to include a section on map projections and to devise and give directions for their construction. After Ptolemy, the western world lapsed into the Dark Ages and the knowledge of projection was one of the casualties.

Elsewhere however, notably in the Arabic world, mathematics, geography, and projections were kept alive, and when, in the fifteenth century, Ptolemy was "rediscovered," the western world again made great strides in cartography and discovery. This period was as much a Renaissance in cartography as it was in anything else, and probably the greatest and most influential map projection ever devised, the Mercator projection, was developed during this period.

The Mercator projection is an excellent example of the relation between the requirements of a map and the manner in which the earth grid may be projected in order to meet the needs. The sixteenth century was a time of exploration and sea travel. Columbus had discovered the Americas; Magellan's ships had succeeded in circumnavigating the globe; the earth's land areas were beginning to take shape on the world map; and ships were setting out "to all points of the compass." One of the major trials of the navigator, however, was that, although he had a rough idea of where lands were and had the compass to help him, he had no way of plotting or sailing a course with any degree of certainty. It was pointed out earlier that the problem of the navigator is that he must sail a loxodrome, a line of constant compass direction, because he cannot readily travel any other course. Mercator's solution was to project (mathematically) the earth's coordinate system in such a way that a straight line anywhere in any direction was a loxodrome. Thus if a mariner knew from whence he was starting he need but draw a straight line (or a series of straight lines) to his destination, and, if he made good allowances for drift and winds, he had a reasonably good chance of arriving somewhere near his destination. The projection suited perfectly the purpose of the map. It still does.

In the less than four hundred years since Mercator devised his projection the world of man has changed tremendously. Distances have been "reduced" a thousand fold; man has investigated and mapped an untold number of subjects; and all branches of science, including cartography, have progressed immensely. The development of map projections kept pace with the developments in other fields, and as the needs arose for ways of presenting particular geographic relations, a means of projecting the grid to accomplish the purpose was usually available.

Not all projections, by any means, were developed in answer to specific needs as was the Mercator. The transformation of the spherical surface to the plane in such a manner as to maintain on the plane certain of the numerous spherical relationships is a most intriguing mathematical problem. Consequently, a number of projections have been devised simply as solutions to interesting problems rather than with a specific utility in mind. Also it should be remembered that some of our common projections were originally contemplated and worked out by the ancients and were only resurrected a thousand years or more later when their utility was appreciated. Such was the case with the gnomonic, orthographic, and stereographic projections, all of which were imagined or devised before the time of Christ, but were not employed thereafter until more than fifteen hundred years later.

The correlation between the purpose of the map and the projection used is strikingly revealed by the tremendous advances made during the last century or so. As transportation abilities have increased and social consciousness has developed the need for maps for air navigation and other nonoceanic travel, and for the display of population, land use, and other geographic factors, has likewise increased. Many new projections have been devised and ways of adapting many old ones worked out, and today there is literally an unlimited number of projections from which to choose.

It may reasonably be asserted that at present cartographers need to devote little time to devising new projections but rather would do better to become more proficient in selecting from the ones available. On the other hand, if a new and particular use of maps requires a special type of projection, undeveloped as yet, such a projection might well be worth the time and effort spent in devising it.

32 The Classification of Projections

It was pointed out above that there are an unlimited number of possibilities for representing the earth grid systematically on a plane. Consequently, it would be desirable to be able to classify them in some manner so that their recognition and choice would thereby be made easier. Like many other phenomena, however, the classification of projections is "easier said than done." The various methods of projection overlap and shade into one another so that any single classification leaves much to be desired.

The usual classification of projections is based on the method of construction, and that approach is used in the following chapter concerning the construction of projections. Theoretically, and sometimes actually, projections are constructed on "developable surfaces." These surfaces are those geometric forms capable of being flattened such as a cone or a cylinder (both of which may be cut and laid out flat) or a plane (which is already flat). The grid of the earth is "projected" geometrically or mathematically on to the surfaces which are then developed, i.e., flattened. Conventionally the axis of the earth is aligned with the axes of the cylinder and cone (see Fig. 10) so that in a projection based upon a cone meridians converge in one direction and diverge in the other, and on the flattened cylinder meridians are straight parallel lines. Projections on a plane are not so conventionally aligned, and no generalizations can be made about their appearance. Such a grouping of projections, geometrically, results in categories called cylindrical, conic, azimuthal (plane), and miscellaneous (those based on no geometric form). Occasionally the cylindrical group is called rectangular. Whatever the terminology employed the grouping is, strictly speaking, not a classification but a listing.

This constructional approach cannot entirely satisfy the cartographer, since before he can set about to construct a projection he must first choose it from the possibilities. Consequently, for the purpose of the following brief discussion of the principles of choosing and employing projections another approach, that of utility, is adopted.

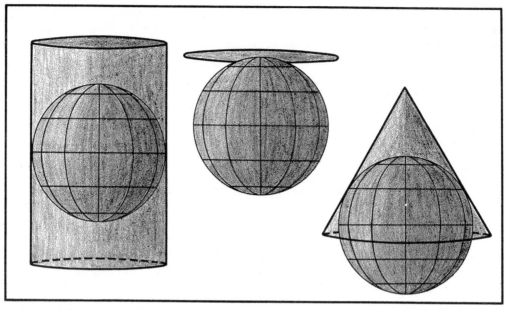

Fig. 10. Surfaces on which the earth's grid may be projected. The origin of the projecting lines may assume various positions. For example, it may be at the center of the earth, or at the antipode of the point of tangency of the plane.

There is a tendency, common among those who do not quite appreciate the nature of projections to think of them as but poor representations of an actual globe surface and thus to select on the basis of "the least of the evils." Such an attitude leads to the conviction that one projection is better intrinsically than another. Nothing could be farther from the truth. Projections are commonly advantageous for reasons other than the fact that it is cheaper to make a flat map than a globe map. The majority of projections enable us to map distributions and derive and convey concepts that would be quite impossible or at least undesirable on a globe. Imagine trying to navigate and draw straight precise courses or loxodromes on a globe surface, or trying to compare distributions of population on a globe when you could see less than half at a time, and that disturbed by perspective. The truth of the matter is that regardless of how

much we concern ourselves with "deformation," "alteration," "distortion," and all the other concepts used in analyzing projections, a projection is a triumph of ingenuity and is a positive, useful device.

The notion that one projection is by nature better than another is as unfounded as saying pliers are better than screwdrivers. Each (tool or projection) is a device to use for a particular purpose, and some will be good for one purpose and bad for another. There are some projections for which no useful purpose is known, but there is no such thing as a bad projection— there are only poor choices.

The following sections consider the various kinds of deformation (angular, area, distance, and direction) that may occur when the transformation from the spherical to the plane surface is made. The discussion in the balance of the chapter separates projections into classes (equivalent, conformal, azimuthal, and others) based primarily upon their major property (quality). Each property, e.g., equivalence, is of sufficient significance so that it is usually the first distinguishing characteristic with which the cartographer begins to make his choice. The classes, unfortunately, are not entirely mutually exclusive, for there are some azimuthal projections that are also conformal or equivalent. The inherent qualities of the projections in each class are relatively distinctive, and when one projection is chosen from a class on a utilitarian basis the fact that it has properties of another class is usually of minor significance.

33 The Deformation in Map Projections

No matter how the earth grid may be arranged on a plane surface, the result can never duplicate the relationships existing on a globe. The alteration of the grid and, of course, the land and sea areas plotted on the map according to it may take several forms.

1. Similar angles at different places on the earth may not be shown as similar on the map.

2. The area of one section may be enlarged or reduced in proportion to that of another region.

3. Distance relationships among points on the earth cannot be shown without distortion on the map.

4. Directions among divergent points cannot be shown without distortion on the map.

There are many other specific spatial conditions which may or may not be duplicated in map projections such as parallel latitude lines, the poles being represented as points, and so on which may assume great significance for certain maps. But the major alterations which may occur are those listed above. In order to provide the student with an understanding of the basic problems resulting from these alterations a brief résumé of their characteristics follows.

34 Angular Alteration

The compass rose, except at the poles, is everywhere the same on the globe surface; that is to say, the cardinal directions are always 90° apart and each of the intervening directions is always at the same angle. This is the case because all parallels and meridians cross one another at 90° and our angular concepts are based on this arrangement.

It is possible to retain this property of angular relations to some extent in a map projection. When it is retained the projection is termed *conformal* or *orthomorphic*, and the meanings of both words imply "correct form" or "shape." This is a bit misleading for no projection can provide correct shape to areas of any extent.

The property of conformality (or orthomorphism) is obtained by retaining in the map projection two conditions of the globe grid. One is that the parallels and meridians cross at 90°, and no projection can be conformal whose coordinates do not do so. The second concerns the fact that on a globe the distance scale will obviously always be the same everywhere. That is to say, all pairs of points 10 miles apart anywhere on the earth will be the same distance apart on the globe or spherical surface. If this condition is not retained in the projection then it is apparent, with a little reflection, that the angles between points cannot be the same. Naturally the second condition could not be duplicated on a flat projection, but it is possible to construct a grid so that *around each point* on the projection the scale is the same in all directions although it necessarily must vary from point to point. Consequently, on all conformal projections the scale will vary from one point to another. Figure 11 illustrates in part the necessity for this relationship.

It is important to realize that just because a projection has parallels and meridians that cross at 90° does not mean that it is conformal. Both the above requirements must be satisfied.

35   Area Alteration

Just as any distance on the earth is "correct" so also are all areas in "proper" proportion; i.e., they are the given material. That statement is so obvious that it seems ridiculous even to suggest that it has any importance. Yet these two conditions, existing on the spherical earth, are of considerable significance when we examine their relationship on a flat projection surface. It has already been pointed out that it is impossible to duplicate all distance relationships on a flat surface; i.e., we cannot keep the map distances between all points correct. Consequently, it might be concluded that, since area is a function of dimension, it is likewise impossible to duplicate the areas in proper proportion to one another. But it is possible.

An area of 1 square inch may have sides of 1 inch in length. By reducing one side to ½ inch and enlarging the other side to 2 inches we have certainly changed the shape, but the area enclosed remains unchanged. So long as the relationship between the sides is varied so that the product of the two is always the same the area enclosed will also be the same; $1 \times 1 = 1$, or $2 \times 0.5 = 1$, or $3 \times 0.33 = 1$, or $4 \times 0.25 = 1$, and so on.

To state the proposition in general terms, if, in a map projection, the scale is manipulated in such a way that whenever it is enlarged above unity in one direction at a point it is correspondingly reduced in the direction perpendicular to the other, the areas represented will be the same *in size*, although, of course, the shapes will be changed from those on the sphere. A more detailed analysis of the facts involved is given in Appendix D.

A map projection that retains the **area** relationships in this way is called an *equivalent* or *equal-area* projection. Such **a** projection can have the scale the same in *all* directions only at one or (at the most) two points or along one or two lines, these being construction lines or points around which the rest of the projection is developed. At all other places the scale will **be** greater than unity in one direction **and** correspondingly less in the perpendicular direction.

Since this is the opposite of one of the requirements for conformality (scale the same in all directions at each point), it is apparent that no conformal projection can be equivalent.

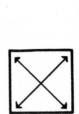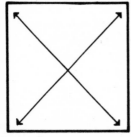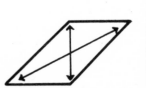

FIG. 11.   Angular and areal relations. The two squares on the left show that relative directions may be maintained even if size is different. On the other hand, the three right-hand shapes show that if relative dimensions are changed angles must be changed also.

Thus all conformal projections will distort most earth areas and all equivalent projections will distort most earth angles.

36   Distance Alteration

The alterations of areas and angles which occur when the spherical surface is represented on a plane are the most important for the majority of cartographic representations. Two others, however, need to be considered in order that the student may have a sound understanding of what may, or rather must, happen when the one surface is projected to another. One of these concerns the problem of the alteration of distances.

It must be thoroughly understood that it is quite impossible to represent at a consistent scale *all* distances of the sphere on a plane. It is possible, on the other hand, to maintain some elements of distance, and on certain types of maps, this may assume an importance above even conformality or equivalence. If, for example, one is mapping certain aspects of temperatures on the earth it may be that these are so intimately related to latitude that it might be necessary to retain on the map the appearance of the latitudes at their correct spacing. This is possible, but only at the expense of considerable angular alteration, or other distortion.

Distance representation is a matter of retaining scale; that is, for distances to be represented "correctly" the scale must be uniform along the line joining the points being scaled. The following are possible:

1. Scale may be maintained in one direction, e.g., north-south or east-west, but only in one direction. When this is done the parallels or meridians that are the correct scale are called *standard* (see Article 48).

2. Scale may be maintained in all directions from *one* or *two* points, but only from those points. Such projections are called *equidistant.*

Any other scale relationship must be a compromise in order to gain better distance relationships in some or all directions in one part of the map at the expense of some other part.

37   Direction Alteration

Just as it is impossible to represent all earth distances with a consistent scale on the flat projection, so also is it impossible to represent all earth directions correctly with straight lines on the map. It is true that the Mercator projection provides "straightened" loxodromes so that if you were to follow a straight line on the map with a constant compass bearing you would actually pass through the points on the line. But straight lines on a Mercator chart are not "true" directions in the sense that we think of lines of direction on the earth. All loxodromes, except for the meridians and the equator, are curved and spiraling lines of constant compass direction. As a matter of fact if one were to point to western Siberia from central United States he would point north, for that is the direction of the great circle joining the two areas. Yet if he were to follow a north direction on the Mercator he would be attempting to reach infinity, not Siberia. On the Mercator chart western Siberia is shown east or west from central United States, a departure of nearly 90°.

When directions are defined properly as great circle bearings, and if we think of a correct direction as being along a great circle on the map which has the proper azimuth reading with the local meridian, then certain representations are possible.

1. Straight great circles between all points may be shown for a limited area although they will not have proper angular relations with the meridians (azimuths).

To do this causes such a strain, so to speak, on the transformation process that it is not possible for even an entire hemisphere.

2. Straight great circles with correct azimuths may be shown for all directions from *one* or, at the most, *two* points. Such projections are called *azimuthal.*

Any other direction relationship must be a compromise, just as in the case of distances.

38   Analysis of the Deformation

The cartographer must be able to recognize the deformation that is inherent in the projection of any map with which he is working. He must also know the deformation characteristics of the common projections so that he may be able intelligently to choose, from among the multitude of possibilities, the best one for whatever kind of map he may be contemplating. The former may be accomplished in a general way by becoming familiar with the characteristics of the earth's coordinate system and then analyzing the projection grid. The latter involves the analysis, for each projection, of the amount of alteration that takes place in so far as it is commensurable and the comparison of the values of different projections.

The visual characteristics of the earth grid, some of which have been discussed previously, are given in the following list.*

1. Parallels are parallel.
2. Parallels are spaced equally on meridians.
3. Meridians and great circles are

---

* In the following list several slight variations have been approximated in order that the principles may be more clearly grasped. In number 2, parallels actually vary in their spacing by about 0.7 mile; in number 6, the discrepancy is negligible; and in number 7, there is a difference of about 0.1 mile. None of these approximations would be of significance in a general-use map with a scale smaller than 1:2,000,000.

---

straight lines (if looked at perpendicular to the earth's surface as is true on a map).*

4. Meridians converge toward the poles or diverge toward the equator.

5. Meridians are equally spaced on the parallels, but their distance apart decreases from the equator to the pole.

6. Meridians at the equator are spaced the same as parallels.

7. Meridians at 60° are half as far apart as parallels.

8. Parallels and meridians cross one another at right angles. (Therefore, with 10 below, the compass rose is the same anywhere.)

9. The area of the surface bounded by any two parallels and two meridians (a given distance apart) is the same anywhere between the same two parallels.

10. The scale at each point is the same in any direction.

To illustrate the mental processes the cartographer should employ when analyzing a projection Figs. 12 and 13 together with their analyses are given. The numbers of the visual characteristics in the list, referred to in the legends, are placed in parentheses.

39   Tissot's Indicatrix

In a classic treatise published less than seventy-five years ago (*Mémoire sur la représentation des surfaces,* Paris, 1881) M. A. Tissot developed the procedure whereby it is possible to determine the amount of angular and areal alteration which occurs at any point on any map projection. His method of analysis is based

---

* If one looks directly at a globe the great circles passing through the point nearest his eye will appear as straight lines. Most projections are attempts at presenting the spherical surface in plan undistorted by perspective, i.e., so that the eye is assumed to be directly above each point of the map.

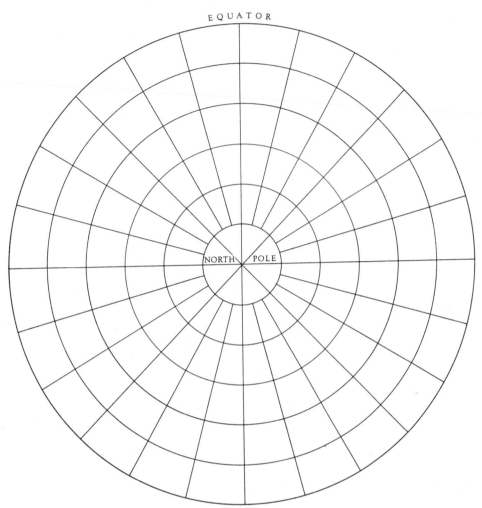

FIG. 12. One hemisphere of the azimuthal equidistant projection. Since a series of straight-line meridians (3), which are, of course, arcs of great circles, converge to a point and are properly arranged around the point as shown by their equal spacing on each parallel (5), the projection must be azimuthal from the point of convergence. The foregoing plus the fact that the parallels are equally spaced on the meridians (2) makes it evident that there is no scale change along the meridians; hence the projection must be equidistant from the point of convergence. Because, however, on the projection the meridians at the equator are not spaced the same as parallels (6) the scale cannot be equal in every direction from each point. Hence it cannot be conformal. Also, since the scale along the meridians has been shown to be correct by the spacing of the parallels (2) and because of the fact that azimuths from the pole are correct it is likely that the central (polar) area is close to truth. If that is true, then the equatorial areas are disproportionately large because of the excessive distances between the meridians (6). Therefore, the projection cannot be equivalent. Courtesy *Annals of the Association of American Geographers.*

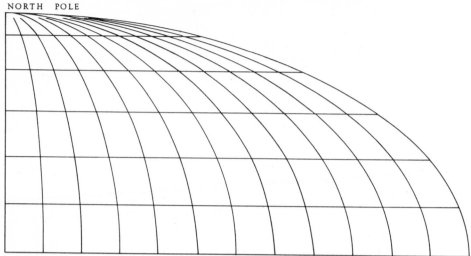

NORTH POLE

EQUATOR

FIG. 13. One quadrant of the Mollweide projection. Since the scale is not the same in every direction (10), as shown by the disproportionate length of the meridian sections at the equator (6), and the compass rose is not the same because parallels and meridians do not cross one another at right angles (8), the projection obviously is not conformal. Because numbers nine (9), and five (5) appear to be satisfied it is likely that the projection approaches equal-area. Because the parallels are not equally spaced (2) and because they do not always cross meridians at right angles (8), it is evident that angular relations are greatly distorted. Courtesy *Annals of the Association of American Geographers.*

on the scale departures from unity that must necessarily, as we have seen, take place when the allside curved surface is represented on a plane. He found that a theoretical circle anywhere on the sphere would be represented by some form of ellipse on a systematic projection. By analyzing the ellipse (which he called the indicatrix), he was able to determine the degree with which angles around a point depart from what they should be or the degree to which areas are exaggerated or reduced. An explanation of the indicatrix is included in Appendix D.

The values derived from the analysis of the indicatrix may be plotted on the projection and thereby show the distribution of angular alteration or areal exaggeration. Many of the projections illustrated in this chapter will have such distributions shown on them. For a number of projections the necessary data have not been determined.

40 Other Methods of Recognizing Deformation

Tissot's indicatrix is limited in its analytical function to values at a point, and by plotting these values over the projection, we may see the change of deformation from point to point. It does not, however, provide much help in the other aspect of deformation inherent in projections, that of the distance and angular relation between widely spaced points or areas such as continents. To date this kind of deformation has not been found to be commensurable, and consequently graphic means have been employed to help show the change of spatial relations.

Various devices have been employed to this end, such as a man's head plotted on different projections to illustrate elongation, compression, and shearing of areas. Another device has been the covering of the globe with equilateral triangles and then reproducing the same triangles on the different projections. This appears to be particularly helpful, and the reader is referred for this subject to the book by Fisher and Miller entitled *World Maps and Globes*, Essential Books, New York, 1944, for excellent illustrations of this use of triangles.

41 The Equivalent Projections

The property of equivalence, or equal-area, is of fundamental importance in the

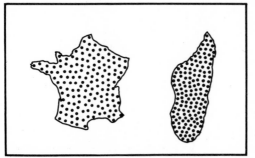

FIG. 14. These two areas (France, left; and Madagascar, right) are nearly the same size on the earth. Areas were considerably altered, however, on the projection from which these two outlines were traced, so that France appears larger than it should by comparison to Madagascar. The same number of dots has been placed within each outline but the apparent density is not the same, although it should be.

presentation of distributions of geographic and economic data. The mapping of many types of statistical and other kinds of information requires that the reader receive the correct impression of the relative sizes of the areas involved. If he does not he is likely to gain an erroneous impression of relative densities. This, of course, is fatal to the purpose of the map which is to present correct visual densities. An example of how this can come about is illustrated in Fig. 14. Furthermore, even for more general uses an equivalent projection is usually desirable (if the purpose does not specifically require another property), for many of our general impressions of the

relative extent of various regions are gained subconsciously through frequent experience. For this reason most people think Greenland is a great deal larger than Mexico (nearly the same size) and that Africa is smaller than North America (Africa is more than 2,000,000 square miles larger). It is, of course, obvious that if any area measurement is contemplated the projection must have a uniform area scale.

The choice of an equivalent projection depends upon two important considerations:

1. The size of the area involved.
2. The distribution of the angular deformation.

There are a great many possibilities from which to choose, and if the cartographer will but keep these two elements in mind he will rarely make a bad choice. In general, the smaller the area to be represented the less significant is the choice of projection for a general map. Any equal-area projection will have points (perhaps only one) or lines of no angular deformation. Consequently, if the area is not large a projection may be chosen with fortuitous deformation relationships for the area involved, and the representation will be practically unassailable. For large areas or the whole earth the distribution of the deformation becomes of paramount significance. The areas of topical importance on the map should be represented in the best fashion possible by the choice of a projection with an advantageous distribution of deformation.

A few representative types of equivalent projections are shown and brief notes on their employment given. Most of the illustrations show lines of equal angular deformation so that the pattern of deformation will be apparent. The values of the lines vary so that it is necessary for the reader to note the values carefully if he wishes to

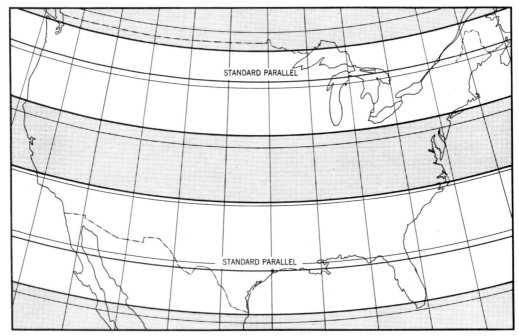

STANDARD PARALLEL

STANDARD PARALLEL

Fig. 15. The Albers conic projection. Values of lines of equal maximum angular deformation are 1°.

compare the various projections. The lighter portion of the projection shows the area of lesser deformation. For definitions of the terms used see Appendix D.

The Albers projection (Fig. 15) has two standard parallels along which there is no angular deformation. Deformation zones are arranged parallel to the standard parallels as shown. Any two parallels in one hemisphere may be chosen as standard but the closer together they are, of course, the better will be the representation between them. Because of the neat appearance of the straight meridians and the concentric arc parallels which meet the meridians at right angles this is a good projection for middle-latitude areas of greater east-west extent and a lesser north-south extent. Parallel curvature ordinarily becomes excessive if the projection is extended for much over 100° longitude.

The Bonne projection (Fig. 16) has a standard central meridian along which there is no deformation. The representation decreases in quality outward from the central meridian so that this projection is a better choice for an area of greater north-south extent and lesser east-west extent.

The sinusoidal projection (Fig. 17) has the merit of a straight central meridian and equator along both of which there is no angular deformation. A further merit of this projection is that the parallels are the same vertical distance apart, giving the *illusion* of proper spacing so that it is useful for representations where latitudinal relations are significant.

The oval Mollweide projection (Fig. 18) does not have the pointed polar areas of the sinusoidal and thus appears a bit more realistic. In order for it to be equal-area within the oval shape it is necessary to de-

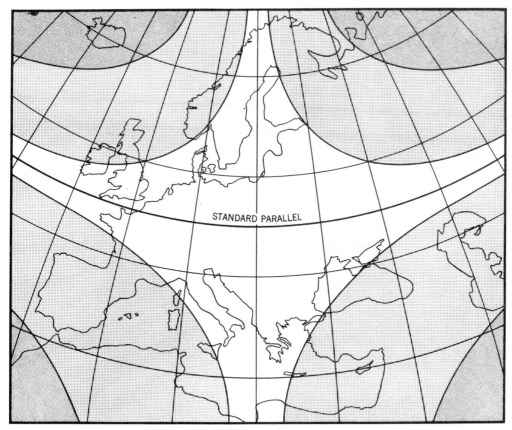

Fig. 16. The Bonne projection. Values of lines of equal maximum angular deformation are
1° and 5°.

crease the north-south scale in the high latitudes and increase it in the low latitudes. The opposite is true in the east-west direction. Shapes are modified accordingly. The two areas of least deformation in the middle latitudes make the projection useful for world distributions with interest concentrated in those areas.

The Eckert IV (Fig. 19) is the best known of several similar equivalent projections. The pole is represented by a line instead of a point so that the polar areas are not quite so compressed in the east-west direction as on the preceding two projections. This takes place however at the expense of their north-south representation. As in the Mollweide the equatorial areas

are stretched in the north-south direction. Deformation distribution is similar to that of the Mollweide.

The Lambert equal-area projection (Fig. 20) is both azimuthal and equivalent. Since deformation is symmetrical around the central point, which can be located anywhere, the projection is useful for areas whose east-west and north-south dimensions are nearly equal. Consequently, areas of continental proportions are well represented on this projection. It is limited to hemispheres. Its azimuthal properties are described in Article 43.

The cylindrical equal-area projection (Fig. 21) is one example of this method of projection which is capable of variation

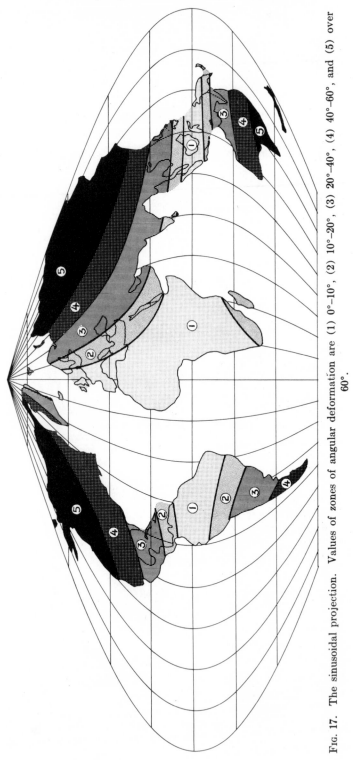

FIG. 17. The sinusoidal projection. Values of zones of angular deformation are (1) 0°–10°, (2) 10°–20°, (3) 20°–40°, (4) 40°–60°, and (5) over 60°.

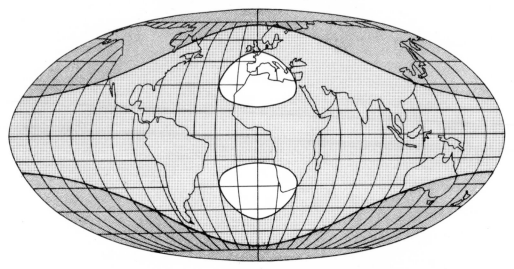

FIG. 18. The Mollweide projection. Values of lines of equal maximum angular deformation
are 10° and 40°.

like the Albers conic. That is, the projection is constructed on the basis of two standard parallels. The two parallels may "coincide," so to speak, and be the equator, or they may be any others so long as they are homolatitudes (the same parallels in opposite hemispheres). Deformation is arranged, of course, parallel to the parallels.

There are many other methods of equal-area projection most of which are in the world-projection class. Naturally there can be only one conic or cylindrical equivalent method with two standard parallels, but there is an infinite number of possibilities for world projection.

42 The Conformal Projections

The property of conformality has many important uses in cartography. The fact that the compass rose is correct anywhere on the projection makes a conformal projection desirable whenever the directional relations at a series of points are important as, for example, in a map of wind directions. It must not be assumed, however, that the directions between points some distance apart are likely to be correct on a

conformal map. On the contrary, they are likely not to be correct. Perhaps the most important use of conformal projections is for navigational maps such as nautical and aeronautical charts and for weather and survey maps where the angular qualities are frequently used.

Because there is no angular deformation at any point on a conformal map the notion is widespread that shapes of countries and continents are well presented on projections having this quality. Although it is true that very small areas on conformal projections are practically perfect, it is also true that in order to retain angular representation it is necessary to alter the area relationships. Thus, on conformal projections the area scale varies from point to point, and consequently large areas are imperfectly represented with respect to shape. It is difficult to express area deformation on a conformal projection, for, in a sense, there is nothing deformed since all angular relationships at each point are retained. All that changes is the linear scale, and one point is as "accurate" as another; only the scales are different. Thus one may

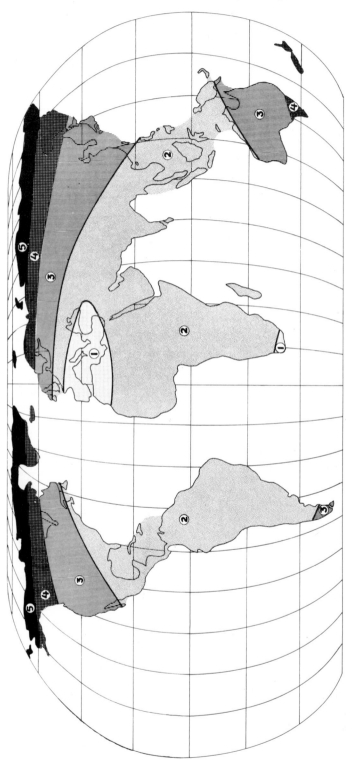

Fig. 19. The Eckert IV projection. Values of zones of equal maximum angular deformation are (1) 0°–10°, (2) 10°–20°, (3) 20°–40°, (4) 40°–60°, and (5) over 60°.

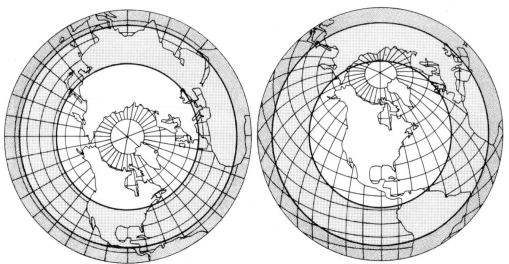

FIG. 20. The Lambert azimuthal equal-area projection. Values of lines of equal maximum angular deformation are 10° and 25°.

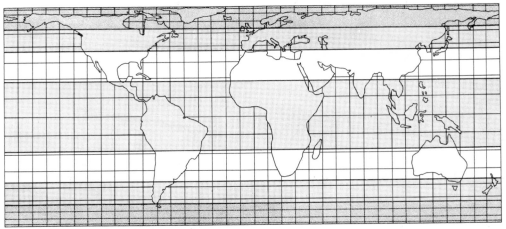

FIG. 21. The cylindrical equal-area projection, with standard parallels at 30°. Values of lines of equal maximum angular deformation are 10° and 40°.

refer to the standard lines or points of origin as having a particular scale and then refer to the other areas as being exaggerated in comparison, for on conformal projections the linear and areal scales always increase away from the origin of the projection.

Some of the conformal projections together with some notes on their qualities are presented.

The Mercator projection (Fig. 22) is one of the most famous projections ever devised. It was invented in 1569 by the famous Dutch cartographer as a device for navigation, and it has served this purpose well. In addition to being conformal it has the added advantage that all loxodromes are represented as straight lines, an obvious advantage to one trying to proceed while watching a compass. Except for the

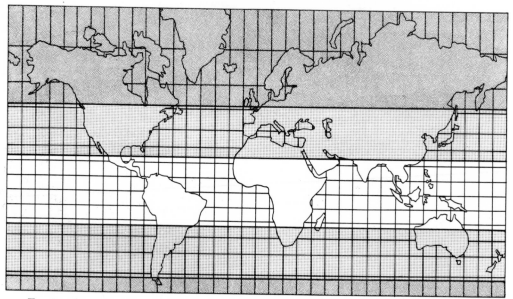

FIG. 22. The Mercator projection. Values of lines of equal areal exaggeration are 25% and 250%.

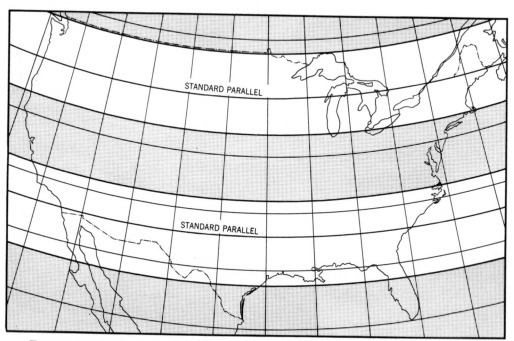

FIG. 23. The Lambert conformal conic. Values of lines of equal areal exaggeration are 2%.

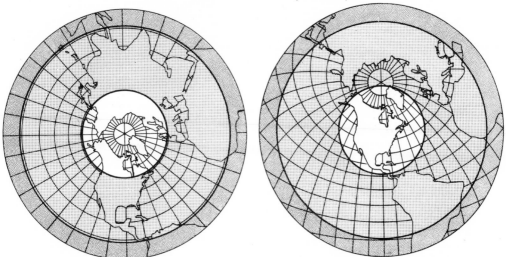

Fig. 24. The stereographic projection. Values of lines of equal areal exaggeration are 30% and 200% (approx.).

meridians and the equator, directions (great-circle courses) are not straight lines, so this projection does not show "true direction"; but such courses can be easily transferred from a projection (gnomonic) that does so. A series of straight "chords" or rhumb lines can thus approximate a great circle. It is apparent that the projection enlarges (not distorts) areas greatly in the higher latitudes, so it is of little use for purposes other than navigation. Also the poles cannot be represented for they are "at" infinity on the conventional Mercator. This is a distinct handicap in these days when the polar areas are of more than usual significance. The Mercator projection is particularly useful for navigation in the equatorial and middle latitudes. Almost all nautical charts are made on this projection.

The Lambert conic projection (Fig. 23) is very similar in appearance to the Albers equivalent projection, for it, too, has concentric parallels and equally spaced, straight meridians that meet the parallels at right angles. Like the Albers it has two standard parallels, but the spacing of the

other parallels on the Lambert increases away from the standard parallels. Area exaggeration between and near the standard parallels is relatively small, and thus the projection provides exceptionally good directional and shape relationships for an east-west latitudinal zone. Consequently, the projection is much used for air navigation in intermediate latitudes (4° to 72°) and for meteorological charts.

The stereographic projection (Fig. 24) belongs also in the azimuthal group. Like the other azimuthal projections the deformation (in this case area exaggeration) increases outward from the central point symmetrically. As in the case of the equivalent azimuthal this is desirable when the area to be represented is more or less square or of continental proportions. In addition to being conformal and azimuthal the stereographic has an additional attribute which no other projection has. All circles on the earth remain as circles on the projection. It is possible therefore to plot the ranges of radiating objects, from radio waves to airplanes, merely with a compass.

This projection, centered on a pole, is much used for navigation in the very high latitudes.

43   The Azimuthal Projections

The azimuthal projections have long been known but only recently have they been resurrected to a position of prominence, or perhaps notoriety, among map projections. The popular notion that we have entered an "air age" provided many map makers with the need for displaying the earth on projections that were better fitted for the requirements of this modern era. They chose the azimuthal projections. It may turn out that the choice of just any azimuthal in many cases was not a wise selection. Like the other categories the azimuthal group has a number of types, each with quite different properties.

All azimuthal projections do have, however, certain qualities which are peculiar to this class. The projections are theoretically (or actually) "projected" upon a plane tangent to the sphere at any desired point. Consequently, the projections are symmetrical around the chosen center; that

is, the scale variation (and it must vary either linearly, angularly, or areally) radiates outward from the center in every direction. There is no deformation of any kind at the center. Furthermore, since all these projections are "projected" on a plane tangent to the sphere, all great circles passing through the point of tangency (center of projection) will be straight lines on the map and will show the correct azimuths from the center to any point. It should be emphasized that only azimuths (directions) *from the center* are correct on an azimuthal projection.

At the center point all azimuthal projections are identical, and the variation among them is merely a matter of the scale differences along the straight great circles that similarly radiate from the center. Figure 45 illustrates this relationship. Any azimuthal projection may be changed to any other one by changing the scale relations along the azimuths. There is no deformation at the center, and the fact that the deformation radiates symmetrically makes this class of projections useful for areas having more or less equal dimensions

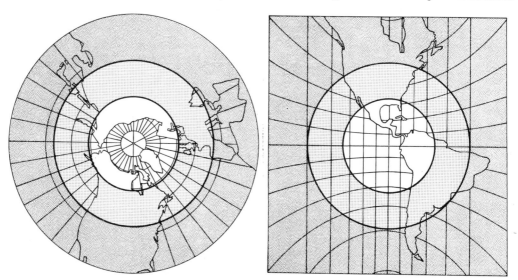

Fig. 25.   The gnomonic projection. Values of lines of equal angular deformation are 10° and 25°. Areal exaggeration, extreme toward the peripheries, is also present.

in each direction, or for maps in which interest is not localized in one dimension. Because any azimuthal projection can be centered anywhere and still present a reasonable appearing grid the class is rather more versatile than others. We frequently see an azimuthal projection with the north pole as the center, for it is easy to draw and provides an illusion of reality because of the regularity of the grid. Except for the basic properties the other qualities of azimuthal projections so centered are somewhat wasted.

The gnomonic projection (Fig. 25), like the Mercator, is one of the most used projections of any class. It has the unique property that all great-circle arcs are represented *anywhere on the map* as straight lines. Therefore the navigator need but join the points of departure and destination with a straight line and his course is determined. Because compass directions constantly change along a great circle, the navigator transfers the course from the gnomonic grid to the Mercator grid and then approximates it with a series of loxodromes which are straight lines on the Mer-

cator. The deformation, both angular and areal, increases rapidly away from the center so that the projection is not much good for any purpose other than showing great circles as straight lines. Because projection is from the center of the earth on the tangent plane, less than a hemisphere can be constructed.

The azimuthal equidistant projection (Fig. 26) has become popular in recent years. It has the unique quality that the linear scale does not vary along the radiating azimuths from the center. Therefore the position of every place is shown in consistent relative position and distance *from the center*. Directions and distances between points whose connection does not pass through the center are not shown correctly. It is apparent, then, that unless movement from the center outward is of major significance, the azimuthal and equidistant qualities may be wasted and some other projection might be a better choice. Any kind of travel that emanates from a center is well shown on this projection. The projection has an advantage over many of the other azimuthal projections

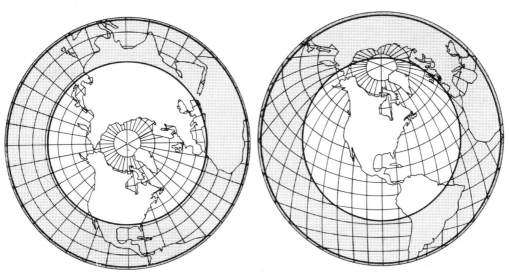

Fig. 26. The azimuthal equidistant projection. Values of lines of equal maximum angular deformation are 10° and 25°. Areal exaggeration is also present.

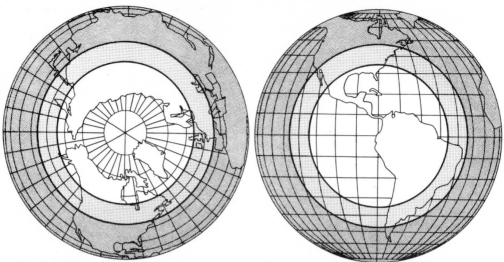

FIG. 27. The orthographic projection. Values of lines of equal maximum angular deformation are 10° and 25°. Areal exaggeration is also present.

in that it is possible to show the entire earth on the projection. Most azimuthals are limited to presenting a hemisphere or less.

The orthographic projection (Fig. 27) looks like a photograph of the earth grid taken from a considerable distance although it is not quite the same. For this reason it might almost be called a visual projection in that the deformation of areas and angles, although great, is not particularly apparent to the viewer since it appears the same as if he were looking at a portion of the globe. On this account it is popular for presenting directional concepts (e.g., Europe as seen from the south), illustrative maps, and for those maps wherein the sphericity of the earth is of major significance.

44 Other Projections

There are a number of map projections that have none of the special properties considered above but that are nevertheless useful for certain purposes. A great many maps do not require any of the special properties but rather are best presented on

a grid that either has some general desirable quality such as ease of construction or is a sort of compromise among the specific properties.

One of the most interesting of these kinds of projections is the minimum-error projection in which the grid of a specific area is presented in such a way that the angular and areal deformation is balanced over the entire area as much as possible. Such a projection will have no precise properties but will give a very "life-like" picture. In other words the angular error will not be as great as it would be if the projection were equivalent; neither will the areal deformation be as great as it would be if the projection were conformal. No purpose would be served by illustrating a minimum-error projection because the projection of each specific area for which it is developed would be different. It would, ordinarily, appear as if it had a conic origin. This type of projection is, in a sense, the ideal kind for general maps or for reference atlas maps, but its construction is too complicated for its use to be widespread.

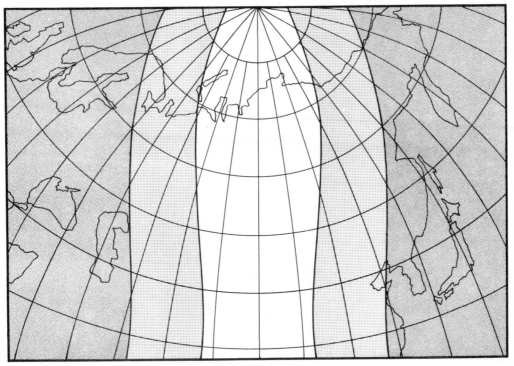

Fig. 28. The polyconic projection. Values of lines of equal maximum angular deformation are 1° and 5°. Areal exaggeration is also present.

The polyconic projection (Fig. 28) is much used in this country for topographic map sheets and is employed, in modified form, for one of the large-scale (1:1,000,-000) maps of the world. It has a straight central meridian along which the linear scale is correct. The parallels are arcs of circles but each is a standard parallel in the sense that it is truly subdivided by the meridians and is drawn with its own center. Thus the parallels are not concentric. The scale along each parallel is correct, but the scale along the curved meridians increases with increasing distance from the central meridian. The projection is, of course, neither conformal nor equivalent, but when used for a small area, bisected by a central meridian, these qualities are so closely approached that the departure is insignificant. For the mapping of a large area on a large scale the development of each small section on its own polyconic projection is therefore desirable. The projection is also easy to construct.

The polyconic used for the so-called Millionth or International Map of the world was modified by making the meridians straight instead of curved, and by making two of them, instead of one, standard on each sheet. This makes it possible to fit sheets together east-west as well as north-south. It is not possible to fit sheets together east-west when the ordinary polyconic is used.

The equirectangular projection (Fig. 29) is one of the oldest and simplest of map projections. It is useful for city plans or base maps of small areas. It is easily constructed, and for a limited area has small deformation. The meridians and central parallel are standard. It may be centered anywhere.

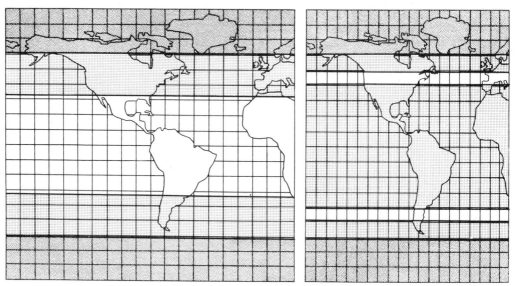

FIG. 29. The plane chart or equirectangular projection. On the left the standard parallel is the equator; on the right, 45°. Values of lines of equal maximum angular deformation are 10° and 40°. Areal exaggeration is also present.

The conic with two standard parallels (Fig. 30) is similar in appearance to the Albers and Lambert conic projections but it has no special properties. It does not distort areas or angles to a very great degree providing the standard parallels are placed close together and provided the projection is not extended far north and south of the standard parallels. It is frequently chosen for areas in middle latitudes of too large an extent for an equirectangular projection, and for maps not requiring the properties of equivalence or conformality.

There are numerous other map projections which have no special properties. Only the major forms have been illustrated, but there are many modifications which have been made for special purposes. For example, O. M. Miller of the American Geographical Society devised a spacing of parallels for a rectangular projection which would allow the poles to be shown but which would have neither the excessive areal exaggeration of the Mercator nor the excessive angular deformation of an

equal-area. This has become quite popular in recent years.

The polyconic and some less important projections are among the more distinctive contributions of the United States to cartography. In this group should also be placed the *homolosine* projection developed by the late Professor J. Paul Goode of the University of Chicago. This projection is a combination of the equatorial section of the sinusoidal and the poleward sections of the Mollweide; thus, it is equal-area. The two projections, when constructed to the same area scale, have one parallel of identical length.* It is an interrupted projection (see next article), and has been widely used in this country. It has been copyrighted, and thus permission is necessary for its use, but whether a map projection is copyrightable has not been entirely determined.

* J. Paul Goode, "The Homolosine Projection: A New Device for Portraying the Earth's Surface Entire," *Annals of the Association of American Geographers,* 1925, Vol. 15, pp. 119–125.

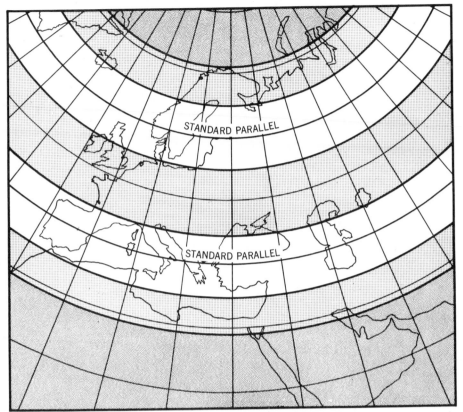

FIG. 30. The conic with two standard parallels. Values of lines of equal maximum angular deformation are 1° and 2° (approx.). Areal exaggeration is also present.

45 Other Criteria for Selecting Projections

A great many maps demand more from the map projection than one or a combination of the properties considered in the foregoing articles. Such projection attributes as parallel parallels, area deformation, and rectangular coordinates oftentimes become of great significance to the success of a map. For example, a map of some sort of distribution that does not require equivalence may have a concentration of the information in the middle latitudes. In a case of this kind a projection that expanded the areas of the middle latitudes would be a great help by allowing details of the significant areas to be presented. Any map of temperature distribu-

tions is made more expressive if the parallels are parallel and even more so if they are straight lines allowing for easy longitudinal comparison. A map in which indexing of places is contemplated is more easily done with rectangular coordinates than with any other kind.

The overall shape of an area on a projection is likewise of great importance. Many times the dimensions of the page or sheet (format) on which the map is to be made is prescribed. One map projection may fit this and another may not, but each may have the desirable properties. By utilizing the projection that will fit a format most efficiently a considerable increase in scale can be effected, which may be a real asset to a crowded map.

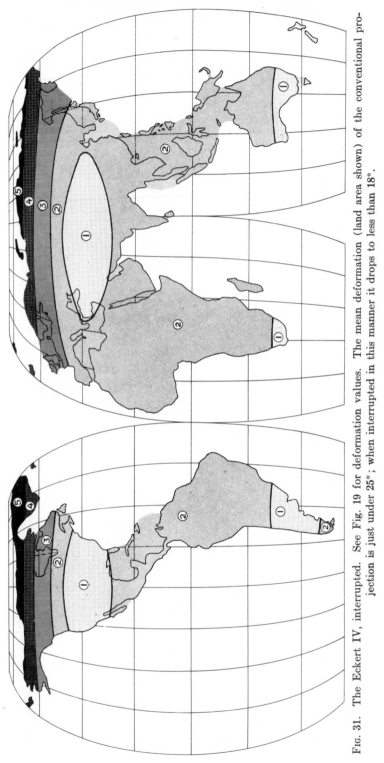

Fig. 31. The Eckert IV, interrupted. See Fig. 19 for deformation values. The mean deformation (land area shown) of the conventional projection is just under 25°; when interrupted in this manner it drops to less than 18°.

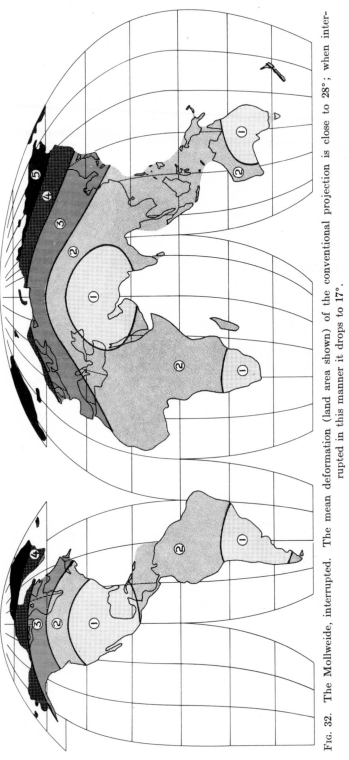

FIG. 32. The Mollweide, interrupted. The mean deformation (land area shown) of the conventional projection is close to 28°; when interrupted in this manner it drops to 17°.

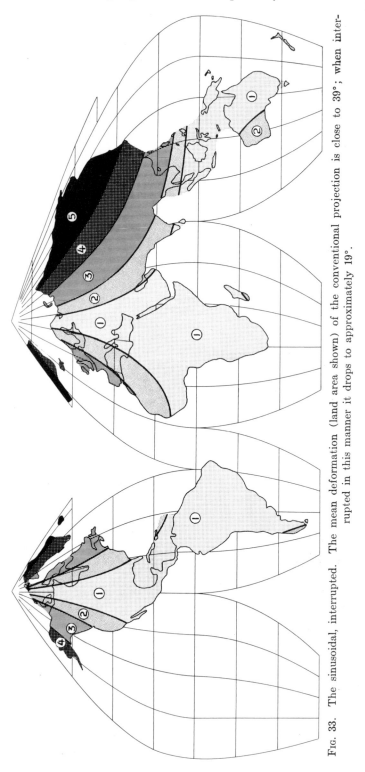

Fig. 33. The sinusoidal, interrupted. The mean deformation (land area shown) of the conventional projection is close to 39°; when inter-rupted in this manner it drops to approximately 19°.

Another expedient occasionally adopted for world maps is to "interrupt" the map, that is, to establish a central meridian for each land mass and to repeat the projection, as the gores of a globe. By repeating the less deformed portions of the grid the angular deformation may be greatly reduced, in most cases by at least a third (see Figs. 31, 32, and 33).

Another useful attribute of a projection concerns whether any portion of it may be cut from the whole and still be a relatively good projection for the smaller area. Any projection in which the meridians are straight lines and meet the parallels at right angles satisfies this requirement. With such a projection it is possible, for example, to make a map of the United States as a whole and then take from it a map of each state centered on its own central meridian.

There are many attributes of projections that when utilized to the full make the difference between a wise choice and a mediocre one. All maps are different, and no rules or principles can be stated, as in the case of the specific properties of projections, which will apply to each projection problem. For example, equivalence is a necessity for an areal distribution map, but the ultimate problem is to choose that equivalent projection which will best serve the specific display purpose of that map.

46 Relation of the Earth Grid to the Projection

There is no need for the earth grid to be presented in the conventional manner by a system of projection. Actually a map projection is a device for representing the spherical surface on a plane. Although a projection is usually constructed in such

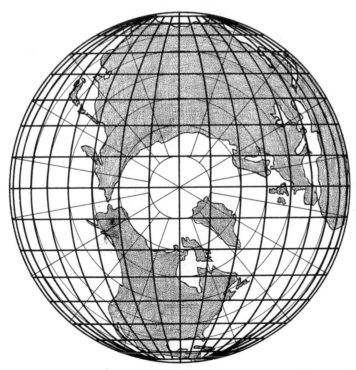

FIG. 34. A polar orthographic projection with an equatorial grid. Since the earth is spherical the coordinate grid will "fit" it in any position.

a fashion that the origin is the equator or some other parallel or parallels, this is not a requirement insofar as making the projection is concerned. An example is the azimuthal class of projections which may be centered anywhere. Although the earth grid will appear differently, the angular and areal relations of the projected surface will not vary because the surface of a sphere does not vary and neither does the surface of the plane on which it is projected.

One way of visualizing an origin other than usual for projections is to think of the earth grid as loose on the sphere while the land and water bodies remain stationary. Then it would be possible to slide or shift the grid in any way we desired. We might even go so far as to turn it 90° so that the equator of the grid coincides with

a meridian and runs through the Arctic and Antarctic regions, while the poles of the loose grid are antipodal points, both where the equator used to be, as in Fig. 34. If we then constructed a Mercator projection along the equator, we would have a projection which is, of course, conformal, but which, instead of representing the areas in the tropics in the best fashion, would present the areas along a meridian and across the poles in the best fashion (Fig. 35). It should be pointed out that most loxodromes would not be straight lines on this form of the Mercator.

Projections of the earth that are not conventionally oriented with respect to the earth grid are usually called *oblique* (Fig. 36) if the grid has been shifted less than 90° from its normal position and *transverse*

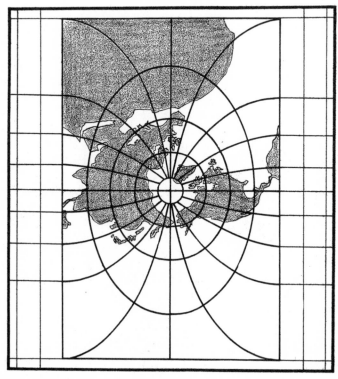

Fig. 35. The transverse Mercator. This form of the Mercator gives a conformal representation with the least deformation along the meridian chosen as the "equator." It is useful for an air chart of a route in a north-south direction. The conventional grid is shown on the sides.

if the full 90° shift has been made. Sometimes the transverse is also termed *polar*.

Any projection may be treated this way, and since the structural relations of the projection are not changed, regardless of the appearance of the grid, many earth relations can be bettered by "shifting the land masses" to bring about a better distribution of the deformation characteristics with respect to the areas of interest.

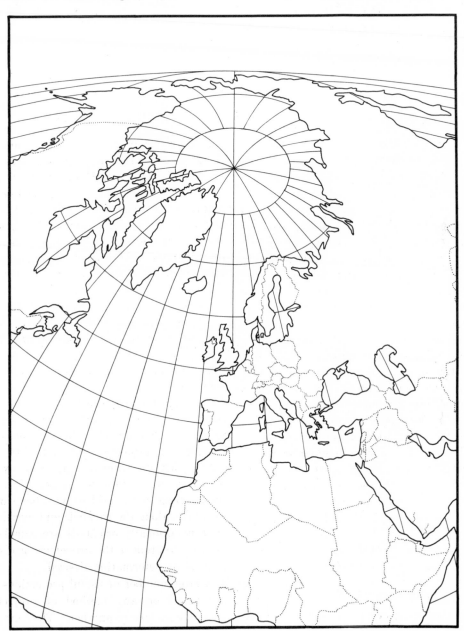

FIG. 36. A portion of an oblique Mollweide. North Atlantic relations are well presented on this representation, which gives somewhat the appearance of a portion of a globe but is, of course, equal-area.

4

The Construction of Projections

47 The Classification of Projections for Construction

In the last chapter, when considering projections on the basis of their employment, it was helpful to categorize them according to their properties. It was apparent, however, that projections having similar properties were markedly different as to their origin. For purposes of construction it is more convenient to consider projections on the basis of their appearance and their theoretical origin.

Projections may be thought of as being a kind of geometric transfer of the grid from the spherical form to some kind of surface that may then be developed into a plane. Thus, we may wrap a cylinder around a globe, in some fashion "project" the grid to the inside of the cylinder, and, finally, cut the cylinder lengthwise which allows it then to be flattened. Similarly, the grid may be projected to a cone perched on the globe, and the cone may be slit from base to apex; or the grid may be projected to a plane tangent to the surface and, of course, need no cutting. The line of tangency between the globe and the cylinder or cone and the point of tangency of the plane are the lines or points of origin. The projection depends upon the system of "projecting" the grid. Many projections are possible, but only a few of them pro-

vide desirable properties. The significant thing to remember is that whatever the deformation which results, it will, in most cases, be arranged parallel to the lines of origin in the case of the cylinder or cone and concentric to the point of origin in the case of the plane. The student should bear in mind that this same arrangement will ordinarily obtain no matter how the earth may be oriented inside the cylinder, under the cone, or with respect to the plane.

The equator is conventionally chosen as the line of origin for the cylindrical projections, and a parallel for the conic projections, but this is not necessary—it is merely convenient.

Although the theoretical method of construction is a valuable way by which to visualize mentally the three-dimensional problem of projection, in actuality not many grids are projected this way, except for those on a tangent plane. Instead, the spacings of the grid or, in other words, the scales along the parallels and meridians (if conventionally oriented) are calculated in order to produce the properties or distributions of deformation desired.

A large number of useful projections are not based on any method of projection from one surface to another. They are, instead, strictly mathematical arrangements of the grid oriented around axes of construction along which a desired scale relationship obtains, such as in the plane chart, or are projections of the grid within a prescribed shape, such as in the case of the oval projections.

Because of similarities of construction methods, and in order to enable the student to make comparisons more easily, projections for construction purposes will be grouped according to whether they are cylindrical, conic, oval, or azimuthal. The grouping is merely an expedient.

48　The Central Meridian and the Standard Parallel

When projections are constructed it is customary and convenient to begin the construction by first drawing one or two of the grid lines and then using them as lines of reference. Most conventional projections are drawn around a *central meridian,* which is a straight line, and with the projection symmetrical on each side of it. It is necessary therefore to draw only one side of the projection; the other side will simply be the reverse and may be copied from the first.

Any line along which the linear scale is the same as that of a generating globe of the same scale is called a *standard* line. In some cases the central meridian may also be a standard meridian as, for example, on the Bonne and polyconic, but more often central and standard do not go together. The term standard is more commonly applied to parallels along which the linear scale is constant and the same as on the generating globe. Thus, for instance, in the polyconic or sinusoidal all parallels are standard, whereas in the Albers and Lambert conics only two are standard.

49　Construction of Projections to Scale

Projections may be constructed in two ways. A number of the common projec-

tions may be graphically derived to fit a format, and provided (after construction) with a graphic bar scale. A numerical scale, or RF, for such a projection would be a very uneven number in most cases, such as 1:11, 453, 421, which would be inconvenient and hardly worth noting. Whenever possible it is better practice to construct the grid to a precise scale. This has the merit of promoting accuracy of construction (distances, etc., may be more easily checked for accuracy with known values), and of providing the map user and reader with an even, readily understood, and usable fractional scale.

Scale in map projections is, as we have seen, an elusive thing, for only in equivalent projections is there such a thing as consistent scale all over the projection. In *all* projections the linear scale varies in some way from place to place. On all cylindrical projections, for example, since the parallels are all the same length it is obvious that not more than two of the parallels can be their true length. To construct a projection at a given linear scale requires, in principle, a quite different operation than the construction of one at a given areal scale.

A projection at a linear scale is constructed so that the standard lines are the same length as those on a generating globe of a chosen size. The length of the line on the projection in relation to the length of the same line on the earth is the scale. To determine this is, of course, very easy, for: (1) the length of a meridian on the sphere is πR, and (2) the length of a parallel is the cosine of the latitude (ϕ) × the circumference of the sphere ($\cos \phi \times \pi D$). These may be determined either by calculating first their true length for the earth and then reducing the values by the desired ratio or by first reducing the earth (radius or diameter) by the chosen ratio to a globe and then calculating the map lengths desired.

To construct an equivalent projection at a given scale requires that the map outline enclose an area that is exactly the (scale) fractional part of the same area on the globe. For example, an equivalent projection of the world at a scale of $1:40,000,000^2$ would contain an area of about 3.4 square feet. In practice it is usually determined by finding the radius (R) of a globe whose surface area (A) bears the desired scale relation to the surface area of the earth. The area of a sphere is $4\pi R^2$. Therefore, if the surface area of the earth has been reduced by the square of $40,000,000$ $\left(A = \dfrac{\text{area of earth}}{40,000,000^2}\right)$, then to find the radius of the globe which has that area merely requires use of the formula $R = \dfrac{1}{2}\sqrt{\dfrac{A}{\pi}}$. Most equivalent world projections are regular shapes the axes of which bear a certain relation to R. The specific relationship for each projection will be stated in the description of its construction.

50   Techniques of Construction

Projections may be mechanically constructed in a number of ways depending upon the origin of the projection and the complexity of the grid to be produced. They can be constructed by working from an elevation of the globe drawn to the proper scale, and then by geometry and transfer the grid may be derived; they can be constructed by calculating the radius of curves and the spacings of parallels and meridians; or they can be constructed by consulting tables showing the x and y plane coordinates of the intersections of parallels and meridians, and then joining the points thus established by smooth lines to form the grid.

Tables are available for the construction of many map projections having specific properties. These tables frequently are given in some unit of distance (meters, miles, minutes of longitude at 0° latitude, etc.) calculated at a scale of 1:1, that is, actual earth size. To construct to scale it is necessary to reduce each unit by the scale ratio. It should be remembered that the scale relationship is an arithmetic linear relationship. It is necessary in the case of equivalent projections to establish the linear relationship by the proportion of squares.

51   The Construction of Cylindrical Projections

All conventional cylindrical projections may be constructed with a straightedge, dividers or scale, and a triangle. In cylindrical projections all meridians are the same length and all parallels are the same length; merely their spacing varies. In practice the length of the equator or standard parallel and the length of a meridian are determined. These are drawn at right angles to one another. The standard parallel is then subdivided for the longitudinal interval desired. The meridians are drawn through these points as parallel lines. The spacing of the parallels is then plotted along a meridian, and the parallels are drawn.

52   The Mercator Projection

Numerous tables of the spacing of the parallels on the Mercator projection are available. The values in Table 3 are taken from *Special Publication 68* of the U.S. Coast and Geodetic Survey, which shows values of the distance of each minute of latitude from the equator. A 5° grid interval is here presented. For any smaller interval it is necessary to consult the original table.

The values of Table 3 are given in minutes of longitude on the equator, which is simply a convenient unit of distance. The scale of the table is, of course, 1:1, making it necessary to reduce the values to the scale desired. A conversion procedure for a projection at 1:50,000,000 is here presented step by step so that the student may follow the reasoning.

1. The equatorial diameter of the earth is 7,928 miles. Reduced by 1 part in 50,-000,000 the diameter of a globe at 1:50,-000,000 becomes about 10.05 inches.

2. The circumference of a globe at a scale of 1:50,000,000 would be πD, or $3.1416 \times 10.05 = 31.56$ inches.

3. There are 21,600 ($360° \times 60'$) minutes of longitude in the equatorial circle.

4. Each minute of longitude on a globe 1:50,000,000 would be 0.00146 inch in length ($31.56 \div 21,600$).

5. Therefore, each value in the table would be multiplied by 0.00146 to find the distance in inches on a projection at 1:50,000,000 of the minutes of longitude.

The same value can be determined by dividing the length of the earth unit in inches by the denominator of the scale ($72,960 \div 50,000,000 = 0.00146$).

TABLE 3. DISTANCES OF THE PARALLELS FROM THE EQUATOR ON THE MERCATOR PROJECTION IN MINUTES OF LONGITUDE AT THE EQUATOR. (From Deetz and Adams, *Elements of Map Projection.*)

0°	000.000	50°	3 456.581
5°	298.348	55°	3 948.830
10°	599.019	60°	4 507.133
15°	904.422	65°	5 157.629
20°	1 217.159	70°	5 943.955
25°	1 540.134	75°	6 947.761
30°	1 876.706	80°	8 352.176
35°	2 230.898		(The pole is in-
40°	2 607.683		finitely dis-
45°	3 013.427		tant)

Note. Values for each minute of latitude are given in the reference from which the above abbreviated table is taken.

53 The Plane Chart

This projection is more precisely called the equirectangular projection, the name plane chart being reserved for the phase wherein the equator is standard. In any case its construction is relatively simple.

A standard parallel is chosen, and its length is calculated or determined from tables. The length of any parallel (ϕ) may be calculated by multiplying the circumference of the earth by the cosine of the latitude. It may also be obtained by referring to the table of lengths of the degrees of the parallel (Table 17, Appendix C) and multiplying the value given for the latitude by the number of degrees the map is to extend. It must then, of course, be reduced to scale. The results, however determined, are then marked on a straight horizontal line. This is the standard parallel. Vertical lines are drawn through the points to establish the meridians. The other parallels are determined by pointing off the actual distance between the parallels (reduced to scale) as determined from the table of meridional parts (Table 18, Appendix C).

If the equator is made the standard parallel the projection will be made up of squares; any other standard parallels will make rectangles whose north-south dimension is the long one; if the poles were made the "standard parallels" the "projection" would be but a straight vertical line!

54 The Cylindrical Equal-Area Projection

The cylindrical equal-area projection is, like all cylindrical projections, relatively easy to construct, requiring only a straightedge, dividers or scale, and a triangle. The equator alone or any pair of parallels spaced equally from the equator may be chosen as standard. Since the angular deformation is zero along the parallel or parallels chosen as standard these may be

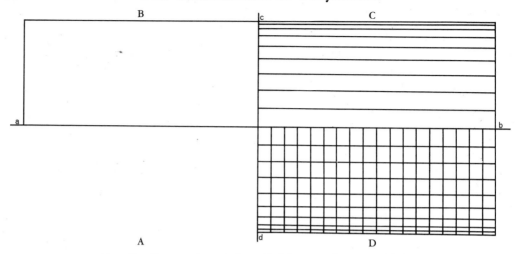

Fig. 37. Construction of the cylindrical equal-area projection.

selected so that they pass through the areas of significance. If the projection is desired for only a portion of the earth rather than the whole, the projection is designed merely as a part of a larger, incomplete world projection.

This projection requires some calculation, but the formulas are elementary and are accomplished merely through the use of arithmetic. The general formulas for any form of the projection are:

1. Length of all parallels is $2R\pi \times \cos \theta$.
2. Length of all meridians is $2R \div \cos \theta$.
3. Distance of each parallel from equator is $R \sin \phi \div \cos \theta$.

R is the radius of the generating globe of chosen *area scale;* θ is the standard parallel; ϕ is latitude.

The procedure for construction is similar to that for other cylindrical projections. Perpendicular lines are drawn to represent the equator and a meridian (Fig. 37). The length of the parallel chosen as standard (*ab*) is marked off on the equator. The length of a meridian (*cd*) is determined. These dimensions define a rectangle forming the poles and the bounding meridian of the projection. The distances of the paral-

lels from the equator are then laid off on a meridian, and the parallels are drawn parallel to the equator as in quadrant *C*, Fig. 37. The parallels are, of course, equally subdivided by the meridians as in quadrant *D*.

55   The Construction of Conic Projections

Conic projections may be constructed either from tables by the x and y coordinate system, or by the use of a straightedge and a compass capable of drawing large arcs. In the latter procedure it is necessary to determine the radii of the parallel arcs and the spacing of the meridians on the parallels. In all true conic projections the meridians are equally spaced along each parallel, and the parallels are arcs of circles which may or may not be concentric. The meridians may or may not be straight lines.

All conic projections are symmetrical around the central meridian. Thus, it is necessary only to draw one side of the projection; the other side may be copied by either folding the paper or copying it onto another paper with the aid of a light-table.

If the paper is opaque a sheet of transparent paper may be laid over the projection, the intersections pricked, and the paper then "flopped over" and the points pricked through again.

56 The Conic with Two Standard Parallels

It is possible to make a projection that in theory results from a cone that intersects the earth at two parallels. This is sometimes called a secant conic projection. As can be seen from Fig. 38, the scale would not be correct along the meridians, for the parallels would be too close together between the standard parallels and too far apart outside them. It is better to construct the projection so that the scale is correct along all the meridians.

To construct the conic projection with two standard parallels first draw a vertical line, ab in Fig. 39, in the center of the paper. Select the two parallels, ϕ_1 and ϕ_2, to be made standard, and determine their actual distance apart on the generating globe of the desired linear scale. If c and d are then positions on ab, and if the radius, R, of the globe to be projected, at

scale has been determined, distance cd may be determined by

$$cd = 2\pi R \frac{\phi_1 - \phi_2}{360}$$

This distance may also be determined by reducing to scale the actual spacing on the earth. Points c and d should be placed in a convenient location on the paper so that the developed projection will be centered properly. Points c and d being the intersections of the standard parallels with the central meridian, it is next necessary to determine the position on ab of the center, x, from which the two concentric arcs may be drawn. This may be done by

or

$$\frac{xc}{cd} = \frac{\cos \phi_1}{\cos \phi_2 - \cos \phi_1}$$

$$xc = \frac{\cos \phi_1 \times cd}{\cos \phi_2 - \cos \phi_1}$$

Draw arcs with x as the center through c and d. Extend these arcs (*ecg* and *fdh*) a distance equal to the length of the standard parallels which is to be included between the extreme meridians of the map.

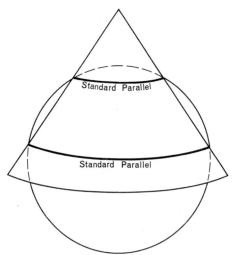
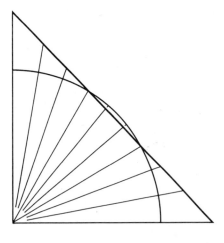

Fig. 38. The theory of the secant conic projection with two standard parallels.

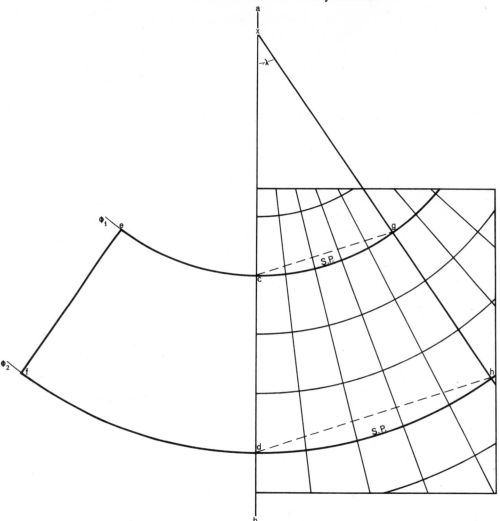

FIG. 39.   Construction of the conic with two standard parallels.   Note that this is not a secant conic.

Space the arcs of the other parallels equally on *ab*.

The meridians are equally spaced on the parallels and are correctly spaced on the two standard parallels.   The most nearly accurate means of doing this is by first determining the chord distances of the bounding meridian, chord *cg* on ϕ_1 and chord *dh* on ϕ_2.   The procedure for doing this is shown in detail below, for it is a useful means of subdividing arcs.

To determine the chord distance *cg* on ϕ_1:

1. Determine longitude on ϕ_1 to be represented by *cg*, for example, 25°.

2. The length of ϕ_1 on the sphere of chosen scale $= 2\pi R \cos \phi_1$.

3. Let *xc* be radius *r*.   The circumference of a circle with radius $r = 2\pi r$.

4. Therefore, angle λ (angle *cxg* on Fig. 39) may be determined by

$$\lambda = \frac{2\pi R \cos \phi_1}{2\pi r} \times 25° = \frac{R \cos \phi_1}{r} \times 25°.$$

5. Chord distance $cg = 2r \sin \dfrac{\lambda}{2}.$

Lay off the chord distance cg. Determine in similar fashion chord distance dh. Subdivide the parallels in question (with dividers) into the desired number of equal parts for the meridians. Join homologous points with straight lines.

Linear distances along the meridians and along the standard parallels are correct, but the projection has no special properties. For a limited area, however, it has little distortion, and its ease of construction and neat appearance make it a useful projection.

57 The Lambert Conformal Conic Projection

This projection is similar in appearance to the Albers and the simple conic. It too has straight-line meridians that meet at a common center; the parallels are arcs of circles, two of which are standard; and the parallels and meridians meet at right angles. The only difference is in the spac-

ings of the parallels and meridians. In the Lambert conic they are so spaced as to satisfy the condition of conformality.

The calculation of this projection requires mathematical computations and facility beyond the average cartographer. On account of its relatively wide use for air-navigation maps, many tables for its construction with various standard parallels have been published. For example, a table for the construction of a map of the United States with standard parallels at 29° and 45° is given in the U.S. Coast and Geodetic Survey *Special Publication 52*. As in the case of the Albers projection it is advisable, if equal distribution of scale error is desired, to space the standard parallels so that they include between them two-thirds of the meridional section to be mapped.

A Lambert conic with standard parallels at 36° and 54° is useful for middle-latitude areas. Table 4 gives the radii of the parallels in meters for a scale of 1:1. It is, of course, necessary to reduce each value to the scale desired.

To construct the projection draw a line, cd in Fig. 40, which will be the central

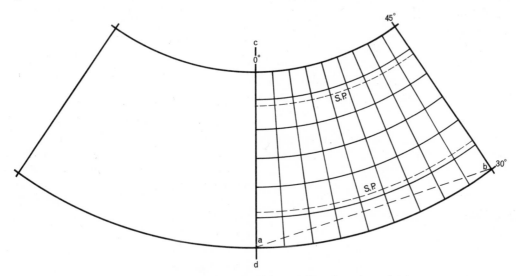

Fig. 40. Construction of the Lambert conformal conic projection.

meridian. The line must be sufficiently long so that it will include the center of the arcs of latitude. With a beam compass describe arcs with radii, reduced to scale, taken from Table 4.

TABLE 4. TABLE FOR THE CONSTRUCTION OF A LAMBERT CONFORMAL CONIC PROJECTION. STANDARD PARALLELS 36° AND 54°. (From Deetz and Adams, *Elements of Map Projection*.)

Lat.	Radii, meters	Lat.	Radii, meters
75°	2 787 926	40°	6 833 183
70°	3 430 294	35°	7 386 250
65°	4 035 253	30°	7 946 911
60°	4 615 579	25°	8 519 065
55°	5 179 774	20°	9 106 796
50°	5 734 157	15°	9 714 516
45°	6 283 826		

To determine the meridians it is necessary to calculate the chord distance on a lower parallel from its intersection with the central meridian (0°) to its intersection with an outer meridian. This is done by means of the following formula:

$$\text{chord} = 2r \sin \frac{n\lambda}{2}$$

where $n = 0.7101$; $\lambda =$ longitude out from central meridian; $r =$ radius of parallel in question.

The above formula (without n) is the general formula for the determination of chord distance. It is necessary to introduce the constant n (in this case 0.7101) for the projection in question.

Example. On parallel 30° the chord of 45° (see Fig. 40) out from the central meridian =

1. $0.7101 \times 45° = 31° 57' 14'' = n\lambda$; therefore
2. $n\lambda/2 = 15° 58' 37''$.
3. Sin $15° 58' 37'' = .27534$.
4. $2r = 15{,}893{,}822$ meters.
5. $15{,}893{,}822 \times .27534 = 4{,}376{,}200$ meters.

The value thus determined, ab in Fig. 40, is reduced by the desired scale ratio and measured out from the intersection of the parallel and the central meridian to the bounding meridian. If point b, thus located, is connected by means of a straightedge with the same center used in describing the parallels, this will determine the outer meridian. If a long straightedge is not available the same procedure may be followed (determining the chord) for another parallel in the upper part of the map, and the two points, thus determined, joined by a straight line. This will produce the same result. Since the parallels are equally subdivided by the meridians, the other meridians may be easily located.

58   The Albers Equal-Area Projection

The construction procedure for this projection is essentially the same as for the preceding projection, the Lambert conic. Like the Lambert, the Albers conic is suited to representation of an area predominately east-west in extent in the middle and high latitudes.

Table 5 gives the radii of the parallels and the lengths of chords on two parallels for a map of the United States with standard parallels 29° 30′ and 45° 30′. The scale of the table is 1:1, and the values are in meters. As in the preceding projection, reduction to the desired scale is necessary.

59   The Polyconic Projection

In general the polyconic is not suitable for small-scale maps. On account of its balance of error and ease of construction it is primarily a survey projection, and this book is concerned more especially with smaller-scale cartography. Consequently, procedures for constructing the polyconic are not included. The student who may have need to construct one is referred to the directions in the U.S. Coast and Geodetic Survey *Special Publication 68*, p. 60, and the tables in *Special Publication 5*.

TABLE 5. TABLE FOR CONSTRUCTION OF ALBERS EQUAL-AREA PROJECTION WITH STANDARD PARALLELS 29° 30′ AND 45° 30′. (From Deetz and Adams, *Elements of Map Projection.*)

Lat.	Radius of parallel, meters
20°	10 253 177
21°	10 145 579
22°	10 037 540
23°	9 929 080
24°	9 820 218
25°	9 710 969
26°	9 601 361
27°	9 491 409
28°	9 381 139
29°	9 270 576
29° 30′	9 215 188
30°	9 159 738
31°	9 048 648
32°	8 937 337
33°	8 825 827
34°	8 714 150
35°	8 602 328
36°	8 490 392
37°	8 378 377
38°	8 266 312
39°	8 154 228
40°	8 042 163
41°	7 930 152
42°	7 818 231
43°	7 706 444
44°	7 594 828
45°	7 483 426
45° 30′	7 427 822
46°	7 372 288
47°	7 261 459
48°	7 150 987
49°	7 040 925
50°	6 931 333
51°	6 822 264
52°	6 713 780

Chord Distances in Meters

Long. from central meridian	on Lat. 25°	on Lat. 45°
1°	102 185	78 745
5°	510 867	393 682
25°	2 547 270	1 962 966
30°		2 352 568

60 The Bonne Projection

The Bonne projection is a useful projection when an equal-area conic projection is desired for a limited area, but when one does not wish to go to the trouble of preparing an Albers. The Bonne is, like all useful conics, a modified projection in that it cannot actually be projected on the enveloping cone.

Theoretically, the cone is tangent to a parallel (ϕ) which is selected near the cen-

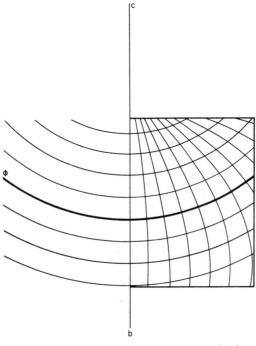

FIG. 41. Construction of the Bonne projection.

ter of the area to be mapped. The radius (r) of this parallel on the map will be

$$r = R \cot \phi$$

in which R is the radius of the generating globe of the desired area scale. To construct the projection draw a vertical line, *cb* in Fig. 41, that is long enough to include the latitudinal extent desired and the center (*c*) of the "standard" parallel. Describe an arc for the "standard parallel" with *r* as the radius. Plot points on *cb* north and south of this parallel spaced equally at scale for the other parallels. Through these points draw arcs with *c* as their center. Subdivide the arcs truly and draw smooth lines through homologous points for the meridians. Meridians cannot be located by computing the chord distance for a given longitude out from the central meridian and then subdividing that distance with dividers along the parallel. This would result in straight-line meridians and the projection would not be equal-area.

61 The Construction of Oval Projections

Most useful oval projections are equivalent, and they are constructed to an area scale. The linear dimensions, for construction purposes, of an oval projection depend upon the shape of the bounding meridian which encloses the projection. It is obvious that the axes of two dissimilar shapes would be different if both shapes enclose the same area, that is, if they were the same area scale. Most oval projections have a vertical axis half the length of the horizontal axis; and, in the conventional equatorial phase, this is the relation to be expected between a meridian and the equator. The relationship between the generating globe and the particular projection being constructed is merely one that states the length of the central meridian on the projection compared to the radius (R) of the generating globe of the same area scale. The equator being twice the length of the central meridian, no further calculation is necessary. The determination of the radius (R) of the globe of equal area was explained in Article 49.

On the majority of the oval projections the meridians are equally spaced along the parallels. The spacing of the parallels along the central meridian varies from projection to projection. These values are available in tabular form.

62 The Sinusoidal Projection

The sinusoidal projection is particularly simple to construct, since the spacings of the parallels and meridians are the same (to scale) as they are on the earth. The length of the central meridian is 3.1416 times the radius (R) of a generating globe of equal area. The equator is twice the length of the central meridian.

To construct the projection a horizontal line representing the equator, *ab* in Fig. 42, is drawn twice the length of the central meridian. The equator is bisected, and at point *o* a perpendicular central meridian (*cd*) is constructed. The positions of the parallels on *cd* are determined by spacing them as they are on the globe. For a small-scale projection this means equally; for a large-scale projection the exact spacings may be taken from Table 18, Appendix C. Through the points thus established the parallels are drawn parallel to the equator as in quadrant *B*. The lengths of the various parallels are their true lengths (to scale) as on the earth and may be determined by multiplying the length of the equator (*ab*) by the cosine of the latitude. One-half this value is plotted on each side of the central meridian. The meridians are drawn by subdividing, as in quadrant *C*, each parallel equally, with dividers, and drawing smooth curves (with a French curve) through homologous points as in quadrant *D*.

The linear scale along the parallels and the central meridian is correct (same as the generating globe), and is the square root of the area scale; i.e., if the area scale is 1:50,000,000² the linear scale along the parallels and the central meridian will be 1:50,000,000. This is the only equivalent oval projection in which this relationship exists, although some others come close to it.

63 The Mollweide Projection

The Mollweide projection does not have the simple relationship to the sphere that characterizes the sinusoidal. The merid-

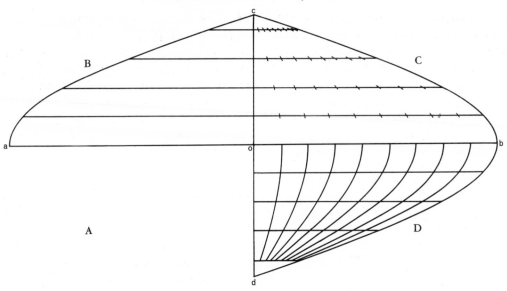

FIG. 42. Construction of the sinusoidal projection.

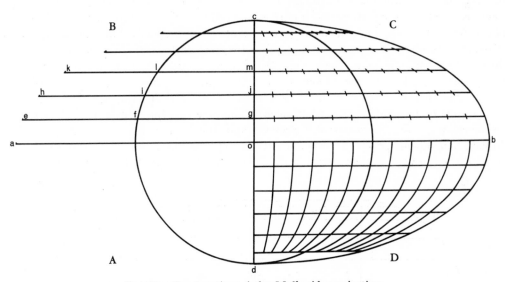

FIG. 43. Construction of the Mollweide projection.

ians of the sinusoidal are sine curves which produce a pointed appearance near the poles, whereas in the Mollweide the meridians are ellipses, which provide a projection shape that is somewhat less of a radical departure from the globe impression. The length of the central meridian is 2.8284 times the radius (R) of a generating globe

of equal area. The equator is twice the length of the central meridian.

To construct the projection a horizontal line representing the equator, *ab* in Fig. 43, is drawn twice the length of the central meridian. The equator is bisected, and at point *o* a perpendicular central meridian (*cd*) is constructed. A circle whose radius is *oc* is constructed around point *o*. This contains a hemisphere. The spacing of the parallels on the central meridian is given in Table 6, in which *oc* equals 1. These posi-

TABLE 6. DISTANCES OF THE PARALLELS FROM THE EQUATOR IN THE MOLLWEIDE PROJECTION (*oc* = 1). (From Deetz and Adams, *Elements of Map Projection*.)

0°	0.000	50°	0.651
5°	0.069	55°	0.708
10°	0.137	60°	0.762
15°	0.205	65°	0.814
20°	0.272	70°	0.862
25°	0.339	75°	0.906
30°	0.404	80°	0.945
35°	0.468	85°	0.978
40°	0.531	90°	1.000
45°	0.592		

tions are plotted on the central meridian, and the parallels are drawn through the points parallel to the equator. Each parallel is extended outside the hemisphere circle a distance equal to its length inside the circle. Thus, in quadrant *B* of Fig. 43, *ef* = *fg*, *hi* = *ij*, *kl* = *lm*, etc. Each parallel is subdivided equally with dividers, as in quadrant *C*, to establish the position of the meridians. The meridians are drawn through homologous points, as in quadrant *D*, with the aid of a French curve.

64 The Eckert IV Projection

The Eckert IV projection is representative of a large group of projections in which the pole is represented by a line half the length of the equator, rather than by a point, as in the case of the Mollweide and the sinusoidal. The rather excessive shearing of the higher latitudes is somewhat lessened by this device, at the expense, however, of increased angular deformation in the lower latitudes. As in the other oval projections the length of the central meridian is half the length of the equator. In the Eckert IV projection the length of the central meridian is 2.6530 times the radius (*R*) of a generating globe of equal area.

To construct the projection a horizontal line representing the equator, *ab* in Fig. 44, is drawn twice the length of the central meridian. The equator is bisected, and at point *o* a perpendicular central meridian (*cd*) is constructed. On each side of the central meridian a tangent circle is drawn. In quadrant *B* the center of one circle (*e*) is on *ab* and midway between *a* and *o*. The pole is a line (*fg*) perpendicular to *cd* and equal in length to *ao* and *cd*. The spacing of the parallels on the central meridian is given in Table 7, in which *oc* = 1.

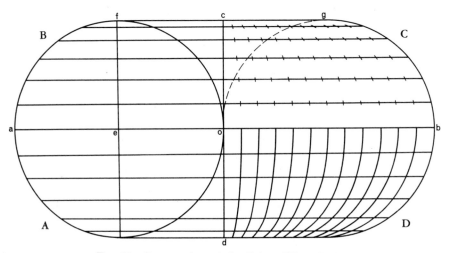

FIG. 44. Construction of the Eckert IV projection.

TABLE 7. DISTANCES OF THE PARALLELS FROM
THE EQUATOR IN THE ECKERT IV PROJECTION
$(oc = 1)$.

0°	0.000	50°	0.718
5°	0.078	55°	0.775
10°	0.155	60°	0.827
15°	0.232	65°	0.874
20°	0.308	70°	0.915
25°	0.382	75°	0.950
30°	0.454	80°	0.976
35°	0.525	85°	0.994
40°	0.592	90°	1.000
45°	0.657		

These positions are plotted on the central
meridian, and the parallels are drawn
through the points parallel to the equator
as in quadrant B, Fig. 44. Each parallel
is subdivided equally with dividers, as in
quadrant C, to establish the position of
the meridians. The meridians are drawn
through homologous points, as in quadrant
D, with the aid of a French curve.

65 The Construction of Azimuthal Projections

Although azimuthal projections have
more in common with each other than any
other class of projections, the uses and
common methods of construction are quite
varied. Some can be easily constructed
geometrically; some cannot in any way be
constructed geometrically. Some are most
expeditiously put together by using x and
y coordinates to locate grid intersections;
others by transforming one projection into
another. It is this last method that is
the key to understanding these projections.
Any azimuthal projection can be transformed into any other by merely relocating the grid intersections along their azimuths from the center of the projection, for
the projections vary only as to the radial
scale from the center of the projection (see
Fig. 45).

There are a great many azimuthal projections (theoretically an infinite number
are possible), but only a few have desirable properties. Of these few, one, the

gnomonic, is used primarily as a planning
map in connection with navigation, and a
cartographer is rarely called upon to construct it. The remaining common azimuthal projections, the Lambert equal-
area, the orthographic, the stereographic,
and the azimuthal equidistant, are much

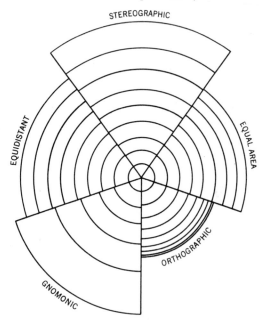

FIG. 45. Comparison of azimuthal projections centered at the pole. Note that the only variation
is in the spacing of the parallels; in other words,
the only difference among them is the radial scale.
The relationship obtains wherever the projections
may be centered.

in demand in these days of "one-world"
consciousness, and methods for their construction will be suggested here. In the
interests of brevity not all the possibilities
will be detailed, and the reader is referred
to any of the standard works on map projections for a fuller account of possible
procedures.

Since the azimuthal projections can,
theoretically at least, be projected on a
tangent plane, and since the point of tangency may be anywhere on the sphere, it is
evident that each projection may have

many different appearances. The names *equatorial, meridional, oblique,* and *polar* are variously employed to refer to them. It is perhaps better and clearer practice when labeling to name the projection, as Lambert equal-area, and follow it with a statement as to where it is centered, since changing the point of tangency does not change in any way the quality of the projection.

66 The Stereographic Projection

The stereographic projection is the conformal graticule in the azimuthal group of projections. In addition to being conformal, it has a quality shared by no other projection, namely, that all circles on the earth are represented by circles on the projection. This being the case, the parallels and meridians in the stereographic are arcs of circles, which makes the projection relatively easy to draw. As is true in all azimuthal projections, great circles passing through the center of the projection are represented by straight lines. They may be considered as arcs of circles whose radii are of infinite length. Because it is a projection composed of straight lines or arcs of smaller circles, all that is necessary to draw this projection, centered anywhere, is a straightedge and a compass, preferably a beam compass.

It is relatively easy to calculate the values necessary to center the projection anywhere. The method is given in Appendix F, together with tables for constructing the projection at 10° latitude intervals. The table for centering the projection at 40° is included here to illustrate the construction procedure. It is much easier and quicker to construct the projection from calculated tables, and such procedure also eliminates errors that usually creep in when one works with a maze of construction lines, protractors, and the like.

Table 8 has been calculated for a globe the diameter (*D*) of which is unity. This

TABLE 8. TABLE FOR CONSTRUCTING THE STEREO-GRAPHIC PROJECTION CENTERED ON 40°.

$D = 1$

Parallels	Upper		Lower
North pole		0.46631	
80°	0.57735		0.36397
70°	0.70021		0.26795
60°	0.83910		0.17633
50°	1.00000		0.08749
40°	1.19175		0.00000
30°	1.42815		−0.08749
20°	1.73205		−0.17633
10°	2.14451		−0.26795
0°	2.74748		−0.36397
10°	3.73205		−0.46631
20°	5.67128		−0.57735
30°	11.43005		−0.70021
40°	−0.83910	−0.83910	−0.83910
50°	−1.00000		−11.43005
60°	−1.19175		−5.67128
70°	−1.42815		−3.73205
80°	−1.73205		−2.74748
South pole		−2.14451	

Homolatitude = −0.83910

Meridians	Bow	Center
10°	0.11421	7.40335
20°	0.23018	3.58658
30°	0.34986	2.26104
40°	0.47513	1.55573
50°	0.60872	1.09537
60°	0.75368	0.75368
70°	0.91406	0.47513
80°	1.09537	0.23018
90°	1.30541	0.00000

means that the values (and those in Appendix F) need only to be multiplied by the number of inches, or other units, contained in the diameter of the generating globe of chosen scale.

To construct the projection first draw a vertical line, *ab* in Fig. 46. Locate on *ab* the center of the projection (*o*), in this case 40°, and with *o* as the center describe a circle the diameter of which is twice the diameter of the generating globe. The parallels are drawn by locating on *ab* the upper (*U*) and lower (*L*) points of each parallel. The center of the circle representing the parallel is midway between the points *U* and *L* for each parallel. For ex-

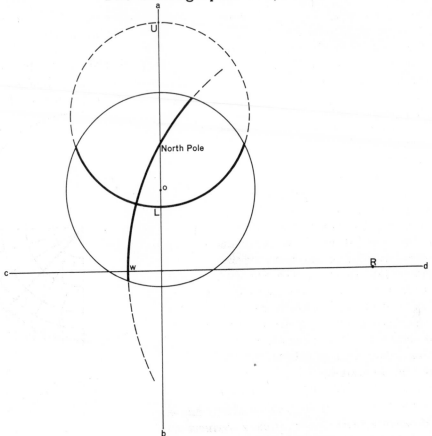

Fig. 46. Construction of the stereographic projection.

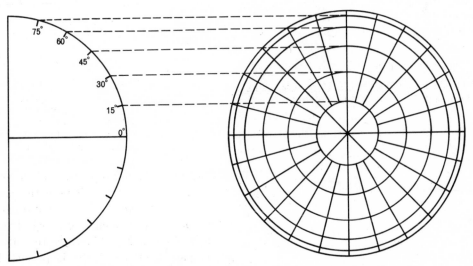

Fig. 47. Construction of the orthographic projection centered on the pole.

ample, from Table 8 the upper intersection with *ab* for the parallel of 20° is 1.73205 above *o* and is at *U* in Fig. 46. The lower intersection is 0.17633 below *o* (shown by the minus sign) and is located at *L*. Midway between these points is the center of the circle representing the parallel of 20°.* The other parallels are similarly located and drawn with a compass.

The centers of the arcs representing the meridians are all located along a straight line, *cd* in Fig. 46, perpendicular to *ab* which is the homolatitude of the center of the projection. The homolatitude of any point is the same latitude in the opposite hemisphere. In Fig. 46, the homolatitude is located 0.83910 below *o*. The *bow* distance is the distance from the central meridian (*ab*) along the homolatitude (*cd*) to the intersection of the meridian with the homolatitude. The center distance is the distance along the homolatitude, on the opposite side of *ab*, to the center of the arc that represents the meridian. In Fig. 46, the bow distance for the meridian of 30° is 0.34986 and the intersection is at *w* on *cd*. The center distance is 2.26104 on the other side of *ab* and is located at *R*. The arc drawn through *w* must pass through the pole. The other meridians are drawn in similar fashion, first for one side and then repeated for the other side. They may, of course, be numbered in any desired sequence depending upon what part of the earth is being mapped.

It will be noted that the spacing of the parallels on the central meridian increases away from the center. Since the parallels are evenly spaced on the earth this establishes the radial scale for the projection.

* It should be noted that any circle on the earth is found on the projection by plotting first the ends of its diameter on a great circle through the center. Midway between these points is the *construction* center of the circle, but not the actual center.

The scale is the same from the center to the periphery in any direction.

67 The Orthographic Projection

The orthographic projection is a view of the globe as it would appear (if it could

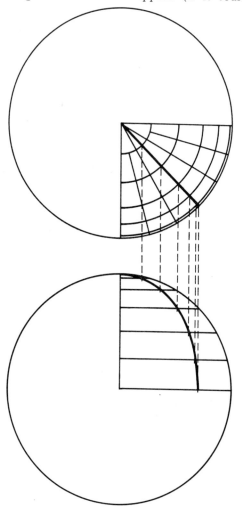

Fig. 48. Construction of the orthographic projection centered on the equator.

be seen) from infinity; that is to say, it is projected upon a plane with parallel lines. In this sense it is like an architect's elevation. The principle of its construction can be seen in Fig. 47, where the latitudinal spacing on the globe is projected by parallel lines to the central meridian of the projection. Being an azimuthal projection all great circles through the center are straight lines and azimuths from the center are correct. When the pole is the center all great circles that pass through it are meridians; hence, all meridians on the projection are straight lines and are correctly arranged around the pole.

The construction of the projection centered on the equator is no more involved. The procedure is illustrated in Fig. 48. The parallel spacing on the central merid-

ian is the same as in the polar case, but the parallels are horizontal lines. The positions of the meridians on the parallels is carried over from the polar case as illustrated. Since all four quadrants are images of one another only one need be drawn. The others may be traced.

The orthographic projection centered on the pole or the equator is seldom used. It is more often centered on some point of interest between the pole and the equator. This may be accomplished by employing a polar and equatorial case as in Fig. 49.

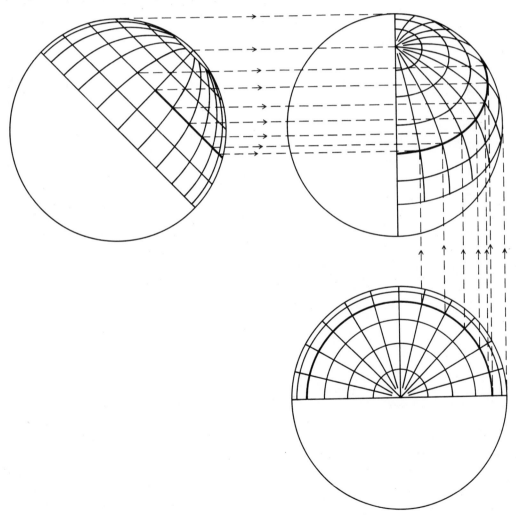

FIG. 49. Construction of the oblique orthographic projection.

It may also be drawn by using the equatorial case as a nomograph as described in Article 70. A third method is to trace a photograph of the globe centered at the desired spot. A photograph of the globe is not a true orthographic, for some perspective convergence is bound to occur in the photographing, even when the camera is at a considerable distance. Neverthe-

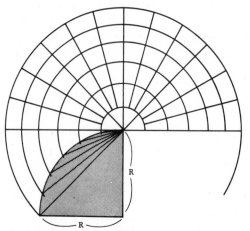

FIG. 50. Construction of the Lambert equal-area projection centered on the pole.

less, the result is a true azimuthal projection and is very nearly the same as the orthographic. Since the only useful precise property is its azimuthality, nothing is lost by using a photograph.

68   The Lambert Equal-Area Projection

Like the orthographic, the Lambert azimuthal equal-area projection is most useful when centered in the area of interest, although the projection is frequently seen in the polar case to accompany other projections that distort areas considerably. The polar case is easily constructed as illustrated in Fig. 50. A segment of the globe is drawn with R as the radius of the generating globe of chosen area scale. The chord distances from the pole to the parallels are carried up to a tangent with a compass and establish the positions of the

parallels on the projection. The meridians, as in other azimuthal projections, are straight lines through the poles.

The equatorial case of the projection is somewhat more difficult to construct graphically and is more easily accomplished by plotting the x and y coordinate positions of the grid intersections from tables. Tables 20 and 21 in Appendix E give values for every 10°.

As with most of the azimuthal projections the oblique case centered on some area of interest is the most useful. The oblique case may be derived from the equatorial by using the latter as a nomograph in the manner outlined in Article 70. Coordinates are given in Appendix E for a grid centered at latitude 40°, which is an appropriate place for maps of the United States or North America, among others, to be centered.

Since this projection is equal-area it should be constructed to an area scale. The tables referred to above have been prepared on the basis of $R = 1$, so that each value in the tables needs only to be multiplied by the length of the radius of the generating globe of chosen area scale.

69   The Azimuthal Equidistant Projection

The azimuthal equidistant projection is a most useful projection when directions or distances from a particular point are of interest, and it is not difficult to construct the projection centered on any spot. The polar case is constructed by first drawing an appropriate set of meridians and then constructing equally spaced circles concentric around the pole. This may be extended to include the whole earth, in which case the bounding circle is the opposite pole as in Fig. 51. As may be seen the area and linear distortions become large as the periphery is approached. A world map centered on a pole is not a very appropriate use of the azimuthal equidistant projection for reasons outlined in Article 43.

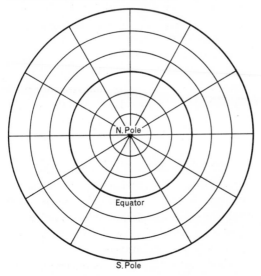

Fig. 51. The azimuthal equidistant projection centered on the pole.

For an oblique case the simplest procedure is to prepare first a stereographic projection centered at the desired latitude. This may then be transformed (to any other azimuthal projection) by merely relocating the positions of the intersections of the new grid along their azimuths from the center. This is accomplished by marking off on one edge of a strip of paper the radial scale of the stereographic and on the other edge the radial scale of the equidistant. The strip is then placed on the stereographic and the distance of a grid intersection from the center noted. This distance is transferred to the radial scale of the equidistant and the position plotted *along the same azimuth*. Figure 52 illustrates this procedure. Of course, the scale of the new projection may be changed, if desired, at the same time.

Positions outside the inner hemisphere of the stereographic may be located in the following manner. When the equidistant hemisphere has been completed the stereographic is no longer needed. The position of every point on the earth is obviously 180° from its antipode; each point and its antipode lie on a great circle through the center of the projection; the diameter of the hemisphere is 180°; and the scale is

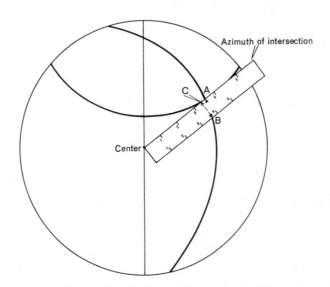

Fig. 52. The transformation of one azimuthal to another. *A* is the distance from the center of a point according to the radial scale of the stereographic. *B* is the distance of the same point according to the radial scale of the equidistant. *C* is the location of the point along the same azimuth on the equidistant.

uniform from the center. Thus, all that is necessary is to mark on a straightedge the diameter of the hemisphere and keeping the edge on the center of the projection locate all the outer intersections from their antipodes in the inner hemisphere.

70   Shifting the Center of the Projection

In the previous chapter it was shown that each projection has a specific pattern of inherent deformation. Most distribution maps of hemispherical or world-wide extent have a sort of "center of gravity" of distortion, and it is frequently desirable to "balance" the projection around this distribution, rather than merely constructing it in its conventional equatorial or polar orientation. This was suggested in the section on azimuthal projections, but it is by no means limited to that class of projections.

There are several ways of changing the "viewpoint" of a projection, that is to say, of centering it anywhere on the sphere. The general procedure involves locating the positions of the grid intersections on the sphere when the earth grid has been "shifted" in the manner suggested in Article 46. This is relatively easy when working with the azimuthal projections, and the procedure for viewing the sphere in any fashion has been treated in those

sections. It is frequently the case, however, that one is desirous of producing an "oblique" azimuthal without the necessity of going through the process of transformation from the stereographic. If one has available the equatorial case of the projection desired, it is possible to do this by employing an ingenious nomographic process best described by R. E. Harrison. The following explanation is slightly modified from his paper which appeared in *The Geographical Review*, 1943.

"To illustrate the procedure the construction of an orthographic projection centered at 35°N is here described. The same procedure is followed in making any azimuthal projection, with only minor and rather obvious differences.

"First, the circular nomograph (the equatorial case) is placed on a drawing board and covered with a rectangular piece of tracing paper that overlaps the nomograph on the sides but not at the top and bottom. The tracing paper is fixed to the board. A needle or round-shanked thumbtack is thrust firmly through tracing paper and nomograph at the center of the latter. As the needle or tack remains in position until the new grid is completed, it is well first to reinforce the nomograph at the center with cellulose tape or similar material. The nomograph is positioned so that its equator is vertical (stage I, Fig. 53).

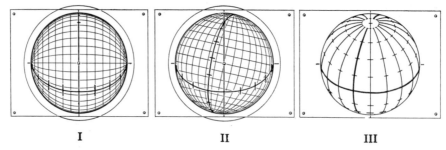

| I | II | III |

FIG. 53. Three stages in the construction from a nomograph of an orthographic grid centered at 35°. Light lines show the nomograph, heavy lines construction on the tracing paper. Courtesy of *The Geographical Review* published by the American Geographical Society of New York.

The intersections of the equator and the central meridian with the bounding circle are then lightly marked on the tracing paper. Thirty-five degrees are counted off below the center along the equator of the nomograph; the meridian passing through this point becomes the equator of the new grid. This is traced, and the intersections of the parallels of the nomograph with the new equator are marked at the desired interval of the grid. This should be done so that the angles of the intersections are correctly preserved, because of a remarkable feature of the nomographic method: instead of providing horizontal and vertical coordinates to establish the points of crossing as in mathematical and other graphic procedures, it gives not only the point but the correct angle of any intersection on the projection. Before changing the orientation of the nomograph, the North Pole is marked by counting 90° from the new equator along the upright center line. (When making an azimuthal equidistant or equal-area projection, the South Pole is also marked.)

"At this stage the North Pole and the equator (with the meridional intersections) are located (stage I, Fig. 53). All the meridians may now be added to the map grid. This is accomplished in the same manner as finding a great circle nomographically, namely, by rotating the nomograph until the North Pole and the meridional intersection of the equator are on the same nomograph meridian or occupy the same relative position between two meridians. The meridian is drawn in its entirety, and while in this position the appropriate crossings of the parallels (with their proper angles of intersection) are noted on the meridian (stage II, Fig. 53). Since the intersections rarely coincide exactly with the parallels on the nomograph, it is generally necessary to interpolate. However, in working with a one-degree nomograph

the proper intersections will be so close to a parallel that they can be drawn directly with little loss of accuracy. Furthermore, one often finds a simple means of checking the accuracy of the interpolations. For example, on the orthographic projection advantage can be taken of the fact that all lines connecting the intersections of parallels along any two meridians are parallel. With a parallel ruling device the intersections along any meridian can be ticked off from the corresponding intersections along the central meridian, since these are already established.

"The nomograph is then rotated to obtain the next meridian, and so on until all are drawn in. At this stage the grid consists of an equator and a complete set of meridians marked with the crossings of the parallels (stage III, Fig. 53), and it is a simple matter to complete the parallels, since these crossings form an almost continuous curve. The grid can be drawn in first in pencil and later in ink, or it can be inked directly. It is a most satisfying experience to draw a brand-new grid in ink without the necessity for any previous pencil drawing, to say nothing of not having to erase horizontal and vertical construction lines.

"The accuracy of the method is limited only by the accuracy of the nomograph and the ability of the draftsman."

The nomographic method can be used with other classes of projections such as the cylindrical, but it is not quite as simple a procedure as it is with the azimuthals.

Another method of transforming the centering of a projection is by calculation of coordinates. For example, if one wished to "shift" the earth grid of a Mollweide projection so that the equator of the conventional projection coincided with another great circle, it would be the same as shifting the earth so that the pole of the grid was at some other point on the earth's surface (see Fig. 54). If the "loose grid" were thus shifted on the earth, all the intersections of

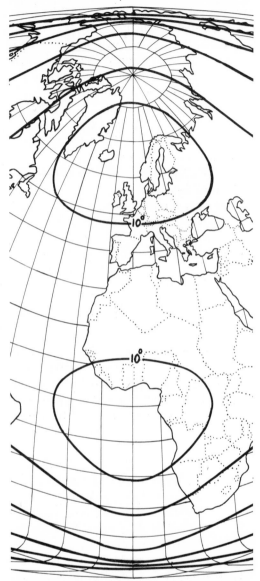

Fig. 54. A portion of a "tilted" Mollweide projection. The lines of equal angular deformation show that the structural characteristics of the projection do not change no matter where the projection may be centered. Compare with Fig. 18.

the new grid positions could be located and expressed in terms of latitude and longitude on the old grid. The calculations are not

difficult, and their appearance should frighten no one. Nothing but arithmetic is necessary for tables of sines and cosines are available. The procedure is as follows, assuming the central meridian is 0° longitude in both old and new grid:

ϕ = the number of degrees the grid has been shifted (90° minus the position of the new pole).
θ = latitude in new system.
λ = longitude in new system.
θ' = latitude in old system.
λ' = longitude in old system.

The problem is to find the latitude (θ') and longitude (λ') on the conventional projection of the *same* latitude (θ) and longitude (λ) of the new system. The formulas are:

$$\sin \theta' = \sin \theta \cos \phi - \sin \phi \cos \theta \cos \lambda$$

$$\sin \lambda' = \frac{\sin \lambda \cos \theta}{\cos \theta'}$$

Tables of the position of θ' and λ' have been computed for every 5° of shift of the grid and are available in E. Hammer, *Über die geographisch wichtigsten Kartenprojektionen* . . . , Stuttgart, 1889.

71 Interrupting or Recentering a Projection

In the second decade of this century an American cartographer, the late Professor J. Paul Goode of the University of Chicago, proposed the technique of interruption as a means of reducing the deformation in world maps. Interruption involves using several central meridians in place of one, and it results in a lobate kind of projection with the continental masses (or oceans) being shown separately on either side of a single equator. Some of these maps are illustrated in Article 45. So long as the parallels are equally divided by the meridians and the equator is a straight line, any projection may be interrupted. Even those projections with a line for the pole instead of a point may be interrupted.

The process of interruption involves only constructing the chosen central meridians and then duplicating the projection around each as far as necessary. This provides several "points or axes of strength" in place of the one or two on the uninterrupted projection. In practice the necessary section of the conventional projection is constructed, and then the appropriate sections or lobes are traced in their proper positions.

5

Drafting, Materials, and Map Reproduction

72 Map Drafting

Many large map-making establishments separate the compilation of maps from the drafting, leaving the latter operation to skillful specialists. The average student and maker of small-scale maps cannot do this, and hence he must become familiar with the basic procedures of map drafting. In addition, if he is ever to direct the work of a draftsman it is necessary for him to be acquainted with the tools, the media, and their capabilities.

The tools and media with which the draftsman works are relatively simple. (See Fig. 55.) They are designed primarily for the purpose of making it easy to obtain precision. Very little instruction and skill are necessary to employ them adequately. As is so often the case in matters involving design and execution, the ultimate appearance of a map depends more upon its design than upon its drafting excellence.

Like any other operation requiring the coordination of the hand, eye, and brain, the skills of drafting require some practice and patience. The student who approaches drafting with the negative attitude that he "couldn't possibly do that sort of thing" is admonished that he can, presumably, write, walk, eat, throw, button buttons, or perform any number of other operations

requiring the same kinds of muscular co-ordination.

Only those who are truly physically handicapped cannot learn to draft.

73 Drawing Equipment

Maps are usually drawn on drawing boards manufactured especially for the drafting process. They are carefully made of soft wood in such fashion as to preserve a flat surface. They are obtainable in a wide range of sizes, but the smallest practicable for general map work is 18 x 24 inches. Larger drawing boards are used to form the top of a table which is adjustable for both height and tilt. If one is not able to employ a drawing table of this sort an acceptable substitute may be improvised by placing a book under the far edge of a smaller drawing board.

Cartographers work with tracing paper or plastics a considerable proportion of the time, and less eyestrain will result if the drawing board is covered with white paper so that the contrast is heightened between the board beneath and that which is on the tracing paper. The drawing material may be affixed to the board with either tape or thumbtacks, but tape is, in general, more satisfactory. Special drafting tape that does not adhere so tightly as Cellophane tape is preferred, for it does not injure the

F𝗂𝗀. 55. Tools and equipment frequently used by the cartographer and draftsman. Courtesy of Rand McNally and Company.

paper when it is removed. Thumbtacks leave holes in the board which are occasionally bothersome, and the tack heads prevent the free movement of flat drawing tools. Many of the drafting operations may be better and more easily performed if the drawing is not fixed to the table but kept loose so that it may be moved about, making it easier to reach the various parts. This is particularly true for the lettering process.

A special kind of table called a tracing or light-table (see Fig. 56) is used when tracing is required on a relatively opaque surface such as drawing paper. The same kind of table is used in the printing business and is there called an opaquing table. A light-table has one surface of ground glass beneath which a light may shine. They are available from drafting supply houses, or one can be improvised.

A T-square and a variety of triangles and curves are used on the drawing surface.

FIG. 56. A tracing table with fluorescent illumination. Cool fluorescent illumination is better than incandescent. Courtesy Hamilton Manufacturing Company.

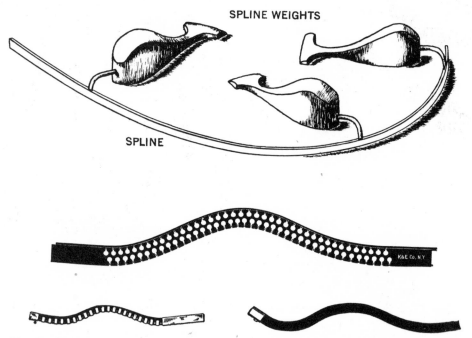

SPLINE WEIGHTS

SPLINE

FIG. 57. Flexible curves and a spline with weights. For large curves the spline is most satisfactory because it can be held rigidly in place by the weights, whereas flexible curves have a tendency to creep and must be held in place with one hand. Courtesy Keuffel and Esser Company.

A plain T-square with a fixed head is adequate for all the requirements of most cartographers, although a T-square with an adjustable head would occasionally be helpful. T-squares are made of metal or solid wood with or without a plastic transparent edge. A transparent edge is desirable for it enables the cartographer to see a bit of the drawing beneath the T-square and helps him to start and stop his lines at the correct places. The T-square is moved up or down one side of the drawing board. If perpendiculars to a horizontal line drawn along the T-square are required they are drawn with the triangle resting against the T-square rather than by hooking the T-square over the top edge of the drawing board, for the two sides are not usually square. The curve is used for constructing bending lines that are not arcs of circles. Many varieties of mechanical curves are available based upon curves of differing characteristics such as sines or ellipses.

For larger curves, the defining points of which are far apart, a flexible curve or a spline with weights is more satisfactory (see Fig. 57).

A useful addition to the drawing edges of the cartographer is a heavy steel straightedge with one beveled edge. As is the case with the spline for curves, the steel straightedge holds its place more readily, and the cartographer has more freedom in drawing long straight lines with it than he has when using the T-square.

A magnifying glass to assist in detailed work and a reducing glass to help plan for reduction are regularly used.

74 Drawing Instruments

Drawing instruments may be obtained either separately or in sets. A drawing set is desirable because it provides a convenient place to keep the instruments in proper storage and is thus an aid toward good

care, but a set is by no means necessary. One may easily start with the basic instruments and build up his own set. The instruments required by the cartographer fall into three classes: ruling pens, compasses, and dividers.

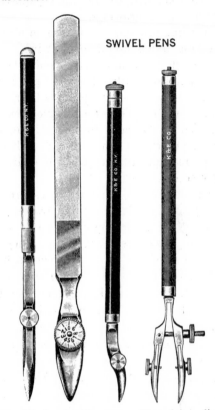

SWIVEL PENS

Fig. 58. Kinds of ruling pens. The plain ruling pen is most frequently used. Courtesy Keuffel and Esser Company.

The ruling pen (see Fig. 58) is perhaps the most used of the drawing instruments, and the cartographer would be well advised to have a good one and especially to keep it clean and in good order. The pen is filled by placing ink between the adjustable blades. In use it is held with the blades parallel to and against a drawing edge. If it is not held parallel the ink will either not flow uniformly or it will "run under" the drawing edge. The ruling pen should be frequently cleaned with a cloth. If ink is kept in the pen too long it will dry a bit, and the same amount will not flow out between the blades; uniformity of lines, then, cannot be obtained. Ink is cheap compared to the time required to produce good drawings.

A ruling pen with the blades on a swivel (see Fig. 58) is useful for drawing smooth curves such as contours. A double-headed swivel called a railroad or road pen is useful for drawing uniform parallel lines. The single- and double-headed swivel pens are handled in the same fashion as the plain ruling pen except that they are ordinarily used freehand, that is, without a drawing edge to guide them.

Dividers, as the name indicates, are used for dividing lines in equal parts and for transferring dimensions from a rule to the drawing paper (see Fig. 59). They are adjustable with a needle point on each leg. When used to divide a distance in equal parts they are "walked" along the line, then adjusted, and the process is repeated until the division is accomplished. Proportional dividers have two sets of needle points, one at each end. The position of the swivel between them can be adjusted so that whatever the opening between one pair, the other opening will remain in a constant ratio with the first pair. They are particularly useful for enlarging or reducing irregular figures with precision.

Compasses are, of course, for drawing arcs and circles (see Fig. 60). There are several kinds for different sizes of circles, but usually only the small and large standard compass is included in a set of drawing instruments. Some makes have an interchangeable pencil or ruling pen; others are made only for pencil or for pen. In either case their use is the same. The large compass in a set usually has an extension arm which may be fitted into a socket to make

even larger circles possible. The drop compass is useful for making small circles. The pen is loose on the pointed shaft, and when the center has been located the pen is

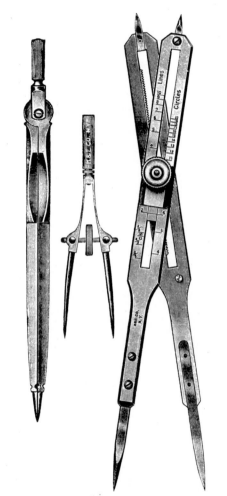

Fig. 59. Kinds of dividers. Courtesy Keuffel and Esser Company.

dropped and twirled, all with one hand. The beam compass is used for drawing large arcs.

There are several makers and distributors of drafting equipment, and almost any drafting supply house has a large selection from which to choose. First-quality instruments are relatively expensive so the

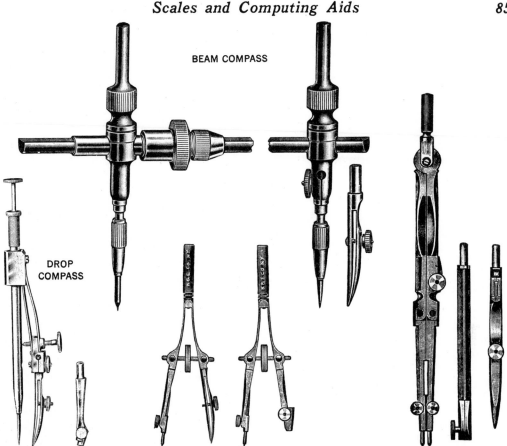

BEAM COMPASS

DROP
COMPASS

FIG. 60. Kinds of compasses. The beam of the beam compass may be several feet long.
Courtesy Keuffel and Esser Company.

beginner is advised to start with inexpensive tools and make replacements as he becomes acquainted with the desirable qualities.

Drawing instruments are precision made of high-quality metal, and it will repay the owner many times over to keep them clean and dry. If they are loose it is easy for the needle points and sharp edges to become damaged. Ruling pens may be kept sharpened with the aid of a thin triangular whetstone. Clean instruments in good operating order will not make the user a good draftsman, but no draftsman can do a good job with dirty or rusty instruments that are out of adjustment.

75 Scales and Computing Aids

The cartographer needs several scales with which to measure distances. The most commonly used scales are triangular and are made of wood. They should be either in the metric system or in the English system, decimally divided. Scales are not meant to be used as straightedges, and pens or pencils should never be run along the edge of a scale. This may dirty the scales, and any marks on them will make the chance of an error in reading values more likely.

If the cartographer does any maps for books he will find it useful also to have a scale that shows picas. The pica (about

⅙ inch) is a unit of typographic measure, and most book type and format dimensions are given in picas.

Every cartographer should have available a slide rule and a table of logarithms. The use of the slide rule and logarithms may be self-taught in a short time, and many calculations are enormously simplified by their use. Calculations of map scales, square roots, percentages, proportions, and many other standard cartographic procedures are a matter of minutes with these aids.

76 Pens

There is a large variety of pens available for drafting different kinds of lines. Some are versatile and can be used for many operations, and some are useful for only a limited range of drawing. Whatever the pen, however, it is important that it be kept clean. Time spent on regular cleaning of pens, is, in the long run, time gained.

Quill-type pens made of metal are among the most used instruments. A large variety is obtainable, and it is helpful to have a good selection on hand. Some are hard and stiff and make uniform lines; others are very flexible and are used for lines, such as rivers, that change width frequently. A favorite is the one called the "crow quill," which requires a special holder. Quill pens may be dipped in the ink bottle, but a better practice is to use the ink dropper to apply a drop to the underside of the pen. This procedure allows frequent cleaning without excessive waste of ink.

The stub pen is like a quill except that the tip ends in a flat section instead of tapering to a point. With such a nib a line may be made of varying width depending upon whether the pen is moved vertically or horizontally on the paper. It is thus a good pen for distinctive freehand lettering.

The Leroy pen (see Fig. 61) was originally designed for use with a lettering device (see Chapter 8) but has been found to be a most useful pen for other purposes. It has a cylinder for a "point," and ink is fed through a small hole in the cylinder. When used freehand in its special holder it is useful for those lines that should maintain a constant width no matter which direction they may follow. Varying pressure makes little difference in the width of the line.

The Barch-Payzant pen (see Fig. 62) was also designed for lettering, but geographers find it an excellent pen for making uniform dots in distribution maps. It operates on a different principle from the Leroy, but the result, so far as lines are concerned, is about the same. The flow of ink is adjustable with a Barch-Payzant, which makes it desirable for the dotting process.

Another versatile pen for cartographic use is the Speedball (see Fig. 63). Several varieties are obtainable, and the shape of the nib provides different kinds of lines. The Speedball has an ink reservoir, and is filled better with an ink dropper than by dipping.

An extremely versatile type of pen is the Pelican Graphos drawing-ink fountain pen with interchangeable nibs. A variety of different kinds of lines, as illustrated in Fig. 64, may be made by inserting different nibs in the special fountain pen.

77 Drafting Surfaces

A most impressive variety of drafting surfaces ranging from cloth to plastic may be used for maps, and the neophyte is hard pressed to choose the right one for the purpose at hand. Each use to which a paper or surface is to be put makes distinct demands on the surface. The follow-

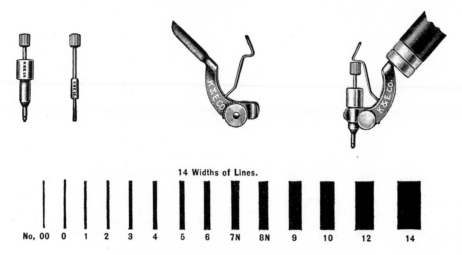

14 Widths of Lines.

No, 00 0 1 2 3 4 5 6 7N 8N 9 10 12 14

Fig. 61. Leroy pens and penholder, and widths of lines made by various sizes of pens. Courtesy Keuffel and Esser Company.

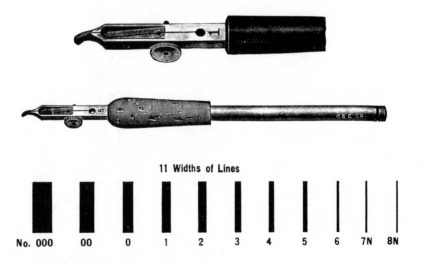

11 Widths of Lines

No. 000 00 0 1 2 3 4 5 6 7N 8N

Fig. 62. Barch-Payzant pens and widths of lines made by various sizes of pens. Courtesy Keuffel and Esser Company.

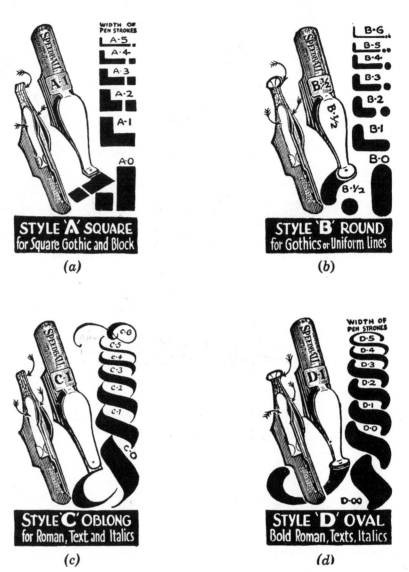

Fɪɢ. 63. Speedball pens and widths of lines made by various sizes of pens. Courtesy Hunt Pen Company

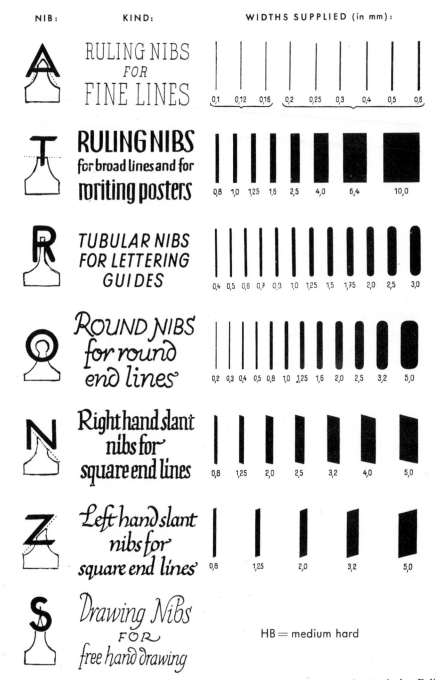

NIB:	KIND:	WIDTHS SUPPLIED (in mm):
A	RULING NIBS FOR FINE LINES	0,1 0,12 0,16 0,2 0,25 0,3 0,4 0,5 0,6
T	RULING NIBS for broad lines and for writing posters	0,8 1,0 1,25 1,6 2,5 4,0 6,4 10,0
R	TUBULAR NIBS FOR LETTERING GUIDES	0,4 0,5 0,6 0,7 0,9 1,0 1,25 1,5 1,75 2,0 2,5 3,0
O	ROUND NIBS for round end lines	0,2 0,3 0,4 0,5 0,8 1,0 1,25 1,6 2,0 2,5 3,2 5,0
N	Right hand slant nibs for square end lines	0,8 1,25 2,0 2,5 3,2 4,0 5,0
Z	Left hand slant nibs for square end lines	0,8 1,25 2,0 3,2 5,0
S	Drawing Nibs FOR free hand drawing	HB = medium hard

FIG. 64. Illustration of the types of nibs and widths of lines that may be made by Pelican Graphos nibs. Courtesy John Henschel and Company, New York.

ing brief listing includes the more important qualities of surfaces for cartographic use.

1. *Dimensional stability.* This refers to the ability of the paper or other surface to withstand changes in temperature and especially humidity without shrinking or expanding. This is particularly important in two instances: (1) when the map must maintain an absolute scale, such as in detailed charting or mapping, and (2) when the drawing must "fit" or register with another drawing.

2. *Ink adherence.* This refers to the ability of the surface to "hold on to" the ink. Some surfaces are rather porous so that the ink sinks in a bit and is held by the fibers when it dries. Other surfaces are so compact that the ink simply dries on the surface, and consequently, it may be easily chipped or rubbed off.

3. *Translucence.* This refers to the ease with which it is possible to see through the material. This is of special concern whenever tracing of any kind is done. Because so much tracing, ranging from lettering and layouts to actual data, is involved in cartography, the quality of translucence frequently transcends the others in importance.

4. *Surface quality.* This refers to the smoothness or roughness of the surface. The smoother the paper the "cleaner" the line that may be drawn on it. Roughness can, however, be a definite asset, as, for example, when "continuous-tone" shading for line reproduction is desired.

5. *Erasing quality.* Some kinds of map work require frequent erasing of pencil lines, as, for example, in terrain drawing, and final inking must be done on the same sheet. Toughness is obviously required.

6. *Strength.* Some drawings must withstand repeated rolling and unrolling or may be made with the idea of frequent revision. For such drawings a strong paper is required.

7. *Reaction to wetting.* Many maps call for painting with various kinds of paints and inks. A paper which curls excessively when wetted is inappropriate for such a purpose.

The above list of qualities is not all-inclusive, but these are the major ones. The cartographer would do well to approach every drafting job with the question "How will the medium react to what I plan to do to it?" The classic cartographic media are tracing paper, tracing cloth, and drawing paper. During the last decade plastics have become common in some kinds of cartographic construction.

Tracing paper is available in two forms, the natural tracing paper and the prepared tracing paper. Natural tracing paper is translucent because the paper is made thin. It is relatively weak and is not recommended for most map work. Prepared tracing paper is made of tougher materials and is made translucent by chemical means. It is much more satisfactory for map work. Tracing cloth or linen is a sized, good-quality cloth. It is tougher than paper and is desirable if unusual handling of the drawing is required. The sizing frequently clogs a pen. None of the tracing papers or cloths can be wetted much without curling. Drawing paper is a fine-grade rag paper available in a variety of qualities, thicknesses, and surfaces. It is opaque, but if translucence is not required it provides a fine drawing surface. Illustration board is a heavy cardboard surfaced with drawing paper. It may be wetted, as may some drawing papers, and is especially useful as a base upon which to mount drawings done on translucent paper.

Translucent Vinylite plastic is available in a variety of surfaces, and it has the definite advantage of being practically dimen-

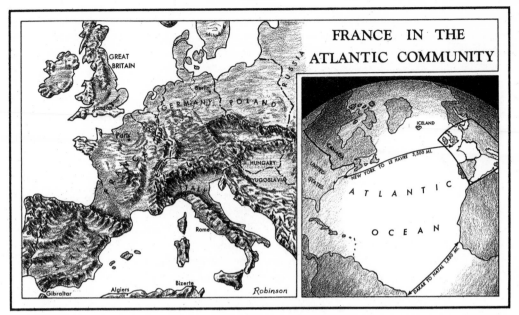

Fig. 65. A map drawn on Coquille board. The reproduction is by ordinary line cut. Reprinted by permission of the publishers from Donald C. McKay, *The United States and France*, Harvard University Press, Cambridge, Mass.; copyright, 1951, by the President and Fellows of Harvard College.

sionally stable, so that it is well adapted to multicolor maps where each color is drafted on a separate sheet and must register with the others. It has the disadvantage, however, that the surface is quite hard and drawing tools wear quickly when used on it. It also requires a different technique of drafting with India ink or the use of a different kind of ink, because standard India ink does not penetrate the surface. Special inks for drafting on plastics are available, but they tend to dry quickly and some corrode the instruments. Mistakes in drafting on plastic are easily corrected, for the ink can merely be scraped off.

There are a variety of other special papers and surfaces that are occasionally useful to the cartographer. For example, large wall maps can be made on sign cloth; transparent overlays can be made on clear plastic; and metal-mounted paper can be used for fine, scale-perfect drawings. The special or unusual map frequently requires some experimentation.

One type of material that is very useful is Coquille or Ross board. This material is prepared in a variety of rough surfaces so that when a carbon pencil or crayon is rubbed over it the color comes off only on the tops of the small bumps (see Fig. 65). For this reason varying shades of gray can be prepared with this material and can be reproduced without the necessity of being halftoned (see Article 89), which reduces the reproduction expense to about half.

78 Inks

The standard ink for drafting purposes is called India ink, and is available in a number of brands. It takes its name from the older product sold in stick form which originally came from India. Modern India ink is a permanent suspension of fine carbon in a liquid medium. It dries a dense

black, which is very important in reproduction. Most brands are waterproof;
that is, they will not run if wetted after
they have once dried. Drawing ink is also
available in colors which can be mixed.

Special inks for use on plastics and different kinds of colored pencils, water colors,
and other paints are available in large
variety. Their uses do not admit of generalization, and the cartographer would do
well to experiment before settling upon any
one product for a particular piece of work.

Tracing cloths and drawing papers commonly pick up oil from the hands, or are
oily or slick because of the method of preparation; it is necessary to remove any film
before inking begins. This is most easily
done by means of a powder, commercially
prepared for the specific purpose. India
ink will either not adhere or will spread if
the surface is oily, and this will result in
poor appearance and poor reproduction.
The draftsman should first clean the drawing surface and then keep it clean by having a piece of paper under his drawing hand
at all times. Fingers should not touch the
paper. A blunt stick is a handy substitute
for fingers when the paper needs to be kept
tight against the board.

For drawings that are to be photographed the best way to "sharpen" lines
and make corrections is to use a white,
opaque paint to cover the ink lines not
wanted. Showcard or tempera-type paints,
although usable, have a tendency to flake
off if the drawing is much handled.

79   Tints and Patterns

An indispensable part of many maps is
the pattern or shading that must be done
to differentiate one area from another.
This may be accomplished either by drafting them laboriously, as in the case of
parallel lines or dotted "stippling," or by
applying a commercially prepared pattern.
Shades of gray as might be prepared by
shading with a pencil cannot be used, for
then reproduction requires halftoning It
can be done with Coquille or Ross board,
but other line work is relatively difficult on
these surfaces.

Preprinted materials, such as area symbols printed on transparent film, are easy
to use and save much of the time which
was formerly necessary. The best-known
and most-used product for map work in
this class is known by the trade name Zip-
a-tone (Paratone Company, Chicago).
More than 150 patterns are available in
black, white, and colors. The colors (except red) are not frequently used in cartography. The patterns are available on
thin transparent film with a wax backing
(see Fig. 66). The material is placed over

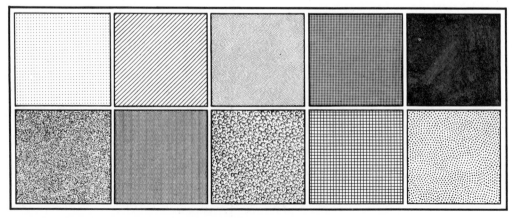

FIG. 66. Samples of Zip-a-tone.

the area desired and is cut out to fit. The excess is stripped away, and the remainder is burnished to the drawing. Patterns printed in red are useful when the pattern is dense, and it would be impossible to see through it (to know where to cut) if it were black. Solid red is also useful because red photographs as black, and large areas of solid black may be easily constructed this way especially on a paper that cannot be wetted. White patterns are useful to break up black areas or other patterns.

Knowledge of the relation of patterns to reduction and the preparation of a graded series of values (darkness) require considerable experimentation by the cartographer.

80 Other Techniques and Media

The foregoing brief résumé of the more important materials and media for average black and white cartography is far from exhaustive. There are other techniques, such as airbrush, intermediate photography, and other media, such as painting with various types of colors, that would require a treatment too exhaustive for a book of this kind. There are several manuals on the graphic-arts techniques which will answer the majority of the special questions the student might have.

81 Map Reproduction

If one surveys the story of the development of cartography he will undoubtedly be impressed by the significance of the development and expansion of the printing process. The invention of printing in the western world during the fifteenth century certainly ranks as one of the major events in cartographic history. Likewise, the contemplation of his first reproduced map is likely to be one of the great events in a cartographer's professional life. Sometimes the event generates sorrow. Of certain results it might be said, "Any resemblance between this printed map and the fair drawing is purely coincidental," for what happens to a neophyte's map when reproduced is sometimes startling. It need not be, however, if the cartographer will but bear in mind that any map to be reproduced must be designed for some particular process of reproduction.

The designing of a map for reproduction involves a number of important decisions and techniques. One of the more important considerations is of the relation between the size of the copy (fair drawing prepared for reproduction) and the printed or reproduced size in terms of the degree of detail, line widths, and lettering sizes. Many maps that appear correct in these aspects in copy form appear crowded and heavy, or the opposite, light and weak, when reduced and printed. This may be a result of poor design, treated elsewhere in this book, or the result of a lighter printing ink on an absorbent paper or some other similar circumstance. In addition, if the map is to be reproduced in color it must be kept in register as the separate plates are drawn. Also, the line work of a drawing must be more carefully drafted on copy that is to be reproduced by the camera, for sensitized paper or film is much more sensitive to differences in blackness than is the human eye. The copy must be appropriate to the process; that is, it must not ask too much of the particular duplicating technique. Very fine lines can be reproduced in only a few copies by some processes, and in many copies by others. The list of caveats is long.

Even before the cartographer begins his map he must learn what choice there is as to method of reproduction, and he must choose the most appropriate one in terms of cost, number of copies required, future use of the map, and a number of other elements. Even after the process has been chosen, there is still considerable choice as to the method of preparing copy for some kinds of maps, especially colored maps.

A thorough knowledge of reproduction processes is desirable for still another reason. In the printing process, and in some other methods of reproduction, photography is an important step. Much of the photography results in film on which there are only two kinds of areas, i.e., opaque and transparent. This fact can be utilized in the construction of a map in a number of ways which will effect great savings of time for the cartographer. Masking of unwanted areas, application of tints and screen patterns, and so on, can often be most expeditiously done during this part of the printing process. The cartographer who is versed in "reproduction cartography" can save himself considerable effort at the same time that he is producing a finer product.

82 Classification of Reproduction Methods

It is difficult to classify reproduction methods in a satisfactory manner, because many processes require more than one technique, and the intermediate techniques in one may be an end in themselves in another, or they may be intermediate in several different processes. For example, photography is a step in the printing process but it can also be considered a separate reproduction process. Perhaps the most practical manner of classification is to group the reproduction methods on the basis of whether or not they involve a decreasing unit cost with increasing numbers of copies. It so happens that segregation on this basis also separates the common processes according to whether or not they require printing plates and printing ink, i.e., whether they are printing processes or nonprinting processes.

In the following descriptions only the widely used and generally available processes are considered. It should, however, be pointed out that there are a number of other processes which produce excellent results in specific "requirement situations," ranging from stencil reproduction and silk screen to gravure and collotype. These and others of the same category (not widely used in cartography) are not considered here, but the interested student can find abundant information about them in the graphic-arts literature.

The widely used nonprinting processes are: (1) photostat, (2) photograph (not including color), (3) blueprint, and (4) dry ammonia or Ozalid.

The widely used printing processes are: (1) letterpress and (2) lithography.

The nonprinting processes are distinguished by providing low-cost, one-color copies at a unit cost that does not vary with the "run," or number of copies. They are therefore ideal for short runs but are not appropriate for large runs. The printing processes, on the other hand, provide low-cost, monochrome or multicolor copies at a unit cost that decreases with the number of copies run. The initial cost is high compared to the nonprinting methods. The printing processes are therefore not appropriate for very small runs.

83 Photostat Process

This process provides direct prints in reverse or negative form on sensitized paper, without the necessity of any intermediate step. It involves the exposure of the copy through a lens to sensitized paper, which is then wet developed. The developing process and the subsequent drying frequently cause unequal shrinkage, so that some distortion of dimensions and directions is often present in a photostat.

The prints are reversed each time through the process. If a drawing of black lines on a white background is photostatted, the result will be a photostat negative, i.e., a reproduction with white lines on a black background. To gain positive copies (same as original copy), it is necessary to repeat the process using the negative as the copy.

Maps may be enlarged or reduced in the photostat process, and the only limitation is the size of the paper and the quality of the lens. Photostatic paper is limited to 18 x 24 inch sheets, but the edges usually are rather badly distorted so that the effective size is somewhat smaller.

Many time-saving and interesting results can be obtained by using the photostat process in cartography. For example, if one wishes to have white lettering on a solid background (reverse lettering) on a printed map, it is a simple matter to do the lettering in black ink on white paper and then to obtain a negative photostat. This may then be pasted on the drawing. It is much easier than attempting to letter with white paint on a black background. Other cases where reversing a drawing photostatically, intermediate in the drafting process, is advantageous will occur to the reader.

The primary use of photostats, however, is for obtaining a few relatively inexpensive copies of a black and white map that has been drawn on opaque or translucent paper. Mistakes can be corrected either on the copy (by painting over, etc.) or on the photostat negative if positives are to be used.

84 Photograph Process

This is the standard process of photography involving camera, film negative, and paper prints. Although the cost of photography per square foot is about the same as photostat, there are certain cases where photography is desirable. Grays and tones may be somewhat better controlled and are available in greater variety photographically. Enlargements or reductions

not in simple proportion are easier to make photographically than photostatically, and photographic enlargements on one sheet are available at a larger size through the use of an enlarger.

To make corrections on the negative is costly and difficult in the photographic process, so that for ordinary work where only a few prints are required the copy must be "ready to go."

85 Blueprint Process

The blueprint process is here used as a general term to cover several processes that produce results by similar techniques, but which are not necessarily the standard blueprint process. In this process the copy is laid next to the sensitized paper and is then exposed to special lights. The exposed print is wet developed and is subject to some distortion. The print appears as the reverse of the copy, i.e., light lines on a dark background. If a positive copy is desired a special "negative" can be made from the original, which is then used as copy, and the prints are then produced as dark lines on a white background. Another variety (B-W) using special papers produces positive copies directly.

It is not possible in the blueprint process to enlarge or reduce so that copy must be designed for "same-size" reproduction. The process depends upon the translucence of the drawing; and therefore painting out imperfections is impossible, for the paint is as opaque as the ink and would appear as a dark spot in the print. Creases on the tracing paper or cloth and heavy erasures which affect the translucence are also frequently visible on the print.

The major use of the process in cartography is to obtain a few relatively inexpensive copies on thinner paper than photostatic or photographic paper. It is also useful for obtaining "same-size" copies of base maps so that a variety of other maps requiring the same base data may be made, without the necessity of redrawing the base data for each map. Blueprint papers have a relatively good drafting surface, but the combination of India ink lines and the blue, "black," red, or brown lines of the print are not particularly satisfactory for subsequent printing reproduction, although the results are not unusable.

86   Dry Ammonia Process

This process, best known under the trade name Ozalid, is similar in some respects to the blueprint in that it requires translucent copy and no reduction or enlargement is possible. It differs markedly, however, because it is a dry process, requiring no liquid developer, and because copies are positive. Prints are obtained by feeding the original drawing into a machine against a roll of the special sensitized paper. The exposure and dry developing take place rapidly within the machine, the drawing is returned, and may be immediately reinserted for another exposure and copy.

Ozalid paper, like blueprint paper, has an acceptable drafting surface, so this process is also useful for obtaining copies of base maps. The same cautions regarding corrections and creasing that were pointed out in the previous article are applicable to drawings for Ozalid reproduction.

Zip-a-tone and similar products on drawings do not produce very good results in the dry ammonia process because of "shadowing" which takes place when exposure is made through the translucent drafting medium. An additional hazard with these materials is present in the Ozalid process, because the drawing must be fed around a roller, and such materials tend to curl off the paper if it is rolled. One way of circumventing this problem is to have a diapositive made by a photographer.

A diapositive, which is a very useful item in reproduction cartography, is a film positive. If the photographer prints his ordinary film negative on another piece of film, instead of paper as is normal, the result is a film positive (diapositive), which is the same as the original copy, except that it is on transparent film instead of paper. If the photographer can arrange the printing of the diapositive so that the emulsion side is on the bottom when the diapositive "reads" correctly, then it may be fed into the Ozalid machine and will produce good results. Of course, Zip-a-tone, etc., may be employed on the drawing used to produce the diapositive since its only function is to be photographed. It is not absolutely necessary to have the emulsion arranged as suggested above, but the results will be more satisfactory if it is.

87   Printing Processes

The earliest printing or duplicating process was undoubtedly that involving a raised surface which could be pressed into a soft medium, such as clay, in order to leave a mark therein. Evidence that this was done several thousand years ago is available. Subsequently, the Chinese carved block characters, inked the raised portion, and transferred the impression to paper. This is the kind of printing from movable type that later was "invented" in the western world in the latter part of the fifteenth century, and is associated with the name Gutenberg. Today printing from a raised surface is known as letterpress and is a standard form of printing.

Another method of reproduction, engraving, involving ink and an uneven surface was developed at about the same time that movable type was first used in Europe. Someone conceived the idea of cutting or engraving grooves in metal, filling them with ink, and then pressing them against paper. In a sense this process of engraving is just the opposite of letterpress printing, for the inking area is "down" instead of "up." Until considerably less than a hundred years ago most printed maps were reproduced by the engraving process.

About a century and a half ago it was discovered that a drawing could be made on a smooth limestone surface with greasy ink or crayon. The unmarked portion of the surface could then be wetted, and if a greasy printing ink, which was repelled by the water, were rolled across the surface, the ink would adhere to the original greasy areas but not to the dampened areas. Paper pressed against the stone would pick up the ink. On account of its original form the process was named lithography. Today stone is no longer used, except in rare instances, and thin metal plates have been substituted, but it is still known as lithography. It is also frequently called offset, because the image is offset by the press to a rubber roller, which in turn prints it on the paper.

The three kinds of printing and printing surfaces, relief, intaglio, and planographic, are still used, but most maps are printed by either letterpress or lithography. Larger maps are usually done by lithography and the smaller, such as book "cuts," by letterpress.

Today all ordinary printing-plate preparation involves photographing the original copy or fair drawing, making a film or glass negative, retouching (correcting and changing the negative), exposing the negative on a sensitive plate, and printing from the resulting plate.

88 Steps in the Printing Process

The basic steps in the printing process, from the time the printer receives the copy until he delivers the printed maps, are much the same whether the process is letterpress or lithography. For a normal piece of copy involving no complications the process consists, in the main, of the following operations:

1. Photographing the original (the copy).
2. Processing the negative.
3. Making the plate.
4. Presswork.

The cartographer is concerned with one or all of the first three. Beyond understanding the problems of the pressman he is little concerned with the fourth stage.

Perhaps the major difference between letterpress and lithography, in so far as the cartographer is concerned, results from the fact that commonly the lithographer handles all four operations in his establishment and is therefore a somewhat more satisfactory person with which to deal. In letterpress, on the other hand, it is not unusual for the first two or three steps, as listed above, to be accomplished by a photoengraver who does no presswork. This means, so to speak, that one more cook is concerned with the broth making, and the danger of spoilage due to inadequate planning is thereby increased.

Photographing the original drawing or copy is an exacting process requiring the use of what is called a copy camera, which is a large, rigidly mounted camera capable of making large or small exposures. The copy is first placed in a vacuum frame, with a glass cover, which holds it perfectly flat, and is exposed for several seconds under illumination by arc lights. Relatively slow film is used in order to give the photographer greater control over the quality of the negative. For the printing processes (lithography and letterpress), the resulting negative must be composed of either opaque areas or transparent areas and nothing intermediate. Grays are not permitted on the negative as they, of course, are in ordinary photography. The printing plate, to be made subsequently from the negative, must be entirely divided into two kinds of surfaces, one which takes ink and one which does not. For this reason all copy should be drafted with marks of uniform blackness. Lack of dense, uniform blackness on the copy makes it very difficult if not impossible for the photographer to produce a satisfactory negative.

Any reduction that is to be made is done at this stage. The photographer can adjust the camera precisely either by calculating the ratio of reduction or by actually measuring the image in the camera before the exposure.

It is important that the nature of the emulsion normally used be fully understood. This emulsion is sensitive to black and to the red end of the spectrum but is not particularly sensitive to the blue end. Consequently, red photographs black, but light blue (and some similar colors) do not photograph at all. For this reason the cartographer should, so far as possible, draw any guide lines with a light-blue pencil. Filters may be used in special circumstances.

After exposure the negative is developed, washed, and dried and is then ready for the next step. The emulsions are on film or glass backing, and for some plate making it is necessary for the photographer to make a diapositive which then is treated as the "negative."

Processing the negative is one of the more important steps in the cartographic process, for it is in this stage that some results can be obtained better than in the drafting stage. No matter what processing or modification is to take place, however, the negative must be brought to perfection by removing all "pinholes" and blemishes in the emulsion so that the image is left sharp and clear. This is done by placing the negative on a light-table and opaquing with paint or scraping clean those spots and areas requiring repair or change (see Fig. 67). In addition to the process of perfecting the negative, called by the general term "opaquing," other changes can be

made such as (*a*) adding or subtracting material, (*b*) color separation, and (*c*) screening.

Depending upon the circumstances it is sometimes possible at this stage to add or subtract names and lines. If an important piece of information has been omitted or a word misspelled, a new piece of emulsion or

FIG. 67.   Opaquing a negative. Courtesy Rand McNally and Company.

emulsion-like material may be "stripped" into place on the negative. If material has been omitted it can sometimes be added by "engraving" it in the emulsion or, in the case of a diapositive, added by painting. Such operations are costly and time consuming, so it is better if the cartographer prepares his copy correctly in the first instance.

If a map is to be printed with two or more colored inks it is necessary that there be a negative and printing plate for each color ink. Copy for separate plates may either be drafted by the cartographer, or he may draft all colors in black on one drawing. If the latter is done the photographer supplies as many identical negatives as there are colors-to-be. The negatives are then opaqued so that only those items which are to be printed in a single color are left transparent on each negative. They are then treated as different negatives. In many instances this insures better registry as well as saving time for the cartographer. It is obvious, however, that on some complicated maps this would not be feasible.

Screening of the negative involves the positioning of thin transparent sheets containing patterns of lines or dots (called screens) over particular areas of the negative. This accomplishes the same end result on the printing plate as applying Zip-a-tone or similar shading film to, or drafting such shading on, the original drawing. Better results are obtained with extra-fine patterns of lines or dots by applying them at this stage, after photography, than by making them "stand up" through the photographic process. Furthermore, opaquing can be done first and screening second, which is desirable because the negative is more difficult to opaque if the emulsion already contains a fine pattern of lines or dots in addition to the other data.

After the negative has been processed it is masked as necessary with opaque paper, marked for position on the plate, and in general made ready for plate making. Printing plates for both lithography and letterpress are now made of various metals, but whatever their composition the printing surface is made light sensitive (see Fig. 68). The negative is placed on the surface of the plate, and the two are put in a vacuum frame and exposed to arc light long enough so that the light may effect a change in the sensitive surface. Whether the plate is to be etched deeply for letterpress, lightly for deep-etch lithography, or practically not at all for standard lithography makes no difference to the cartographer. By the time this stage of the printing process has been reached the "die is

almost cast," for that map. It is possible, however, to take advantage of one opportunity at this stage—double exposing of the plate. This may be done by using two negatives with printing areas that are mutually exclusive. They are "burned" on the plate one after the other so that the printing plate is a composite. The advan-

Fig. 68. Sensitizing the printing plate. The printing plate is here shown in a "whirler," which rotates it to spread smoothly the emulsion being poured on it. Courtesy Rand McNally and Company.

tage of this will be described in Article 91. It is also possible at this stage to apply screens directly to the printing plate. These are called Ben Day patterns and may also be added during the negative stage as previously described.

Presswork involves placing the completed plate in exact position on the press, inking the press so that just the right amount is applied to each part of the plate, and feeding the paper through the press (see Fig. 69). Except for the fact that rough changes, such as removing a mark, can be made on the plate after it has been made ready for the press, the cartographer has no further part in the printing process. He must depend at this stage on the skill of the pressman for such things as an even impression, proper inking, and maintenance of correct registry.

Although the principles of the process are straightforward, the details may vary considerably because of the different

FIG. 69. A modern printing press. This is a two-color offset press. Courtesy Rand McNally and Company.

methods, letterpress and lithography, and because of variations resulting from different metals, emulsions, and the like. Consequently the student should take the opportunity to visit several printing establishments in order to observe this fascinating process which is so important in present-day cartography.

89 Line and Halftone

All copy (or fair drawings) belongs to either of two classes, line copy and halftone copy. The distinguishing characteristic that places a piece of copy in one or the other class is whether or not it contains any shading or gray. If it does, it is halftone copy and must be dealt with in

the reproduction process by a different (and more costly) procedure. The significance of this division results from the fact that the ordinary printing processes depend upon printing from a surface that is either inked or is not inked. There is no such thing in lithography and letterpress as "halfway inking."

It is possible, however, to make a printed area appear gray, or shade from light to dark (continuous tone), as if the surface had more or less ink on it. The process, halftoning, is accomplished by transforming the tone area into a large number of small dots of different sizes depending upon whether it is to be dark or light. The dots print ink, and the spaces between do not. The dots are so close together that the eye is unable easily to distinguish them, so that the combination of black spots and white spaces blends and appears as a tone.

The tone area is broken up by inserting a special screen in the rear of the copy camera between the lens and the emulsion. This screen is made of two circular sheets of glass on which fine, parallel, closely spaced grooves have been cut. The grooves are filled with opaque paint, and the two sheets are cemented together so that the grooves are at right angles to one another. The light that passes through the screen is rendered as dots on the emulsion. All other things being equal, the closer the grooves the smaller and closer together the dots will be. The closer together they are, the more difficult it is for the eye to see them individually and the smoother and more natural the result will appear. A screen of 120 lines to the inch is common. This provides more than 14,000 dots per square inch! (See Fig. 70.)

The size of the printing dots relative to the white spaces between is dependent upon the darkness or lightness of the tones on the copy. It should be remembered, however, that unless special additional process-

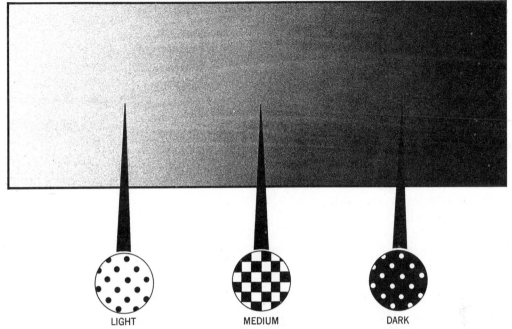

Fig. 70. An example of "continuous tone" reproduction. The three drawings show the different sizes of halftone dots as they might appear if the areas indicated in the drawing were enlarged many times.

ing takes place, no part of a halftone will be without dots. All lines and lettering will therefore have fuzzy edges. Pure whites on copy will, in ordinary halftoning, have very small black dots and therefore a light tone, whereas black areas will reproduce with small white spaces rather than solid black. These effects can be removed by opaquing or scraping on the halftone negative, but this is difficult if the areas involved are complex.

Ordinary halftoning at least doubles the cost of reproduction, so that it provides a considerable saving if the cartographer can gain a similar effect with line copy. This can be done by

1. Shading either uniformly or for continuous-tone effect by hatching or stippling with pen and ink.

2. Using Zip-a-tone, etc., on the copy for uniform shading.

3. Screening the negative for uniform shading.

4. Using Ross or Coquille board for continuous-tone effect.

5. Using Ben Day screens on the negative or on the printing plate for uniform shading.

6. Using specially prepared drawing papers, such as Craftint Singletone or Doubletone.

The variety of methods available, and the commercial materials that have been developed to simulate continuous tone by line methods, is ample evidence of the significant savings that can be accomplished if copy does not require halftoning.

90 Color Reproduction

The reproduction of maps in color does not differ from black reproduction except that different colored inks are used. Each separate ink requires, of course, a separate printing plate, and thus a complete duplication of the steps in the whole process. Thus, generally speaking, the costs of color reproduction are many times that of the single-color (usually black) reproduction. There are, however, two basically different color reproduction processes, and it is unwise to generalize further about relative costs. The two processes are called "flat color" and "color process." The major difference between them is that the color copy for process color is prepared as a single color drawing, whereas that for flat color is prepared in black and white and usually requires a different drawing for each ink.

Flat color is the process most often used for maps and involves a straightforward procedure that varies little from the procedure described previously. For the flat-color procedure the map is planned for a certain number of colored printing inks, and a separate drawing is prepared for each ink. Of course, many combinations of line and halftone effects are possible.

The basic problem of multicolor map preparation is register, i.e., making the colors print exactly where they should. To facilitate register, small crosses, called register marks, are placed on the four margins of every plate (drawing) of the copy in exactly the same place on each (see Fig. 71). The marks are retained on the negatives and on the printing plate. As soon as the plate has been properly adjusted on the press they are removed. Register may be maintained in a number of ways, such as: (1) using a dimensionally stable drawing surface, (2) using blue-line boards, and (3) negative separation. Whatever the method employed, great care must be expended to maintain as perfect registry as possible.

The larger the drawing and the reproduction the more important is the use of dimensionally stable materials. Plastics

(Vinylite) are stable, and some drawing papers and tracing papers can be used in the smaller sizes. If drawing papers or tracing papers are used, care must be taken that the grain of the paper runs in the same direction on each overlay or plate, so that if expansion or contraction does take place it will be more nearly uniform on each.

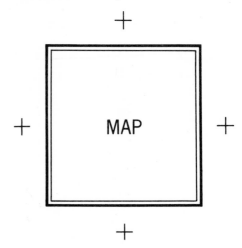

FIG. 71. Register marks showing their usual position.

The blue-line board, if carefully used, is an excellent method of maintaining register for relatively complex color maps. In this process the original copy for the black plate is drafted and all boundaries of color areas are included. The printer can supply from this drawing any number of same-size reproductions in light blue on a white drawing surface. The common blue lines are on heavy paper or illustration board. The light blue is nonphotographic and serves as a guide for further drafting. All areas and lines (including register marks) to be printed in red are drafted in black, screened, etc., on one board; all areas in blue, or whatever the color may be, are drafted on another, and so on. The lines used only for color guides on the original black plate drawing may be removed from the drawing, or opaqued on the negative later. The cartographer then delivers a series of black and white "separation drawings," properly labeled, to the printer who treats them as single pieces of copy through the entire process. The pressman prints them on top of one another in the appropriate inks, and a multicolor map results.

Another method of insuring register, which is appropriate under some circumstances, is for the cartographer to draft all lines of all colors on the same drawing. These are photographed, and as many duplicate negatives are made as there are colors-to-be. These may then be opaqued in such a way as to leave on each negative only that which is to be printed in a particular color. Screens, etc., may be added as usual to the negatives, and the final separation negatives are the same as would have resulted from separation drawings.

There are many ways of accomplishing the same end result in the flat-color procedure, and each engraver or printer has special ways of operating. It is always wise to confer with the printer before initiating work if there is to be anything at all unusual in the procedure.

Process color, or more properly four-color process, is the name applied to an essentially different procedure. This method is based on the fact that almost all color combinations can be obtained by varying mixtures of red, yellow, blue, white, and black. The copy consists usually of two pieces, the color drawing and a black line plate. The black plate usually contains the border (if any), lettering, grid, outlines, etc., and is the base for a blue-line board. On the blue line all color work is done by painting, airbrush, etc. The color copy is photographed three times, each time through an appropriate color filter and a halftone screen, so that the three printing plates are halftones of the varying amounts of the primary colors. The black plate is treated as a line drawing. When printed together again the halftone dots and transparent inks merge and recreate the colors of the original drawing. The process is expensive because it is exacting. Much work by highly skilled persons is necessary on the halftone negatives, and the combination of halftone negatives, their modification, and careful processing throughout the printing process is time consuming.

The above explanation of the principal color processes used in reproducing maps is greatly simplified but is included in order that the student may have an idea of the basic procedures. If one is to have a color map reproduced he is advised to investigate these interesting processes more carefully through reading (see bibliography) and especially by visits to printing plants where this type of work is done.

91 Negative Manipulation

It has perhaps occurred to the student that the processes previously described lend themselves to various combinations. For example, it is possible to expose two negatives, one a halftone and the other a line negative, on the same printing plate, or the negative for one plate may be used as a positive and be the basis of another plate.

An example will serve as an illustration of short cuts. Suppose a map of North America is to be made, and on the printed map it is desired that the oceans be a blue tint (screened), the land be a brown tint (screened), and the line work (boundaries, etc.) on the land be black. This will involve three printing plates, one for each color. Yet only two need be drafted and one of those is very simple. (See Fig. 72.) The two drawings are:

A. All line work drafted in black including
   a. Grid on oceans.
   b. Boundaries and coastline.
   c. All lettering in black.

DRAWINGS

A   B

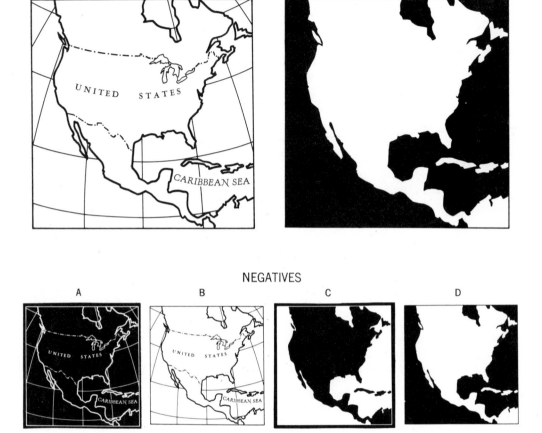

NEGATIVES

A   B   C   D

PRINTING PLATES PRODUCE

Negs. A + D produce   Neg. D, screened, produces   Negs. B + C, screened, produce

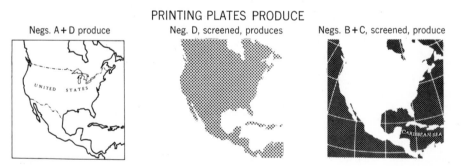

FIG. 72. An example of possible negative manipulation and combination. The letters are keyed to the explanation in Article 91. The coarseness of the screens is, of course, exaggerated.

B. A masking drawing consisting of
   a. Black oceans (most easily done with red Zip-a-tone).

The processing of these two drawings is as follows:

A. One negative of the line drawing is made (transparent lines on opaque background).
B. One diapositive of the line drawing is made (opaque lines on transparent background).
C. One negative of the masking drawing is made (opaque land on transparent ocean).
D. One diapositive of the masking drawing is made (opaque ocean on transparent land).

The printing plates are made as follows:

1. Negative A is combined with diapositive D to provide a black printing plate with coastline, boundaries, and lettering on the land.
2. Diapositive D is screened and provides a brown printing plate with a tint on all the land.
3. Diapositive B is combined with screened negative C which provides a blue-tint ocean with white (reversed) lettering and white grid ending at the land.

There is an unlimited number of possibilities of producing interesting effects by combining various types of negatives and by various kinds of screenings. An interesting and instructive exercise for the student of cartography is to try to analyze the methods by which the color or black and white maps that are available to him have been reproduced, and to suggest alternative ways of arriving at the same or better results.

6

Compiling and Preparing the Map Base

92   The Map Base

All special-purpose maps are made on the foundation of a base map. This base map is compiled first, and the accuracy with which it is made determines in large part the accuracy of the final map. This is due to the practical requirement that the cartographer must compile much of the special data by using the base data as a skeleton on which to hang it. Base data consisting of coasts, rivers, lakes, and political boundaries are available from larger-scale, generally accurate, survey maps; but, on the other hand, the kinds of specialized data usually put on special-purpose maps for the social sciences are commonly organized according to the civil divisions of the area concerned. It is absolutely necessary, therefore, that the cartographer take special pains to be accurate in his compilation of the base data.

Large-scale maps, 1:150,000 and larger, are not usually compiled maps, but are maps made from surveys ranging from photogrammetric to plane table survey. Their accuracy is controlled as carefully as possible, and within the limits of human error and scale they are correct. Some medium-scale maps are made by tracing selected data from the larger-scale maps and reducing the result photographically.

These are essentially mechanical processes, for relatively little interpretation and generalization takes place.

The special-purpose map is quite a different operation. The compiling of base data requires using many maps from which to gain the desired information; they may be on different projections; they may differ markedly in level of accuracy; the dates of publication may vary; and their scales will probably be different. The cartographer must pick and choose, discard this, and modify that, and all the while he must place the selected data on a new projection, locating each item precisely by eye. For although it is possible to transform by tracing and photography a 1:50,000 map into one at 1:250,000, it is quite impossible to transfer mechanically between scales of a much greater range. This is easily understood if one but remembers that 1 square inch at a scale of 1:62,-500 will occupy only 0.01 square inch at a scale of 1:625,000. The latter is still a fairly large scale for special-purpose maps.

The process of compilation requires that the selected data be transferred by eye. The projection grid in each case constitutes the guide lines, and all positions must be estimated. Lest the reader be concerned about the accuracy of such a process he should remember that 90 per cent of all

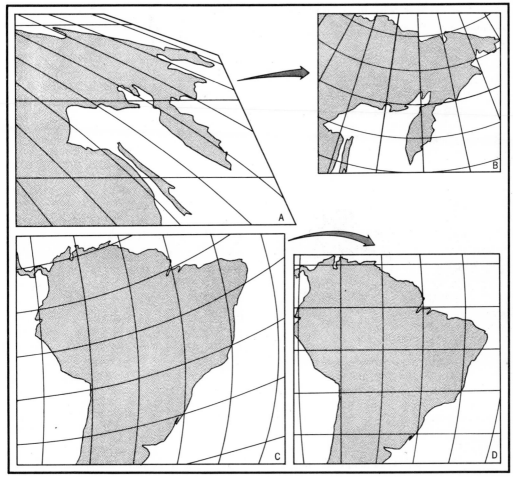

Fig. 73. Changing shapes in the compilation procedure. Maps *B* and *D* are derived from *A* and *C*. The compilation of *B* would have been made easier if the intermediate parallels of *B* had been drawn on *A*.

small-scale maps have been compiled in this manner. Since the projections commonly differ as between those of the sources and that of the base being compiled, it is necessary for the cartographer to become adept at imagining the shearing and twisting of the grid from one projection to another and to modify his lines accordingly. He must continuously be generalizing and simplifying. The difficulties occasioned by projection differences between the sources and the compilation can be largely eliminated by making the projection grids comparable. That is to say, the same grid interval on each will greatly facilitate the work (see Fig. 73).

Compilation is most easily undertaken by first outlining on the new projection the areas covered by the source maps, as in Fig. 74. Such an outlining is similar to the index map of a map series. The sheet outlines may be drawn, and the special grid spacing of each source (5°, 2°, etc.) may be lightly drawn on the base.

It is worth reiterating that the care with which the cartographer approaches this part of his task will, in large part, determine the accuracy of the final map.

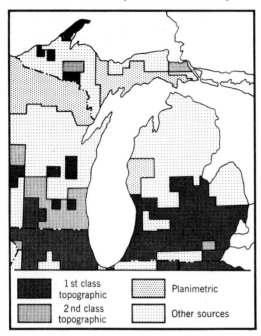

1st class topographic

2nd class topographic

Planimetric

Other sources

Fig. 74. Indexing of sources preliminary to compilation. This makes it possible for the cartographer to see immediately what gaps in source material there may be. It also aids him in pursuing the task systematically.

93 The Importance of Base Data

The importance of including on the finished map an adequate amount of base data cannot be overemphasized. Nothing is so disconcerting to a map reader than to see a large amount of detail presented on a map and then be confronted with the realization that there is no "frame" of basic geographic information to which he can relate the distributions.

The amount and detail of the base data will, of course, vary considerably from map to map. The average special-purpose map must have on it the coastlines, the major rivers and lakes, and at least the basic civil divisions. The projection grid, in most cases, should be indicated in some fashion. The purpose of the map will dic-

tate the degree of detail required, but it is a rare map that can be made without the above kinds of information to aid the reader to appreciate the relationships presented.

94 Determining the Scale

All maps must, of course, be drawn to a scale. In actual practice most special-purpose maps are drawn to fit a prescribed format, the format being the size and shape of the sheet on which the map will appear. The format may be a whole page in a book or an atlas, a part of a page, a separate map requiring a fold, a wall map, or a map of almost any conceivable shape and size. Whatever the format may be the map must fit within it.

The first operation in planning the map is to arrive at a layout. (See Article 115.) The layout need not be in precise final form, but should be sufficiently exact so that the cartographer may proceed with the base map.

As we have seen the shapes of areas vary considerably depending on the projection upon which they are plotted. Hence the first concern of the cartographer regarding scale is the projection on which the map will be made. If the map is one for which almost any projection could be used, the cartographer need concern himself only with the dimensions of the format. This circumstance is not, however, likely to occur, or at least it ought not to occur frequently, for it is difficult to imagine a map that would be equally presentable on any projection. When the projection choice has been narrowed to a smaller class or group of projections, then the variations in the shapes of the mapped area on the different projections must be matched against the format in order to see which will provide the best fit and maximum scale.

The easiest way to do this is to establish the vertical and horizontal relationship of the format shape on a proportion basis and then compare the proportion against representations on the various projections. The proportion can be set on a slide rule or plotted on graph paper, so that for any

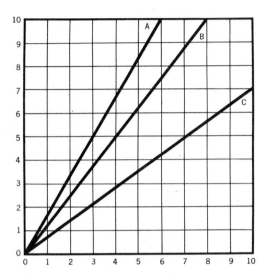

FIG. 75. Dimension proportion graph. The ratio is constant along each line. *A* defines a rectangle with sides in a 5:3 ratio; *B*, a 5:4 ratio; and *C*, a 7:10 ratio. Whatever pair of values is obtained by reading the ordinate and abscissa of a point on one line the shape will remain the same.

one dimension the other may be readily determined. (See Fig. 75.) With the proportion established, any scale projection can be used to test for shape fit.

When the projection has been selected that best fits the purpose and format of the proposed map the scale may be determined. This, of course, may be done in a number of ways, but the simplest is to calculate the scale from the length in degrees of the central meridian.

The cartographer must also decide at this stage whether he is going to compile on an already drawn projection or base map,

or construct his own projection and compile on it. Most projections may be used more than once by simply copying the projection and renumbering the longitude. One must be careful, however, not to use a projection that has been copyrighted or patented unless permission is obtained (see Article 106). As a general rule it is far better to construct the projection to fit precisely the purpose of the map. Most projections are not difficult to construct except in special phases, and it is poor practice to produce an inferior map "projection-wise" in order to save a few hours' time. Frequently mapped areas such as continents or countries have, however, appeared on most of the appropriate standard projections, and if available there is no reason why a good projection already available should not be used. One should, however, always test such a projection to be certain that it has not been improperly constructed.

95 Reduction

Most maps are made for reduction by photography. This is not always the case, for some processes of reproduction cannot change the scale, but whenever reduction of the fair drawing is possible its advantages make it desirable. The amount of reduction will depend upon the process of reproduction and upon the complexity of the map. It will also depend upon whether definite specifications have been determined for the reproduction, as may be the case with maps of a series. In general, maps are made for from one-quarter to one-half reduction in the linear dimensions. It is unwise to make a greater reduction, for the design problem then becomes difficult.

Whatever the reduction, it is frequently necessary to change the scale of a base map or an already prepared projection. This is unnecessary, of course, if the projection is being constructed, for it may be initially computed and drawn at the larger scale.

96 Changing Scale

The scale of a base map or projection may be changed in a number of ways, viz., by photography, by pantography, or by similar squares.

Changing scale by photography is the easiest for the cartographer, but, as might be expected, it is the most expensive. It may be accomplished either by photographic enlargement or reduction through the use of the conventional film process or by the photostat process. Formerly photostat was cheaper, but there seems to be less difference at this writing between the costs. Photography provides a little more precision than does photostat, and there is likely to be less distortion around the edges of a photograph than a photostat. It is usually necessary to specify the reduction or enlargement of photostating work by a percentage ratio, such as 50 per cent or 75 per cent reduction. Change of scale is usually accomplished by setting the machine on a percentage scale. Care should be exercised in specifying the percentage change, since 50 per cent reduction or enlargement means one-half in the linear dimension and is usually the most that can occur in one "shot." A change of more than 50 per cent requires repeating the process. To reduce something by 75 per cent in the linear dimension would require two exposures of 50 per cent each, not one at 50 per cent and another at 25 per cent. Photostat paper is ordinarily limited to 18 x 24 inches, and anything larger must be done in sections. It is difficult to match the sections since the paper commonly changes shape unevenly in the developing and drying.

Photographic enlargement or reduction using film negatives may be made some-

what more precisely, since the image may be projected (if enlarged) or viewed in the camera (if reduced), and thus dimensions can be scaled exactly. All the cartographer need do is to specify a line on the piece to be photographed and then request that it be reduced to a specific length. The ratio can be worked out exactly, and the photographer needs only a ruler to check his setting. Any clearly defined line or border

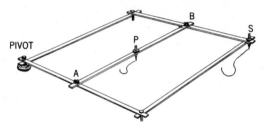

Fig. 76. A pantograph. Stylus (*S*) and pencil (*P*) are interchangeable for enlargement or reduction. Adjustment to the desired ratio is made by moving arm *AB* parallel to itself while the pencil or stylus on *AB* is adjusted so that it, the pivot point, and *S* are kept in a straight line.

will serve as the guide. If none is available he may draw one on the copy. The sizes available are limited only by the photographer's equipment and paper stock.

The pantograph is an ancient device for enlarging and reducing, the common form of which is illustrated in Fig. 76. Simple wooden pantographs cost but a few dollars; large, metal precision models cost much more. They are easy to operate for reduction, but enlargement is relatively difficult and accuracy is hard to obtain.

If a pantograph is unavailable, and if the projection of a map one wishes to copy is either too difficult or not indicated, then one may change scale by similar squares. This involves drawing a grid of squares on the original and drawing the "same" squares, only larger or smaller, on the compilation. The lines and positions may then be transferred from the one grid system to the

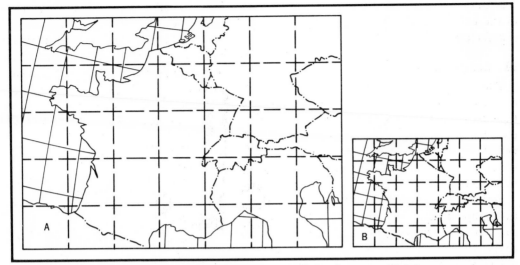

FIG. 77. Changing scale by similar **squares.** Map *B* has been compiled from map *A*.

other (see Fig. 77). With care it is quite an accurate process, for it is the same as compilation.

Occasionally a cartographer is called upon to produce a large wall-size chart or map that involves greatly enlarging a base. In most cases extreme accuracy is not required. If the outlines cannot be sketched satisfactorily because of their intricacies, it is possible to accomplish an adequate solution by projection. A slide or film positive (in some cases, a negative will do) may be projected by means of a lantern to the paper affixed to the wall and the image traced thereon. If an opaque projector with a large projecting surface that is sufficiently cool in operation is available, it may be used directly so that the necessity of making a slide is eliminated. This is similar to the process sometimes used in large cartographic organizations of compiling with the aid of large, overhead, precision projectors.

97 Compilation Procedure

Perhaps nothing helps the mechanical process of compiling so much as a trans-parent or translucent material with which to work. A tracing medium of some sort (paper, plastic, etc.) enables the compiler to accomplish a number of things in addition to the convenience of being able to trace some data. He may lay out lettering for titles, etc., and move the layout around under this compilation worksheet. (See Article 115.) If he wishes to draw a series of lines, or letter at an angle, or place dots regularly, he need only place some cross-section paper under the tracing paper. The use of a lightweight material such as tracing paper occasions, however, the problem of maintaining size, for papers contract and expand with changes in humidity and temperature. Plastic materials such as acetate or Vinylite are more stable but are harder to work with. If, however, registry is a problem, a dimensionally stable material should be used.

Compilation may be done in any colors and inks the cartographer desires. The main problem is to put all the desired data on the worksheet in such a way that each item is clear and will cause no confusion in the drafting process; thus hydrography, coastlines, boundaries, and other elements of the base data may each be compiled in a different color.

98   Coastlines

The compiling of coasts for very small-scale maps is not much of a problem, for they usually require so much generalization that detail is of little consequence. This is not the case when compiling at medium scales, where considerable accuracy of detail is necessary.

Perhaps the major problem facing the cartographer is the matter of source material. It is well to bear in mind that some coasts will be shown quite differently on different maps, yet both may be accurate. Hydrographic charts are made with a datum, or plane of reference, of mean low water, whereas topographic maps are usually made with a datum of mean sea level. The two are not the same elevation, and it is to be expected that there will be a difference in the resulting outline of the land. In parts of the world with higher tides and with special planes of reference the differences will be greater. Another difficult aspect of dealing with source materials is that the coloring of the charts and maps may be quite different. Swamp land, definitely not navigable, is usually colored as land on a chart. The compiler would assume it to be land by its appearance. All low-lying swamp on a topographic map is colored blue as water, and only a small area may be shown as land. On many low-lying coasts the cartographer is faced with a decision as to what is land; the charts and maps do not tell him.

Through the years some coasts change outline sufficiently so that it makes a difference even on medium-scale maps. Figure 78 shows the north coast of the Persian Gulf in the past and at present, and Fig. 79, a portion of the Atlantic coast. If one were making maps of an historical period he should endeavor to recreate the conditions at the period of the map. This problem is particularly evident on coastal areas of rapid silting, which in many parts of the world seem to be important areas of occupance.

Another problem of considerable concern to the cartographer is the representation of

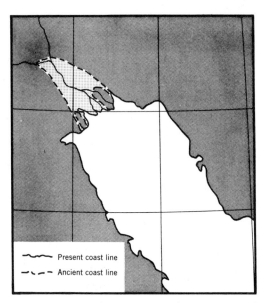

FIG. 78. Major changes in coastlines occur over long periods of time which are significant even on small-scale maps. A portion of the Persian Gulf.

coasts on maps wherein the scale varies considerably over the map. For example, at 60° latitude on the Mercator projection everything is much larger (twice linearly, four times areally) than similar features at the equator. Bays, inlets, fjords, etc., in the higher latitudes take on a great apparent significance on such maps and look more detailed and complex than they should if the coast is not the focus of interest. It may be necessary to vary the simplification and generalization according to the scale variations of the map. Of course, this would never be done on a topographic or chart series.

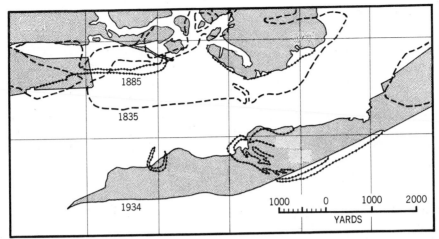

FIG. 79. Frequent changes have occurred in some areas. The various lines show the position of the shoreline of Rockaway Inlet, Long Island, at several periods in the past. Modified from Deetz, *Cartography*, Special Publication 205, U.S. Coast and Geodetic Survey.

In a number of areas of the world, notably in the polar regions, the coastlines, like many other elements of the map base, are not well known. They vary considerably from one source to another. On some maps a particular region may appear as an island; on others, as a series of islands; and on still others, as a peninsula. On simple line maps a broken or dashed line suffices for unknown positions of coastlines, but it becomes a larger problem when the water is to be shaded or colored for no matter what type of line is used to delineate the coast the value or color change outlines it clearly.

99 Drafting Coastlines

Coastlines may be drawn with a crow quill pen or any other fine nib if care is taken to maintain a uniform thickness of line. It is an aid to have the paper loose on the drafting table so that it may be turned around freely and lines drawn toward the cartographer. Occasionally, it is desirable to draw a lighter line in a complex area, and a slightly heavier line in a simple area in order that the two coastlines may appear more nearly uniform as

shown by *A* in Fig. 80. Likewise, embayments, estuaries, etc., may sometimes be drawn with a line lighter than the main trend of the coastline, as shown by *B* in

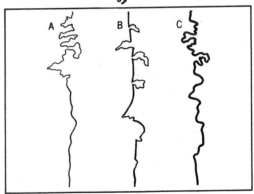

FIG. 80. Various kinds of coastlines. Letters refer to Article 99.

Fig. 80. This is especially desirable for the thick coasts of wall maps.

Coastlines may also be drawn with a pen that makes a uniform line no matter what direction it is moved on the paper, such as the LeRoy et al., shown by *C* in Fig. 80. This is much faster than using a quill pen but is not so precise for detailed work, for no points can be made with these "round-pointed" pens. It is also difficult to vary the width of line, and a very thin line cannot be drawn.

100   Political Boundaries

Compiling political boundaries for base data is sometimes a complex problem, for the boundaries must be chosen for the purpose and date of the map data to be placed on them. The problem becomes more difficult as the area covered by the map increases. Almost all boundaries change from time to time, and it is surprising how difficult it is to search out the minor changes. For example, a population map of the distribution of languages in central Europe prior to World War II, but also showing present boundaries, raises these problems: (*a*) international boundaries today and (*b*) census division boundaries as of the dates of the enumerations in the various countries.

The major difficulties are two-fold, the first being that of finding maps showing enumeration districts that show grid or base data so that the boundaries may be transferred to the worksheet in proper position. The second is that of placing present international boundaries in correct relation to the enumeration boundaries.

The complexity of this type of boundary compilation problem is further increased by the fact that surveys are not all alike. Some are based on three-dimensional geodetic survey, and some are based on two-dimensional plane survey. The two cannot match. A good example is that of the cadastral survey in much of the United States vs. the topographic survey in the same areas. Many county and township maps are available showing straight lines for the various survey lines. In reality the lines may not be straight at all on the earth; yet, if the compilation covers a large enough area, it is necessary to fit the one set of boundary lines to the natural features

of the other. The fact that surveys are of different types based on different systems must be constantly borne in mind by the compiler.

It is not uncommon for official civil division boundary maps to be without any other base data, even projection lines. Such a condition should impress on the cartographer who uses such deficient maps the need for him to provide base data for the users of his maps.

101   Drafting Boundaries

As in drawing other linear symbols, boundaries on base maps are most easily

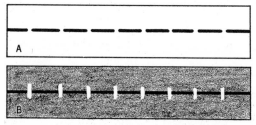

FIG. 81. A line drawn with a round pen (*A*) has round corners; *B* shows one method of sharpening such corners with white paint. They may also be drawn with a stub-type pen, or the corners may be sharpened by touching them up with a crow quill.

made with a pen that will draw a uniform line no matter which direction it is moved. As shown in Fig. 81, such a line cannot, however, have sharp corners, and this is sometimes a disadvantage when boundaries are shown with a dot-dash symbol. One way to overcome this defect is illustrated in Fig. 81, where a solid line is first drawn and then broken into the symbol desired by brushing across it with white paint. This is a good way to clean up corners and other junctions, but it can be done *only when the map is to be photographed on relatively slow film.*

A large variety of symbols may be used to show boundaries, some of which are illustrated in Fig. 82. There is no gen-

erally accepted standardization of boundaries, but many agencies and governments
have standardized boundary symbols for

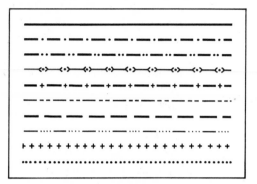

Fig. 82. Some examples of kinds of boundary symbols.

their own official maps. Generally speaking, decreasing significance of boundaries
on a map is accompanied by a decrease
in width of line and an increase in complexity of line.

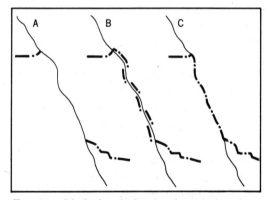

Fig. 83. Methods of showing boundaries along
rivers. *A* and *C* show only that the boundary
follows the river. It may be on either bank or
in the middle of the stream. *B* shows that it is
in the middle. If it is necessary to show that the
boundary follows one bank it may be drawn parallel to the stream on the appropriate side.

One difficulty the cartographer occasionally encounters is the problem of symbolizing the boundary along a water course
also shown as base data. Some possible
solutions are shown in Fig. 83.

102 Hydrography

The compiling of rivers and lakes on the
base map is an important process. These
elements of the physical landscape are the
only relatively permanent interior features
on many maps, and they provide helpful
"anchor points" both for the compilation
of other data and for the map reader's appreciation of the significance of the distribution mapped

The selection of the rivers and lakes depends, of course, upon their significance
to the problem at hand. On some maps
the inclusion of well-known state boundaries makes it unnecessary to include any
but the larger rivers. Maps of less well-
known areas require more hydrography,
for the drainage, which indicates the major
structure of an area, is sometimes a better-
known phenomenon than the internal
boundaries. Care must be exercised to
choose the main "stream" of rivers and the
major tributaries. Often this depends not
upon the width, depth, or volume of the
stream but upon some economic or other
element of significance. Oftentimes it is
necessary to eliminate relatively important
rivers or lakes because they will interfere
with the planned use of the maps. For
example, Lake Winnebago in Wisconsin
becomes a visual focus on many maps to
the detriment of the map data. Often it
need not be included.

Just as coastlines have characteristic
shapes (see Article 104) so do rivers, and
these shapes help considerably, on the
larger-scale maps, to identify the feature.
The braided streams of dry lands, intermittent streams, or the meandering streams
on flood plains are examples. On small-
scale maps it frequently is not possible to
include enough detail to thus differentiate
between stream types, but the larger
sweeps, angles, and curves of the stream's
course should be faithfully delineated.

Likewise, the manner in which a stream enters the sea is important. Some enter at a particular angle, some enter into bays, and some break into a characteristic set of distributaries. Examples of streams are shown in Fig. 84.

Swamps, marshes, and mud flats are commonly important elements of location

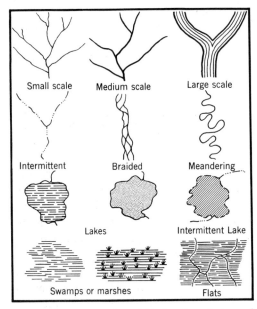

FIG. 84. Some examples of kinds of symbols used for hydrography.

on the base map. They may be represented by various symbols, examples of which are shown in Fig. 84.

103 Drafting Hydrography

It is desirable when representing streams to draw them so that they grow from thin to thicker lines near their mouths. This is most easily done with a flexible, fine, pen nib which spreads with increased pressure. It requires a bit of practice to keep the spreading uniform around curves and angles in the stream.

On all but the largest-scale maps it is impossible to represent the width of a river truly, and, consequently, the width of line chosen is an important consideration. When the existence of a river is known but not its precise location, its unknown portion may be represented by a dashed line the same width as the known course.

Patterns for lakes, swamps, intermittent lakes, etc., may either be drafted or obtained in preprinted form.

104 Generalization

The effective limit of exact representation of earth phenomena having dimension (roads, rivers, etc.) is at a fairly large scale. The limiting scale varies somewhat, of course, depending on the item to be represented. Certainly, however, at any scale smaller than the topographic it is necessary to simplify outlines and shapes, to enlarge the area covered by symbols, and to select from the multitude those things to be represented. This process in cartography is called generalization. Every special-purpose map must be a product of generalization.

Good generalization requires many qualities on the part of the cartographer, chief among which are a thorough knowledge of his subject matter and essential intellectual honesty. The latter is particularly important. A distinguished cartographer and geographer, John K. Wright, puts it thus: [*]

"Fundamental among these qualities is scientific integrity: devotion to the truth and a will to record it as accurately as possible. The strength of this devotion varies with the individual. Not all cartographers are above attempting to make their maps seem more accurate than they actually are by drawing rivers, coasts, form lines, and so on, with an intricacy of detail derived largely from the imagination. This

[*] From "Map Makers Are Human . . . ," *The Geographical Review*, 1942, Vol. 32, p. 528.

may be done to cover up the use of inadequate source materials or, what is worse, to mask carelessness in the use of adequate sources. Indifference to the truth may also show itself in failure to counteract, where it would be feasible and desirable to do so, the exaggerated impression of accuracy often due to the clean-cut appearance of a map."

It is next to impossible to set down any rules for intellectual generalization. The degree of simplification of a coastline, a boundary, or any other data *depends entirely upon the purpose of the map.* If the map being made is a reference map then the data must be placed as accurately as possible within drafting and legibility limits. If, on the other hand, the map is for a special purpose, some of the base data may be simplified to a considerable degree. Experience, knowledge of the subject, and clearly defined purpose are the only possible guides to intellectual generalization.

There is another aspect of generalization that allows the cartographer a certain measure of latitude. This may be called visual generalization to distinguish it from the strictly intellectual, although it is difficult in practice to separate the two. In this kind of generalization we are concerned with the visual effect of the character of the line on the viewer. It is particularly important in the designing of lines to represent coasts and boundaries when the reference value of the line itself is slight, as is the case with a great many maps on which boundaries and coasts appear.

As a general rule we may say that any visual form that appears more complicated than the surrounding forms will draw attention to itself, simply because it is more interesting to the eye. The fjorded coast of Norway is an example. If the reader will refer to Fig. 85 he will at once see that *A*, the more complicated representation of the coast, catches his eye. This is partly due to the fact that the degree of complexity also makes the coastal region a dark

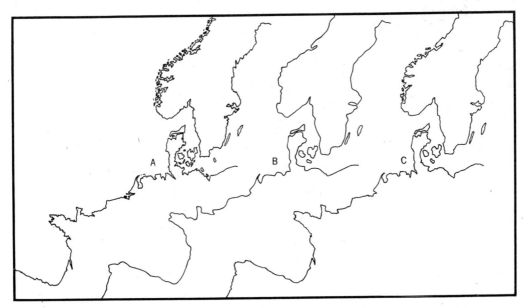

Fig. 85. Generalization of coasts. *A* and *C* are least generalized; *B*, the most. All, however, are greatly simplified from reality.

value area. By simplification the map maker can help the reader refrain from giving attention to details that are extraneous to the purpose of the map.

It is not enough merely to smooth out coasts and ignore islands. The basic shapes must be retained and emphasized in their simplicity, for the eye will not quibble with the representation if the general shapes are as expected.

The cartographer must be careful not to overdo the simplification, for, as has been abundantly shown in many newspaper maps, too much simplification makes a representation of a known shape appear ridiculous.

While the cartographer is learning, and for some time afterward, it would be wise for him to test his generalization by drafting a small portion of the planned map before compilation has progressed far. In this way he may decide upon the generalization needed for his compilation. It will also help him in his design plan.

105 Reliability

One of the most difficult tasks of the cartographer is to convey to the map reader some indication of the reliability of the information on his map. When writing or speaking, words such as "almost," "nearly," and "approximately" can be included to indicate the desired degree of precision of the subject matter. It is not easy to do this with map data. It is unfortunate that this is the case, for a well-made map has about it an aura of truth and exactness that might not be warranted if the facts concerning its accuracy were known.

There are several ways to combat this. One, of course, is to include in the legend a statement concerning the accuracy of any item about which such is necessary. Another, and more common method on larger-scale maps, is to include a reliability diagram (Fig. 86) which shows the relative

accuracy of various parts of the map. A third method is necessary when there are various categories of information that do not lend themselves to areal evaluation as in the preceding case. This is the reliability code or statement (Fig. 87), which may be modified to suit the purpose.

COVERAGE DIAGRAM

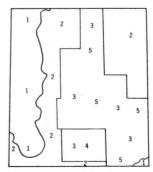

1. USC&GS Charts, (Reliable survey)
2. Luzon, 1:63,360 (Trigonometric survey - reliability fair)
3. PIC&GS Charts (Compiled map - reliability fair)
4. Luzon Island, 1:200,000 (Reconnaissance map - reliability fair)
5. Sectional Aeronautical Chart, 1:600,000 (Compiled map - reliability fair)

Fig. 86. Coverage diagram from a map of the Lingayen Gulf area, Philippine Islands, giving an annotated list of sources together with an index. Courtesy of the Army Map Service.

It is also good practice to include in the legend, if warranted, such terms as "position approximate," "generalized roads," or "selected railroads," in order that an idea of the completeness and accuracy may be given the reader.

106 Copyrights and Credits

It is beyond the purpose of this book to suggest sources of compilation materials, but the cartographer, regardless of what sources he uses, must always give proper credit for materials gathered and presented by others. It is necessary to do this for it is the honest way of doing things. But this does not mean that he must identify the source of every single item on a reference

RELIABILITY OF DATA				
DATA	QUAN.	QUAL.	LOC.	Quantitative & Qualitative Data
CITIES			NE	R - Reliable
INDUSTRY		GR-I	NE	GR - Generally Reliable
				U - Unreliable
				Coverage of Data
				C - Complete
				I - Incomplete
				Location of Data
				A - Accurate
				NE - Not Entirely Accurate
				OA - Only Approx. Accurate

QUANTITATIVE DATA The letters R, GR, and U are an estimate of the reliability of the map's quantitative data, the data which are measurable, including economic or population statistics, hypsometric data, the width of roads, gauges of railroads, etc.

QUALITATIVE DATA The letters R, GR, and U are an estimate of the reliability of the map's qualitative data which shows the types of road surfaces, character of beaches, types of terrain, etc.

COVERAGE The letters C and I in combination with R, GR, or U are an estimate of the degree of completeness of quantitative and qualitative data.

LOCATIONAL DATA The letters A, NE, and OA are estimates of the plotted accuracy of data within the limits of scale and width of line.

R A, OSS

FIG. 87. A reliability statement devised during World War II by the Map Division, OSS, for use on special-purpose maps. From a qualitative map of German industrial locations.

map, even though it is obvious that he could not have gathered any of the material himself in the field by original survey. It does mean that he should identify the source of any material that is not generally common knowledge or does not obviously come from good public authority. He may, however, wish to identify such sources of well-known information in order to justify the quality of his map.

Equally important for the map maker is the problem of copyright protection and the use of materials that have been copyrighted. This is a particularly difficult problem in cartography, for there has never been a clear definition of the way in which the copyright laws apply to maps. In general, no copyrighted map may be used as a source without permission, for the manner in which the material is arrayed and generalized is protected. Most United States government maps and publications may be used, but in the case of specialized materials containing judgments and opinions, it is not only courteous but wise to request permission, for the material may have been copyrighted by the authors separately or some of it may have come from copyrighted sources.

Generally speaking, survey maps of the topographic variety, census material, and the like, may be used freely. Reproduction or copying of private materials *must* be accompanied by permission from the holder of the copyright. Even some projections are copyrighted, but this is not much of a problem to the cartographer for there are many from which to choose.

7

Map Design

107 Map Design and Visual Significance

Of all the aspects of cartography, map design is perhaps the most complex. The manner of presentation of the many map components so that together they appear as an integrated whole, devised systematically to fit the purposes of the cartographer (and thus those of the reader), includes elements ranging from mathematics to art. Regardless of the essential accuracy or appropriateness of the map data, if the map has not been properly designed it will be a cartographic failure.

It is not necessary to be an artist to learn to design effectively. The basic elements of good design lend themselves to systematic analysis, and their principles can be learned. A basic requirement, however, is a willingness to think in visual terms, uninhibited by prejudices resulting from previous experience, or, to put it another way, a willingness to exercise imagination. The imagination must, of course, be disciplined to some extent, for, like many fields, cartography has developed traditions and conventions; to disregard them completely would inconvenience the user of the maps, which would in itself be proof of poor design. Cartography is not art in the sense that one may have complete freedom with techniques and media. The exercise of imagination will soon reveal, however, that the possibilities of variation of shapes, sizes, forms, and other visual relationships of the map components are practically unlimited. The aim of cartographic design is to present the map data in such fashion that the map, as a whole, appears as an integrated unit and so that each item included is clear, legible, and neither more nor less prominent than it should be.

The myriad things we see every day of our lives vary from the visually important to the visually unimportant. Sometimes the striking things are interesting because of some special significance they may have, such as a new-model automobile or darkness at midday. Usually, however, the striking things are *visually significant*. That is to say, they appear so different from their surroundings that they excite our eyes. Since this is a common experience it should be relatively easy to adapt the underlying principles to our cartographic purpose.

Suppose, for example, that we wished to attract the reader's eye to the water or hydrographic features of a map, perhaps even to the extent that he would notice little else. It would be a simple matter to color the water and rivers a bright red to the end that their brilliant and incongruous appearance would dominate. This is, of course, extreme, even for an example, but the principle has not been violated, namely, that every item in a design has some place on the scale of visual significance. The estimation of how visually significant a thing may be is not, however, an easy task, for there are a number of factors which must be analyzed, such as:

1. The degree to which an item departs from its expected appearance. The more it departs, the more interesting it is.
2. The relative complexity of its delineation. The more complex the item is, the more visually interesting it is.
3. The relative size of an item. The larger an item is, the more visually important it is.
4. The relative brightness of an item. The brighter or lighter an item is contrasted with its surroundings, the more visually interesting it is.
5. The position of an item with respect to the other components of the map. The nearer to the visual center of a presentation an item is, the more significant it is visually.

It may be seen from the list that each of the statements is concerned with some kind of varying relationship between an item and its surroundings. Consequently, it is possible to assess the design "strength" of an element, and, in a sense, to locate it on a scale of visual significance.

108 The Visual Outline

Just as when one plans to write something, he first prepares an outline, so is it also necessary to outline a visual presentation. Each item of the design should be evaluated in combination with the other elements in terms of its probable effect on the map reader. To do this requires a full and complete understanding of the purpose or purposes of the map to be made. One can scarcely imagine writing an article or planning a lecture without first arriving at a reasonably clear decision concerning (*a*), the audience to which it is to be presented and (*b*), the scope of the subject matter. With these well in mind, the writer uses them as a framework upon which to plan and as a yardstick against which to measure the significance of the items to be included.

It is impossible to categorize the kinds of maps that can be made in such a way that the rubrics will help provide more than a very general guide to design planning. It is true, however, that many maps generally fall into what we might call a class of "reference maps." These maps, common in atlases, are to be used like a dictionary; they are for the reader to find many kinds of information. Few, if any, of the represented items are more important than the others. Consequently, the elements of clarity and legibility are paramount; but at the same time no emphasis, no differing position on the scale of visual significance, is desirable, at least theoretically. A reference map is only one of many kinds of maps. Others show categories of information, such as roads, railroads, population, resources, movement of goods, and so on; they may show several such kinds of information, and one kind of information may be more significant than another. Furthermore, many maps that are made for geographers, historians, planners, and the like, are intended to make clear special relationships between two or among a number of items.

As an illustration of how the presentation may be outlined, *A*, *B*, *C*, and *D* in Fig. 88 have been prepared. The assumption is made that the planned map is to show two related hypothetical distributions in Europe. The basic elements of the visual outline are:

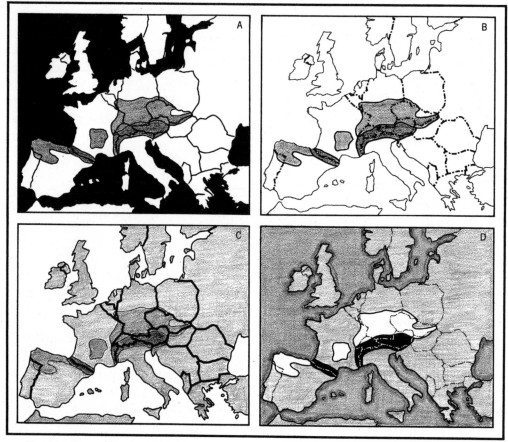

FIG. 88. Examples of variations in the primary visual outline. Letters refer to Article 108.

1. The place, Europe.

2. The data, the two distributions to be shown.

3. The position of the data with respect to Europe.

4. The relative position of the two distributions.

Any one of the above four elements may be placed at the top of the visual outline, and the order of the others following it may be varied in any way the author desires. In *A* in Fig. 88, the outline places the items in the general order of 1-2-3-4; in *B*, 2-3-4-1; in *C*, 3-1-4-2; and in *D*, 4-2-3-1. Other combinations are, of course,

possible. It should not be inferred that the positioning of concepts in the visual outline can be as exact and precise as in a written outline. In the latter, the position is reasonably assured since the reader is more or less forced to start at one point and go systematically to the end, whereas in the visual outline he sees the items all at once, and it is up to the designer to attempt to lead him by manipulating the various elements of visual significance.

It is appropriate at this point to digress slightly in order to emphasize one of the more difficult complicating factors a cartographer must face in visual design. Any component of a map has, of course, an intellectual connotation as well as a visual meaning in the design sense. It is difficult to remove the former in order to evaluate the latter, but many times it is not only necessary but definitely desirable. Artists turn their works upside down; advertising layout men "rough in" outlines, and even basic lettering, as design units without "spelling anything out"; and because the intellectual connotation cannot always be predicted, cartographers will obtain better design if they do likewise, except for obvious, well-known shapes, such as continents and countries. To illustrate this the distributions in Fig. 88 and some other figures in this book have been made incomplete, purely hypothetical, or highly generalized.

It is apparent that there are, in fact, two scales of visual significance for each map. Just as is the case with a written outline, the major items, or the primary outline, are first determined, then the position of the subject matter within each major rubric is decided. In the case of a map, the visual presentation of the detail is primarily a matter of clarity, legibility, and relative contrast of the detail items.

The outlining of a map depends upon an understanding of the contrasts of lines, shapes, colors, brightness (value), and the principles of balance. These topics are treated in the succeeding articles.

109 Clarity and Legibility

To be effective any kind of communication must be clear and legible. The transmission of information by maps is no exception.

Clarity and legibility are broad terms, and many of the techniques and principles considered in other parts of this book are important factors in obtaining these qualities in a presentation. Furthermore, a considerable portion of the task of achieving clarity and legibility will have been accomplished if the map maker has made sure that the intellectual aspects of his map are not open to doubt or misinterpretation. In writing or speaking, the aim is to state the thought with the right words, properly spelled or pronounced, and clearly written or enunciated. In cartography, symbols are ordinarily substituted for written or spoken words; their form and arrangement substitute for the spelling or pronunciation; and their delineation takes the place of writing or enunciation. It is apparent, then, that no matter what the form of a presentation may be, the principles behind clarity and legibility are much alike; only the "vocabulary" varies.

If it is assumed that the geographical concepts underlying the purpose and data of a map are clear and correct, then legibility and clarity in the presentation can be obtained by the proper choice of lines, shapes, and colors and by their precise and correct delineation. Lines must be clear, sharp, and uniform; colors, patterns, and shading must be easily distinguishable and properly registered; and the shapes of symbols, coastlines, and other items represented must not be confusing.

One important element of legibility is size, for, no matter how nicely a line or symbol may be drawn, if it is too small to be seen it is useless. There is a lower size limit below which an unfamiliar shape or symbol cannot be identified. This has been established as being a size which subtends an angle of about 1' at the eye. That is to say, no matter how far away the object may be, it must be at least that size to be identifiable. It is well to point out that this limit sets rather an ideal, for it assumes perfect vision and perfect conditions of viewing. Because of the unreasonableness of these assumptions, it is wise for the cartographer to establish his minimum size somewhat higher. Instead of the ideal of an angle of 1′, it may be assumed that 2′ is more likely to be a realistic value for average (not "normal") vision and average viewing conditions. Table 9 is useful in setting bottom values of visibility.

TABLE 9. APPROXIMATE MINIMUM SYMBOL SIZE FOR VIEWING FROM VARIOUS DISTANCES.

Viewing distance	Size (width)
18 inches	0.01 inch
5 feet	.03 inch
10 feet	.07 inch
20 feet	.14 inch
40 feet	.28 inch
60 feet	.42 inch
80 feet	.56 inch
100 feet	.70 inch

It should be remembered that some map symbols have length as well as width, and in such cases, as for example with lines, the width may be reduced considerably since the length will promote the visibility. In similar fashion, other elements, such as contrasting colors or shapes, may enhance visibility and legibility, but even though the existence of a symbol on the map is made visible by such devices, if it does not stand at or above the sizes given in Table 9 it will not be legible. In other words, it might be seen (visibility), but it might not be read or recognized (legibility).

A second element regarding legibility is also operative in cartography. As a general rule, it is easier to recognize something we are familiar with than something that is new to us. Thus, for example, we may see a name in a particular place on a map, and, although it is much too small to read, we can tell from its position and the general shape of the whole word what it is.

The fact that symbols, lines, and the other elements of a map are large enough to be seen does not in itself provide clarity and legibility. An additional element, that of *contrast,* is necessary.

110 Contrast of Lines and Shapes

No element of the cartographic technique is so important as contrast. Assuming that each component of the map is large enough to be seen, then the manner and the way in which it is contrasted with its surroundings determines its visibility. The degree to which a map appears precise and "sharp" is dependent on the contrast structure of the map.

Contrast is a subtle visual element in some ways, and in others it is blatant. The character of a line, and the way its curves or points are formed, may set it completely apart from another line of the same thickness. The thickness of one line in comparison to another may accomplish the same thing. The shapes of letters may blend into the background complex of lines and other shapes, or the opposite may obtain. If one element of the design is varied as to darkness, thickness, or shape, then the relationship of all other components will likewise be changed. It requires careful juggling of the lines, shapes, and brightness characteristics, on a kind of "trial and error" basis, to arrive at the "right" combination.

Most maps require the use of several kinds of lines, each symbolizing some geographic element or concept, such as coastlines, rivers, railroads, roads, various political boundaries, and so on. In order to make each clearly distinct from the next, it is necessary to vary in some way their character, design, or size. Figure 89 shows some of the many possible variations in line width. Figure 90 shows some of the various possibilities in line design. Figure 91 shows some possible variations in character of line. Only on the largest-scale maps does accuracy require an exact position for every part of a line. On smaller-scale maps the lines, if large enough to be seen, cover much more area than the element they represent on the earth. Therefore, they may be drawn precisely and firmly. A wobbly, wavering line looks weak and indecisive and should be avoided.

Just as lines may have an almost infinite variety, so also may larger shapes vary. Oftentimes shape is given by nothing but

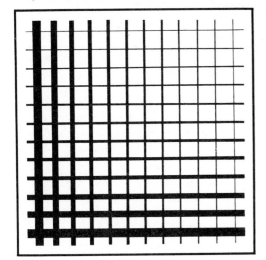

FIG. 89. Size contrast of lines. Uniformity produces monotony. Note that a clear visual difference between sizes of lines requires considerable actual difference.

the bounding line, and there are some components of a map, such as the legend or title box, insets, labels, and so on, that are definite shapes without benefit of a geographic delimitation. Part of the ability of the eye to perceive and take note of the contents of such shapes is due to the way they contrast with their surroundings. Figure 92 shows some of the ways such shapes may be varied.

It is impossible, of course, to catalog all the ways in which lines and shapes may be varied and contrasted. In other portions of the book some specific elements, such as the shapes and lines of letter forms, the delineation of coastlines, and so on,

FIG. 90. A few possible design variations of lines. Others are, of course, possible.

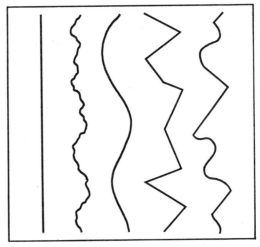

FIG. 91. Variation of shape or character of lines. Irregular "wiggliness" produces an impression of weakness.

have been considered. It is up to the student, however, to let his imagination roam and to consider critically those maps on which the line and shape structure appears well designed in order to become familiar with the range of possibilities.

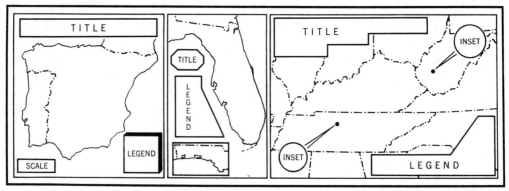

FIG. 92. Variation of larger shapes. Note that no attempt has been made to create additional contrast by varying the brightness of the background.

111 Color in Cartography *

Color is without doubt the most complex single medium with which the cartographer works. The complications arise from a number of circumstances, the major one being that even yet we do not know precisely what color is. We theorize that it consists of differing wave lengths of light, but exactly why color affects man's eyes the way it does is still a mystery. The complexity is increased by the fact that, so far as the use of color is concerned, it exists only in the eye of the observer. The student may obtain an inkling of some of the consequent difficulties by imagining the problem of explaining the appearance of red to a "color-blind" person.

Even the use of a small amount of color seems to produce remarkable differences in legibility and emphasis on maps. Its importance was early realized, and, although facilities for printing color are relatively recent, old maps were laboriously hand colored—an index of the esteem in which color was held. During the last century reproduction facility has increased to

* Portions of this and following articles have been in part modified from Arthur H. Robinson, *The Look of Maps, An Examination of Cartographic Design,* University of Wisconsin Press, Madison, Wis., 1952.

the point where it is possible to reproduce practically any kind of cartographic copy. Unfortunately, as the techniques and scientific knowledge have increased, so has the cost. As a result, it is to be expected that monochromatic techniques will be used for most maps, at least for most special-purpose maps. Although the majority of cartographers will have few opportunities to make colored maps for reproduction, they should be familiar with the bases for evaluating color use. Familiarity with principles of color use will also enable the cartographer to make an intelligent choice of the available alternatives, when economic considerations preclude the use of the ideal. For example, a range of shades or tints may be produced from a single plate in the flat-color process, whereas the best range might involve the more expensive requirement of several plates, or the four-color process. The choice of colors, then, depends on the characteristics of color perception and the purpose of the map.

The choice and use of color must obviously be primarily based on the characteristics of color vision, for maps are to be read. When color is examined from the point of view of its effect on the observer it has several characteristics. First, to the eye, color varies as to hue, e.g., blue or red.

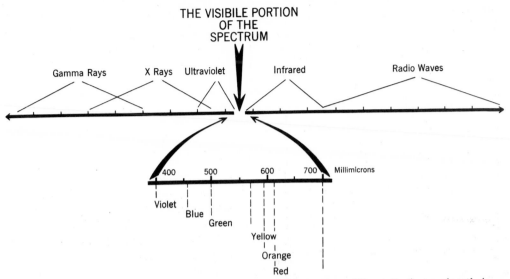

FIG. 93. A portion of the spectrum showing the visible section. The unit of wave length is the millimicron, one-billionth of a meter.

Because of the structure of the human eye and the differing wave lengths of light, human vision reacts in different ways to different hues, and a knowledge of these differences is necessary to the proper employment of colors. Secondly, each individual hue varies both in terms of its inherent brightness or value and in the degree of its intensity or the saturation of the color area. Just as the eye reacts differently to the various hues, so does it have varying sensitivity to value and intensity changes. Moreover, color always appears in an environment, and the environment has a marked influence on its appearance. Also significant in color use are the conventions, preferences, and the traditional significance of colors, cartographic and otherwise. The cartographer must be familiar with all these considerations before he can effectively evaluate the color technique. He should also have some background in the basic elements of color vision and color science, as is suggested by some of the references in the bibliography.

Color is the visual sensation produced by certain wave lengths of light whether singly or in combination. The visible portion of the spectrum is relatively small, as can be seen from Fig. 93. Between the extremes of violet and red occur all the pure or spectral hues. When reflected in combination to the eye they produce white. Black is the absence of light, but as far as the eye is concerned it also is a color, as is white. Almost all the colors we see or use are combinations of hues and can be analyzed by showing the percentage of reflectance of a particular wave length on the ordinate and the wave lengths on the abscissa of a graph. Figures 94 and 95 illustrate this method of visualizing colors, which aids considerably when evaluating them for use.

It is fundamental to the consideration of color that it be clearly understood that, for practical purposes, color exists only in the eye of the observer. The physics of light is of importance in the investigation of the characteristics of color behavior, and its findings provide a solid foundation for the discussion and analysis of color perception. But the study of color, whether in the cartographic technique or in any other aspect of its use, is based fundamentally, not

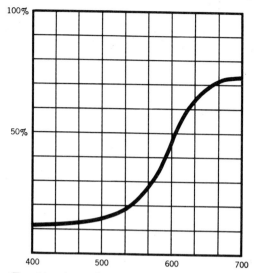

FIG. 94. Approximate color graph of a common red showing per cent reflectance of various wave lengths. Although the eye sees it as a single color the other wave lengths are included.

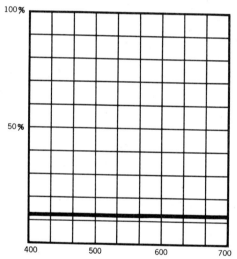

FIG. 95. Approximate color graph of a dark gray, showing it to be a uniform reflectance of all wave lengths. White would be the same kind of curve near the top of the reflectance scale.

on the physics of light, but on the sensations produced by the eye's reaction to colors.

Colors as eye sensations vary according to hue, value, and intensity. Hue is the color itself whether spectral or mixed, for example, a red or a green. Value is the intrinsic lightness or darkness of a color; for example, red is usually darker than yellow. The value scale ranges from black to white, as more completely described in the next article. All colors, mixed or pure spectral hues, have a value rating and can be matched with one of the values on a gray scale. The same hue can be varied in value by varying the amount of black or white mixed with it. Thus we may have a dark, medium, or light red, but all the same hue. Intensity is the term applied to the relative purity and amount of color in a given area. A scale of intensities would range from the pure hue at one end to a neutral gray at the other. At no place would it vary in value.

112 Contrast of Value

It was stated in a preceding article that contrast is the most important visual element of the cartographic technique. It may be further asserted that the variation of light and dark, whether colored or uncolored, is the most important of all contrast elements. Value contrast may be termed either brightness contrast, as the physicist thinks of it, or tone contrast, as the photographer thinks of it. Lightness is termed high value, and white would be the maximum attainable.

Value contrasts are the most important element of seeing, and everyone is familiar with the ease with which it is possible to recognize objects represented in drawings or photographs merely by their tonal or value structure. Since anything that can be seen must have a value rating, and because anything must vary in value if it is to be easily distinguished from its surroundings, it follows that the contrast of values is one of the fundamentals of visibility.

Any object or group of objects on a map has a value rating. Widths of lines, shad-

FIG. 96. A value scale in which the steps are equal in terms of black/white ratios. The middle gray does not appear to be halfway between black and white. Note also the apparent "waviness" or induction. From a Kodak Gray Scale, courtesy Eastman Kodak Company.

ing patterns, names, blocks of lettering, the title, the legend, colors, and so on, are all value areas, and their arrangement within the map frame is a basic part of map designing. It is well for the student to keep in mind the generalization that *visibility and visual importance vary directly with value contrast.* Figure 88 illustrates in a limited way the significance of value contrast.

One of the more important ways in which the cartographer uses values is in presenting a graded series of information. Thus, for example, rainfall, depth of oceans, elevation of land, density of population, intensity of land use, and so on, are usually depicted by some technique that depends for a large portion of its effectiveness upon changing values.

The human eye is not particularly sensitive when it comes to distinguishing value differences. Eight shades of gray, between black and white, is about the limit, and consequently the cartographer must be relatively restrained in this respect. If a greater number of divisions in a series must be shown, he must add hue or some pattern, such as dots or lines, to the areas to aid the user to distinguish among them. Also important is the fact that physically equal fractional steps of black and white ratios from 0 (white) to 1.0 (black) do not appear equal to the eye. Figure 96 is a scale in which the steps are equal in terms of pigment ratios.

The precise ratios of black to white necessary to produce a gray scale of equal

visual steps have not been determined. The results of several tests have given close approximations, however, and it is possible to draw a curve based upon them which is undoubtedly close to reality. Figure 97

ROBINSON

P. 129c

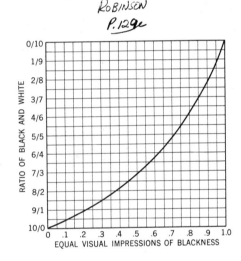

FIG. 97. Graph of the relation of visual gray steps to black/white ratios (approx.).

shows such a curve. The relationship could be graphed several ways, but the generalizations to keep in mind are:

1. The visual gray scale is not the same as an arithmetic progression of black and white ratios.

2. It is easier to distinguish light gradations than dark gradations if the progression is arithmetic.

3. Even eight gradations of gray are difficult for the average person to distinguish.

Another characteristic of vision and its relation to value, hue, and intensity, which the cartographer must bear in mind, is a general phenomenon of vision called simultaneous contrast. In value contrasts it is particularly important. A basic generalization regarding the employment of any color is that the appearance of a color is markedly modified by its environment. With respect to value, we find that a dark area next to a light area will make the dark appear darker and the light appear lighter.

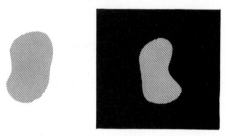

FIG. 98. How environment modifies appearance. The two gray areas are the same Zip-a-tone.

This effect, called induction, makes it difficult for a reader to recognize a given value in various parts of a map when it is surrounded by or adjacent to different values. Figure 96 illustrates one aspect of induction. The "wavy" appearance of the value blocks causes the recognition of values to be difficult, and the difficulty increases in direct ratio to the similarity of the values. The effects of induction may be largely removed by separating adjacent values with a white space or by outlining the areas with black lines. In Fig. 98 the gray spots are the same, but the one on the dark block appears much lighter, and the reverse is true of the other. It is obvious that a reader would have difficulty in recognizing values under such a situation.

113   Contrast of Pattern

Because many kinds of data cannot effectively be shown by value shadings alone, and because the nature of the data dictates that other devices be used, it is common for the cartographer to rely upon various kinds of patterns. These patterns are composed of dots (stippling), lines, or combinations. The possibilities are unlimited.

Very little study has been directed toward the understanding of patterns, their

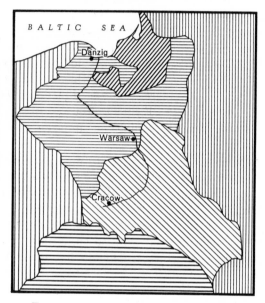

FIG. 99. A map employing line patterns.

effects upon the eye, and the ability to distinguish between them. Consequently, the student can proceed only on a trial and error basis. There are, however, a few generalizations that are of assistance as guides to the use of patterns.

Patterns may be classified broadly into two groups, those composed of lines and those composed of dots. Any line anywhere has, in the eye of the viewer, a direction; that is to say, he tends to move his eyes in the direction of the line. If irregular areas are shaded by line patterns which do not vary much in value, as in Fig. 99, the reader's eyes will be forced to change direction frequently. Consequently, he will experience considerable difficulty in noting the positions of the boundaries.

If the line patterns of Fig. 99 are replaced with dot patterns, as in Fig. 100, the map is seen to become much more stable, the eye no longer jumps, and the boundaries are much easier to distinguish. Lettering is also easier to read against a dot background than against a line background. If, however, the parallel lines are fine enough and closely enough spaced the resulting effect is one of value only and has but a slight suggestion of direction.

Many parallel-line patterns are definitely irritating to the eye. Figure 101 is an example of the irritation that can occur from using parallel lines. The cause is probably that the eyes are unable quite to focus upon one line. The effect is somewhat reduced if the lines, whatever their width, are separated by white spaces greater than the thickness of the lines.

114 Choice of Color

Colors vary in a number of ways, and the cartographer who contemplates using color is hard pressed to make a choice. Since very little experimental research has been undertaken regarding color on maps, the only course for the cartographer to follow is to base his selections on certain fundamental facts regarding the reaction of the mind and the eye to color. In addition, he has a few well-known cartographic conventions upon which he may lean, such as blue water, green vegetation, etc. The reaction of the mind and eye to hue, and the extreme significance of value contrast, as outlined in Article 112, are, however, his major guides.

The eye is not particularly sensitive to hue changes, as is indicated by the relatively few words referring to hues in our language. Consequently, the farther apart, visually, hues can be separated, the better. The eye is, moreover, definitely more sen-

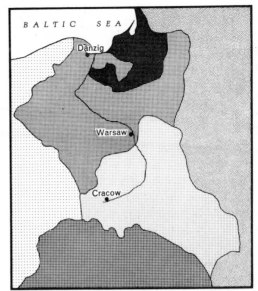

FIG. 100. Same map as Fig. 99 but employing dot patterns.

FIG. 101. Line patterns can hurt the eyes, and the map on which they are used, if they are not carefully chosen.

sitive to some hues than to others, i.e., some are more "noticeable" than others. All observers agree that the eye is most sensitive to red, followed by green, yellow, blue, and purple, in that order. This series provides the cartographer with a partial basis for choice of color, depending upon how much emphasis is desired for the data to be represented by a color. Unfortunately, no satisfactory data seem to exist that make it possible to grade the colors precisely according to relative degree of sensitivity.

In considering the sensitivity of the eye to hues, it is well to remember that pigment hues themselves vary in terms of their inherent value or brightness which, in turn, is of considerable significance with respect to their relative visibility and that of the data placed upon them. The relative luminosity of the spectral colors for the normal eye has been determined and is highest in the yellow-green region (555 millimicrons) and falls to approximately half its maximum within a range of 50 millimicrons each way. Disregard of the obviously significant value relationship by following simply a wave-length progression of hues has led to many visual difficulties in map making. In many atlases, on the International Map, on many wall maps, and in numerous other instances where colors have been used to show altitude, the wave-length progression of colors in the spectrum has been taken as the basis for hypsometric shading. The lower altitudes have been shown in greens, followed by yellows for the intermediate altitudes, and then reds or near reds for the higher. Because of the relative luminosity and pigment values of the colors, by far the lightest areas, and by comparison the most visible, are therefore the areas of intermediate altitude, which are rarely the areas of great importance. Nevertheless, this progression, along with blue water, is almost a convention in cartography, and we have become so used to it that it cannot be ignored. The value of the colors used can,

however, be adjusted to provide the maximum visibility in the significant areas.

It is a well-known fact that some colors appear more individual than others. For example, red is red, but orange seems to be composed of both red and yellow, and purple is made of blue and red. Many colors are named for their apparent components, such as yellowish green, greenish blue, and blue-violet. Normally only blue, green, yellow, red, white, and black appear as individual colors. The reason for this is not definitely known, but, nevertheless, all authorities agree that the phenomena of "pure hues" together with the "intermediate hues" are of considerable significance in color use. Their importance in cartography for showing interrelationships or mixtures of distributions is apparent.

Value is one of the three color sensations which the eye receives simultaneously, the others being hue and intensity. Its greatest significance is in the application of contrast; and the cartographer who works with hues soon finds it necessary to adjust the values of his color areas so that legibility and perceptibility will not be lost. He may do this by watering down paints or mixing white with them. He will also soon learn that he cannot gain as many distinguishable steps in a value scale of yellow as he can in one of gray. It becomes necessary, then, to mix hues to obtain more distinguishable intervals.

Intensity of colors varies, in the color-science sense, when we vary the amount of gray mixed with a color. In practical use on maps intensity may be considered loosely as brilliance. Some colors are bright—they "knock your eye out"—whereas others of the same value and hue are subdued. Undue brilliance acts as a deterrent to easy reading of a map and in general is not necessary, even for emphasis. Soft or subdued shades or tints of low intensity, such as pastels, are fully as visible

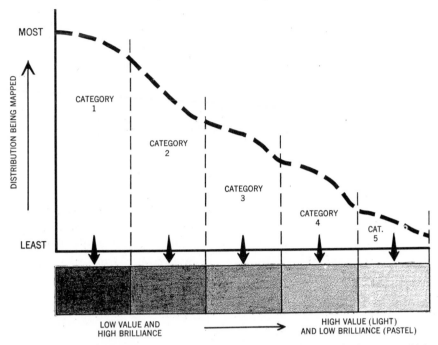

FIG. 102. Theoretical graph of a graded distribution showing the basis upon which one chooses a scale of values or brilliance. The graph could be constructed in a number of ways, but the curve of the "progression" of the data should match that of value and brilliance.

as the more "aggressive" and intense colors.

The average eye and mind unconsciously assigns to value and to intensity a numerical rating. Darkness and brilliance are assumed to represent "more" of something, and lightness and tints represent "less." One would not think of making a map of rainfall distribution whereon the heaviest rainfall was shown by the lightest tone and the least rainfall by the darkest tone. If there is to be a gradation of amounts on a map one can approach the presentation problem by way of a graph, on which value or brilliance is plotted on the abscissa and amount of the phenomena being presented is plotted on the ordinate, as in Fig. 102. This is a relatively simple problem so long as the distribution is limited to a single phenomenon, but it becomes complex when the categories to be shown are comprised of interrelated items, as, for

example, on maps of climatic areas. In such maps, temperature and rainfall are usually the major contributing elements, and the problem of showing an area that has both high temperature and low rainfall is difficult. The tropical areas may be shown with considerable red which is made lighter toward the savanna areas of less precipitation; but a change to another hue such as yellow at the boundary of the dry climates is likely to upset the progression owing to the necessity of using a more brilliant yellow in order to distinguish it from the white paper. It is desirable for the curves of value and brilliance on colored maps showing a graded scheme of things to parallel one another.

115 Balance and Layout

When the cartographer begins the designing and planning of a map he is faced with making a number of preliminary decisions. These involve problems of balance and layout, such as those due to format, projection shape, land-water relations, and the general arrangement of the basic shapes of the presentation.

Balance in visual design is the positioning of the various visual components in such a way that their relationship appears

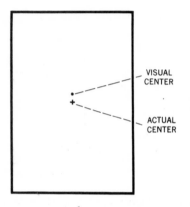

Fig. 103. The visual as opposed to the actual center of a rectangle. Balancing is accomplished around the visual center.

logical or, in other words, so that it does not raise doubt in the reader's mind. In a well-balanced design nothing is too light or too dark, too long or too short, or too small or too large. The importance of the various components is directly related to their position and visual significance. Layout is the process of arriving at proper balance.

Visual balance depends primarily upon the relative position and visual importance of the basic parts of a map, and thus it depends upon the relation of each item to the optical center of the map and to the other items, and upon the visual weights. It may also help to think of the map as a horizontal plane; each item on a balanced map would lie in this plane. If one item

is out of balance it may be prominent and lie "above" the plane visually, or if weak it will recede "below" the balance plane.

The optical center of a map is a point slightly (about 5 per cent) above the center of the bounding shape or the map border (see Fig. 103). Size, value, brilliance, contrast, and, to some extent, a few other factors influence the weight of a shape. The balancing of the various items about the optical center is akin to the balance of a lever on a fulcrum. This is illustrated in Fig. 104, where it can be seen that a visually heavy shape near the fulcrum is balanced by a visually lighter but larger body farther from the balance point. Many other combinations will occur to the student.

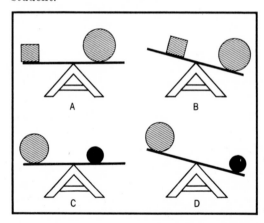

Fig. 104. Visual balance. *A, B, C,* and *D* show relationships of balance. *A* and *B* are analogous to a child and an adult on a "teeter-totter"; *C* and *D* introduce relative density or visual weight.

The aim of the cartographer is to balance his visual items so that they "look right" or appear natural for the purpose of the map. The easiest way to accomplish this is to prepare thumbnail sketches of the main shapes, and then arrange them in various ways within the map frame until a combination is obtained that will present the items in the fashion desired. Figure

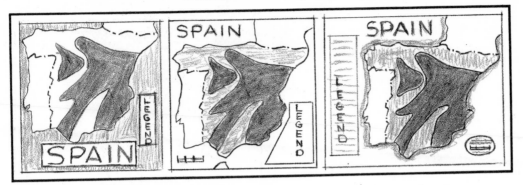

Fig. 105. Thumbnail sketches of a map made in the preliminary stages to arrive at a proper balance.

105 shows some thumbnail sketches of a hypothetical map in which the various shapes, i.e., land, water, title, legend, and shaded area, have been arranged in various ways.

The format, or the size and shape of the paper or page on which a map is to be placed, is of considerable importance in the problem of balance and layout. Shapes of land areas vary to a surprising degree on different projections, and in many cases the necessity for the greatest possible scale within a prescribed format dictates a projection which produces an undesirable fit for the area involved. Likewise, the necessity for fitting various shapes, such as large legends, complex titles, captions, and so on, around the margins and within the border makes the format a limiting factor of more than ordinary concern. Generally speaking, a rectangle with sides having the proportion of 3:5 is the most pleasing shape (see Fig. 106). Of course, when circumstances dictate otherwise, other shapes must be used.

Occasionally the cartographer wishes to emphasize one portion of the map or a particular relationship thereon. For example, he may wish to show territories that changed hands in Europe, and he would like to make them appear above the background base data so that the eye will focus upon these areas and will only incidentally look at the locational base material "beneath" them. In cases like this the map is out of balance intentionally; that is, all

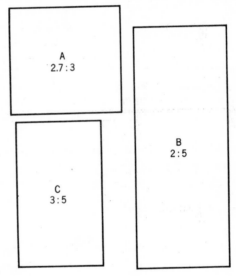

Fig. 106. Various rectangles. *C*, with the ratio of its sides 3:5, is more stable and pleasing than the others.

elements of the map do not lie in the same plane (see Fig. 107). This effect is sometimes referred to as the figure-ground relationship.

The possibilities of varying balance relationships to suit the purpose of the map are legion. The cartographer will do well to

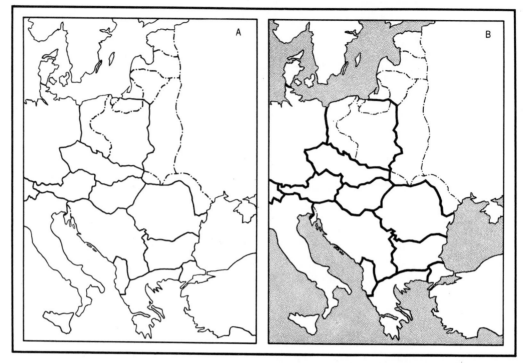

Fig. 107. All elements in map *A* lie generally in the same visual plane. In map *B* the land has been made to rise above the water, and the more prominent boundaries have been made to rise above the "level" of the land. Projection lines on the water only, instead of shading, would also tend to raise the land above the water level.

analyze every visual presentation he sees, from posters to advertisements, in order to become more versatile and competent in working with this important factor of map design.

116 Titles, Legends, and Scales

The titles of maps are an important part of the design, and on different maps they serve a variety of functions. The title sometimes informs the reader of the subject or area of the map, and is therefore as important as a label on a medicine bottle. But this is not always the case, for some maps are obvious in their subject matter or area and in reality need no such title. In these instances the title is often useful to the designer as a shape that he may use to help balance the composition.

It is impossible to generalize as to the form a title should take; it depends entirely upon the map, its subject, and purpose. Suppose, for example, a map had been made showing density of population per square mile of arable land in post-war Hungary. The following situations might apply:

1. If the map appeared in a text devoted to the general world-wide conditions at that time with respect to the subject matter, then only

HUNGARY

would be appropriate, for the time and subject would be known.

2. If the map appeared in a study of the current food situation in Europe, and

if it were an important piece of evidence for some thesis, then

Hungary
POPULATION PER SQUARE MILE
ARABLE LAND

would be appropriate.

3. If the map appeared in a publication devoted to the changes in population in Hungary, then

POPULATION PER SQUARE MILE
ARABLE LAND
1950

would be appropriate, for the area would be known but the date would be significant.

Many other combinations could be worked out, but there is no need to belabor the fact that the title must be tailored to the occasion. Similarly, the degree of prominence and visual interest displayed by the title, through its style, size, and the blackness of the lettering employed, must be fitted into the whole design and purpose of the map.

Legends are naturally indispensable to most maps, for they provide the explanation of the various symbols used. It should be a cardinal rule of the cartographer that no symbol that is not self-explanatory should be used on a map unless it is explained in a legend. Furthermore, any symbol explained should appear in the legend *exactly* as it appears on the map, drawn in precisely the same size and manner. Legend boxes can be emphasized or subordinated by varying the shape, size, or value relationship. Figure 108 illustrates several variations. In the past it was the custom to enclose legends in fancy, ornate outlines which by their intricate workmanship called attention to their presence. Today it is generally conceded that the contents of the legend are more important than its outline, so the outline, if any, is usually kept simple.

The scale of a map also varies in importance from map to map. On maps showing road or rail lines, air routes, or any other phenomenon or relationship that involves distance, the scale is an important factor in making the map useful. In such cases the scale must be placed in a position of prominence, and it should be designed in such fashion that it can be easily used by the reader.

The method of presenting the scale may vary. For many maps, especially those of larger scale, the representative fraction, the RF, is useful for it tells the experienced map reader a great deal about the amount of generalization and selection that

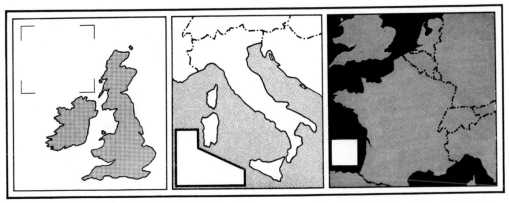

Fig. 108. Variations in prominence of legend boxes.

probably went into the preparation of the map. It should, however, be borne in mind that changing the size of a map by reduction changes the scale of the map, but does not change the printed numbers of the RF. On a map designed for reproduction the RF must be that of the final scale, not the drafting scale.

A graphic scale is much more common on small-scale maps, not only because it simplifies the user's employment of it, but because an RF in the smaller scales is not so meaningful. Graphic scales may be designed in a variety of ways. Some examples are shown in Fig. 109. On scales that are likely to be used precisely it is helpful to the reader if one part of the scale is subdivided in order to make finer readings possible. It is also helpful to show both an English and a metric graphic scale.

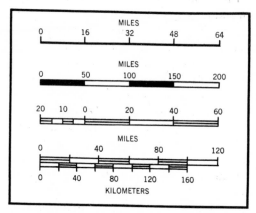

FIG. 109. Kinds of graphic scales.

117 Effects of Reduction

It is usually the practice to draft maps at a scale larger than the reproduction scale. This is done for a variety of reasons, the most important of which is that it is often impossible to draft with the precision and detail desired at the scale of the final map. Also, reduction frequently "sharpens" the line work of the fair drawing. Drafting a map for reduction does not mean merely drawing a map that is well designed at the drafting scale. On the contrary, it requires the anticipation of the finished map and the designing of each item so that when it is reduced and reproduced it will be "right" for that scale. A map must be designed for reduction as much as for any other purpose.

The greatest problem facing the cartographer in designing for reduction is that involving line-width relationships. In general a map on which the line relations appear correct at the drafting scale will appear "light" when it is reduced. Consequently, the map maker must make his map overly "heavy" in order to avoid its appearing too light after reduction. This applies especially to lettering and particularly to lettering from preprinted type impressions. It is necessary for the cartographer to "overdo" his lettering, just as it is necessary for him to make lines and symbols too large and dark on the fair drawing. Figure 110 illustrates these relationships. The use of a reducing glass will aid in visualizing how the map will appear when reduced.

Maps of a series should appear comparable, and since they are drawn for reproduction, they should be drafted at the same scale. This may necessitate changing the scale of base maps, which is troublesome, but which insures that the line treatment and lettering will be uniform.

Specifications for drafting and for reduction are given in terms of linear change, not areal relationships. It is common to speak of a fair drawing as being "50 per cent up," meaning that it is half again larger than it will be when reproduced. The same map may be referred to as being drafted for one-third reduction; that is, one-third of the linear dimensions will be lost in

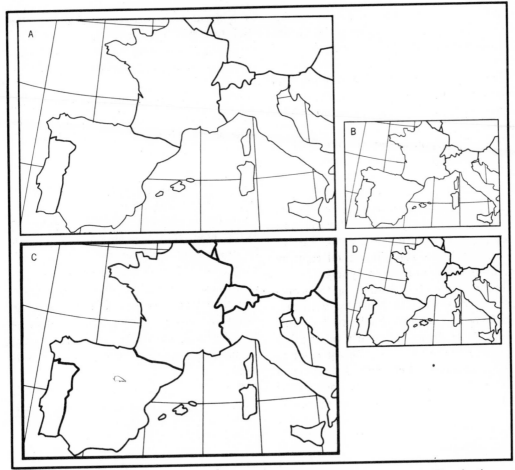

Fig. 110. Effects of reduction. (*A*) When fair drawing is designed at scale, then (*B*) reduction makes it too light. (*C*) When fair drawing is designed for reduction, then (*D*) reduction produces proper relationships.

reduction. Figure 111 illustrates the relationships. Since it is common practice in large printing plants to photograph many illustrations at once, it is also desirable, for economy, to make series drawings for a common reduction.

118 The Worksheet

The cartographer can obviate most of the troubles that beset the finishing of a map by constructing a worksheet. One of the most difficult operations in cartography is that of correcting and changing the fair drawing, for it usually is accompanied by

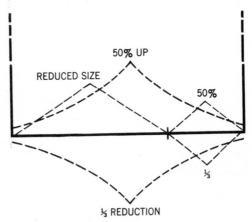

Fig. 111. Relation of enlargement to reduction.

a realization of careless and poor planning. Any such operation is bound to be an unhappy one if, with proper care, it could have been avoided.

The worksheet is the compilation and planning of the map down to the last necessary detail. It is usually done on translucent tracing paper or plastic. On it the lettering is planned, and all line work is done; in short, everything about which there could be any question is determined. When completed, the worksheet is comparable to the handwritten manuscript, for all that is necessary then is for the fair drawing to be drafted by tracing, just as the manuscript is made into good copy by the mechanical process of typing.

The lines and other drawing on the worksheet may be done in pencil or with any satisfactory medium. Each kind of line that is to be drawn differently on the fair drawing may be put in a different color to obviate mistakes. Lettering, if the placing is no problem, may be roughly done; if the placing is important, the lettering should be laid out as to size and spacing. If the first try does not work then it may be erased and done over. Borders and obvious line work need only be suggested by ticks.

When the worksheet and the compilation have been completed, the drafting may be done on tracing paper, cloth, or plastic directly over the worksheet or, if the drafting is to be done on a relatively opaque material, it may be done over a tracing table. If the drawing is to be done by the cartographer he will have in mind the character of the lines, etc.; but if it is to be drafted by someone else he must prepare a sample sheet of specifications to guide the draftsman. This is simple to do if each category is in a different color or otherwise clearly distinguished. Separation drawings for small maps may easily be made from a single worksheet and will register.

The worksheet is a "must" for careful, accurate, efficient map making.

8

Map Lettering

119 The Importance of Lettering

Lettering is one of the symbols used on maps to designate places and items, in the legend, in the title, and especially on the map itself. Because of the familiarity of its forms, it is not commonly considered a cartographic symbol, but in the last analysis it is difficult to draw a distinction between the lines we use to represent such concepts as the land-water boundary and the lines we use to represent the concept of name. The forms the lines assume in lettering are more commonplace, but otherwise there is little difference between this and other symbol forms.

In cartography the study of lettering as a symbol form is especially important, both because of its universal use and because it is a rather complex and, at times, bothersome element of the map. Whether we like it or not, places must be named; and the name may be small and easy to insert as, for example, "Cape Cod," which has the whole Atlantic on which to lie, or it may be long and difficult to insert in a small area, such as "Philadelphia" or "Switzerland" on small-scale maps. The problem of fitting in the lettering among the maze of other symbols is oftentimes nothing short of frustrating.

Lettering is an important element of the design of a map. Most maps have some sort of inherent design quality, such as a repeating pattern of lines, and the letter-ing styles may contrast with this basic characteristic or they may blend with it. Through his choice of lettering style, size, and positioning the cartographer can lead attention to, or direct it away, from the names of the elements it is to identify. Not the least important aspect of lettering is the fact that it provides one of the more noticeable indices of cartographic quality. Striving for elegance can, of course, be carried to extremes, but a well-lettered map is a pleasant thing to contemplate.

Cartographic lettering styles have changed often in the past. Before the development of printing in Europe, all lettering on maps was done freehand with a pen or brush. After printing and engraving became the accepted methods of reproduction, the lettering on maps was the task of the engraver, who cut his letters with a burin or graver in reverse on the copper plate. The great Dutch atlas makers were wont to include many pictures of animals, ships, and wondrous other things for, as Hondius explained, "adornment and for entertainment"; but their lettering was generally well planned in the classic style and well executed, as is that illustrated in Fig. 112.

As might have been expected, when the lettering was done by those more interested in its execution than in its use, it became excessively ornate. The tendency toward poor lettering design continued well into

F<small>IG</small>. 112. The Hondius map of America. This map was included in the Hondius-Mercator Atlas of 1606. The original is in the Newberry Library, Chicago. Courtesy of Rand McNally and Company.

F<small>IG</small>. 113. Ornate lettering on a lithographed map of 1875. The name "Illinois" is more than 1 foot long on the original.

the Victorian era, when lettering and type styles in general became so bad that there was a general revolt against them, which caused a return to the classic styles and greater simplicity. Figure 113 is an example of ornate lettering in the title of a nineteenth century geological map. The fancy lettering of this and earlier periods provides good examples of manual dexterity, being intricate and difficult to execute; but they are examples of poor lettering because they are difficult to read and because they call undue attention to themselves.

In the past century, and especially during the past several decades, many changes have taken place in cartographic lettering practice. No longer does the engraver do the lettering; instead, maps are "engraved" by means of photography, and it is up to the cartographer to plan and execute the lettering on the copy. More recently, new techniques have been developed which make it possible, among other advantages, to apply already printed lettering to the copy, so that there is little excuse for poor style. Mechanical aids for ink lettering have also been introduced.

The above-mentioned developments have combined to relegate the traditional freehand lettering somewhat to the background as a part of the art of cartography. It can be stated without reservation, however, that a map well lettered freehand will be a better-lettered map than one done in any other way, because many cartographic lettering problems involving fitting, design, and positioning are more effectively solved freehand than in any other way. For this reason, if for no other, it is well for the student of cartography to study and practice freehand lettering. Good freehand lettering is a great asset to a cartographer, and it merely involves learning principles and practicing execution. Practically anyone can learn to do an eminently satisfac-

tory job of freehand lettering—if he will but try.

120 Planning for Lettering

Planning the lettering for a map requires careful consideration of a number of things. The more elaborate the map, of course, the more elements must be considered; but, in general, there are at least seven major headings to the planning "checklist." The complexities of the map and its purposes will add subheads to the following major elements.

1. The style of the lettering.
2. The form of the lettering.
3. The size of the lettering.
4. The color of the lettering and its background.
5. The method of lettering.
6. The positioning of the lettering.
7. The relation of the lettering to reproduction.

The style refers to the appearance of the lettering, i.e., its design, and it includes such elements as thickness of line and serifs. The form refers to whether it is composed of capitals, lower-case, slant, upright, or combinations of these and other similar elements. The methods of lettering include freehand, mechanical aids, and preprinted letters to be used as "stick-up," a term recently introduced in cartography to include all methods of applying preprinted lettering. The positioning of the lettering involves a consideration of when and where on the map, and in the construction schedule, the lettering is applied. As is apparent from Chapter 5, different methods of reproduction require variations in parts of the above processes, and this is especially so when various effects are to be gained.

Regardless of the kind of map, the lettering is there to be seen and read. Consequently, the elements of visibility and legibility are among the major yardsticks against which the choices and possibilities are to be measured.

121 The Style of the Lettering

The cartographer is faced with a truly imposing array of possible style choices when he sets out to plan the lettering for his map. He not only has an infinite number of different alphabet designs from which to select, but he must also settle upon the wanted combinations of capital letters, lower-case letters, small capitals, italic, slant, and upright forms of each alphabet. There is no other technique in cartography that provides such opportunity for individualistic treatment, and this is especially true with respect to the monochrome map. The cartographer who becomes well acquainted with styles of lettering and their uses finds that every map or map series presents an interesting challenge. When this attitude obtains, lettering the map ceases to be the mechanical chore some, whose maps reflect their disinterest, consider it to be.

Lettering and type styles have had a complex evolution since Roman times. The immediate ancestors of our present-day alphabets include such grandparents as the capital letters the Romans carved in stone and the manuscript writing of the long period prior to the discovery of printing. Subsequent to the development of printing, the types were copies of the manuscript writing, but it was not long until designers went to work to improve them. Using the classic Roman letters as models for the capitals and the manuscript writing for the small letters, they produced the alphabets of upper- and lower-case letters that it is our custom to use today.

The better designers, of course, kept much of the free-flowing, graceful appearance of freehand lettering so that their letters look as though they had been formed with a brush. The proportion of thick to thin lines is not great, and the serifs with which the strokes are ended are smooth and easily attached. Such letters are known as Classic or Old Style. They appear dignified and have about them an air of quality and good taste that they tend to impart to the maps on which they are used. The lettering or type has an appearance that is neat, but at the same time it

CHELTENHAM WIDE

Cheltenham Wide

CHELTENHAM WIDE ITALIC

Cheltenham Wide Italic

GOUDY BOLD

Goudy Bold

GOUDY BOLD ITALIC

Goudy Bold Italic

CASLON OPEN

FIG. 114. Some Classic, Old Style letter forms. Courtesy Monsen-Chicago, Inc.

lacks any pretense of the geometric. (See Fig. 114.)

A radically different kind of face was devised later, and for that reason it, unfortunately, is termed Modern. Actually the Modern faces were tried out more than two centuries ago, although we think of them as coming into frequent use around 1800. Modern type faces, and lettering, look precise and geometric, as if they had been drawn with a straightedge and a compass, which they have. The difference between thick and thin lines is great and sometimes excessive. (See Fig. 115.)

A third type of style class includes some varieties that are definitely modern in time but not in name, as well as some of older origin. This class is called Sans

Serif (without serifs), and has about it an up-to-date, clean-cut, new, and nontraditional appearance. The forms are angular

BODONI BOLD

Bodoni Bold

BODONI BOLD ITALIC

Bodoni Bold Italic

Fig. 115. Some Modern letter forms. Courtesy Monsen-Chicago, Inc.

or of perfect roundness. There is nothing subtle about most Sans Serif forms. (See Fig. 116.)

The above three classes are the basic groups of the classification of printing types; there are, however, many variations.

MONSEN MEDIUM GOTHIC

Monsen Medium Gothic Italic

COPPERPLATE GOTHIC ITALIC

FUTURA MEDIUM

LYDIAN BOLD

DRAFTSMANS ITALIC

Fig. 116. Some Sans Serif letter forms. Courtesy Monsen-Chicago, Inc.

Freehand lettering generally conforms closely to the Classic and to the Sans Serif, but is ordinarily called, respectively, Roman and Gothic.

There are several other styles of type and of freehand lettering which are not common but which are occasionally used on maps. These are Text, script or italic, and Square Serif. Text, or black letter, is similar to the manuscript writing, and is dark, heavy, and difficult to read. Script

and italic in type are similar to handwriting with flowing lines. They have been traditionally replaced in map work by the slant letter. Square Serif is rarely seen any more, but was popular during the last century. (See Fig. 117.)

The above listing by no means exhausts the possibilities. There are literally hundreds of variations and modifications possible, such as the open letter, light or heavy face, expanded or condensed, and so on. In the selection of type, or in the design of

CLOISTER BLACK

Cloister Black

STYMIE MEDIUM

Stymie Medium

Fig. 117. Examples of Text and Square Serif letter forms. Courtesy Monsen-Chicago, Inc.

his own freehand lettering, the cartographer may be guided by certain general principles that have resulted from a considerable amount of research by the psychologist and others, as well as from the evolved artistic principles of the typographer.

Legibility depends upon the recognition of familiar forms and upon the distinctiveness of those forms from one another. For this reason "fancy" lettering or ornate letter forms are difficult to read. Flowing swash lines and excessively complex letter forms may delight the clever draftsman, but they do not make words easy to read. For this reason Text lettering is particularly difficult. Conversely, well-designed Classic, Modern, and Sans Serif forms stand at the top of the list, and they rate about equally in legibility. Legibility also depends, to some extent, upon the thickness of the lines forming the lettering. The thinner the lines in relation to the size of the lettering, the harder it is to read. The cartographer is therefore called upon in his letter selection to do a bit of experimentation, for, although the bold lettering is more legible, the thicker lines may overshadow or mask other equally important data. It should also be remembered that lettering is not always the most important element in the visual outline of the map; rather it may be desirable, on occasion, that the lettering recede into the background. If so, lightline letter forms may be the effective choice.

The problem of the position of the lettering in the visual outline is one of considerable significance. For example, the title may be of great importance and the balance of the lettering of value only as a secondary reference. Size is usually more significant, in determining the relative prominence, than style, but the general pattern of the lettering may also play an important part. For example, rounded lettering may be lost along a rounded, complex coastline, whereas in the same situation angular lettering of the same size may be sufficiently prominent.

It is the convention in cartography to utilize different styles of lettering for different classes of features, but this may be easily overdone. As a general rule, the fewer the styles, the better harmony there will be. Different size combinations of capitals, small capitals, and lower case provide considerable variety, and most common type faces are available in several variants; it is better practice to utilize these as much as possible. (See Fig. 118.) The cartographer may, of course, do the same sort of thing freehand. If styles must be combined for emphasis or other reasons, good typographic practice allows Sans Serif to be used with either Classic or geometric Modern. Classic and Modern should never be combined.

Whatever the choices of style and combination, the lettering should be well designed. This requires some knowledge of the development of typography and of the elements of letter design. If freehand lettering is the aim, the beginner is *not* encouraged to design his own alphabets, for the result is not likely to be fortunate.

Futura Light

Futura Light Italic

Futura Medium

Futura Medium Condensed

Futura Medium Italic

Futura Demibold

Futura Demibold Italic

Futura Bold

Futura Bold Italic

Futura Bold Condensed

Futura Bold Condensed Italic

Fig. 118. Variants of a single face. This face has a larger number of variants than is usual but the list is representative except that expanded (opposite of condensed) is missing. Courtesy Monsen-Chicago, Inc.

Letter design is an exacting and complex art that reflects the tradition, experience, and the distillation of centuries of effort. It is better for the beginner to spend his time copying the work of the masters of letter design until he has gained a "feel" for the simplicity and the shape and line relationships that characterize good lettering. It is particularly important, whether he use type or letters freehand, that he familiarize himself with the elements of letter design by reading in the copious literature of this fascinating subject.

122 The Form of the Lettering

Alphabets consist of two quite different letter forms called capitals and lower-case letters. These two forms are used together in a systematic fashion in writing, but conventions as to their use are not so well established in cartography. In general, more important names and titles are usually put in capitals, and less important names and places are identified with lower-case letters. Names requiring considerable separation of the letters are commonly placed in capitals.

Kennerley—an upright Classic

Kennerley in the Italic form

Monsen Medium Gothic—upright

Monsen Medium Gothic Italic

FIG. 119. Differences between italic and slant forms. Courtesy Monsen-Chicago, Inc.

Legibility and perceptibility tests have shown without any doubt that capitals are not so easy to recognize or read as are lower-case letters, since the latter contain more clues to letter form. A greater use of well-formed lower-case letters will improve the legibility of a map.

Most styles of type can be had in either upright or italic form, and, of course, freehand lettering may be rendered either upright or slanted. The tendency in cartography is for hydrography, land form, and other natural features to be labeled in slant or italic, and for cultural features (man-made) to be identified in upright forms. This can hardly be called a tradition, for departure from it is frequent, except in the case of water features. The slant or italic form seems to suggest the fluidity of water.

There is a fundamental difference between slant and italic, although the terms are sometimes used synonymously (see Fig. 119). True italic in the Classic or Modern faces is a cursive form similar to script or handwriting. Gothic slant and Sans Serif italic are simply upright letters tilted forward. Italic forms are considerably harder to read than their upright counterparts; however, it is doubtful that there is much difference between the upright and slant letters of Gothic or Sans Serif in so far as legibility is concerned.

123 The Size of the Lettering *

Perhaps the commonest kind of decision regarding lettering, which must be made by a cartographer, concerns the sizes to be used for the great variety of items which must be named on maps. Traditionally, specifications for lettering are usually based on the size of the thing to be named or the space to be filled. Then the lettering must be graded with respect to the total design and intellectual content of the map. Much of the criticism, however, conscious or unconscious, that is leveled at map lettering is aimed specifically at size—or lack of it. There seems to be a widespread tendency among amateur (and even some professional) cartographers to overestimate the ability of the eye and to underestimate the effects of reduction.

Size of lettering or type face is designated by *points*, 1 point being nearly equal to $\frac{1}{72}$ inch. Lettering that is $\frac{1}{4}$ inch high is roughly equal to 18-point type, although not precisely since the size of type refers to the body, not the letter on it. Reduced by one-half, it will be nearly equivalent to 9-point lettering, although not the same as 9-point since each type size in a font (all sizes and forms of one face), and in freehand lettering, is designed separately for more perfect balance than would be

* Portions of this section have been modified from Arthur H. Robinson, "The Size of Lettering for Maps and Charts," *Surveying and Mapping,* 1950, Vol. 10, pp. 37–44.

produced by simple enlargement or reduction of one design.

There have been numerous studies during the past half century of the effect of type sizes and styles on reading habits, but most of them are somewhat limited in their application to the specific problems of cartography. Of much more significance to cartography are the variations in visibility and legibility of type faces and type sizes. Precise studies have been made by Luckiesh and Moss, based on physiologically sound determinations of the ability of the eye. Assuming no other complications (the assumption is a bit unreal), the eye reacts to size in relation to the angle the object subtends at the eye. With normal vision an object that subtends an angle of 1′ can just be recognized. Letter forms are complex, however, and it has been determined that about 3-point type is the smallest, just recognizable type at usual reading distance. Normal vision is, however, a misnomer, for it certainly is not average vision. It is safer to generalize that probably 4-point or 5-point type comes closer to the lower limit of visibility for the average person.

Determinations of the relative visibility of type have significance in cartography. By means of a "visibility meter" investigators have gathered the data shown in Table 10. The values result from rating

TABLE 10. RELATIVE VISIBILITY OF TYPE SIZE.

(From Luckiesh and Moss.)

Size in points	Relative visibility
3	1.10
4	1.60
5	2.11
6	2.64
8	3.64
10	4.65
12	5.66
14	6.67
18	8.67
24	11.68

the tests of one font at normal reading distance with test objects of simple design which subtended known angles and had previously been rated in visibility. The table may be used as a kind of yardstick of prominence for the smaller sizes; e.g., 10-point type is roughly 4 times more visible (or prominent) than 3-point. It should be noted that the relationship is not arithmetic but approaches logarithmic. This relationship, of course, does not continue indefinitely. One may assume that ratings much beyond 24-point would probably have little validity, since anyone who can't see 24-point type would be rated as blind, and visibility in the larger sizes would be more dependent upon factors other than size.

Within the narrow limits prescribed by the familiar "all other factors being equal" the table provides the cartographer with a scale by means of which he can select relative sizes in accordance with the intellectual significance he assigns to the different names appearing on a map. It can rarely, if ever, be exact, for in many cases it is difficult to be precise in the determination of relative significance in the map design, and because so many other factors of design are operative in producing the final "total" impression. But at least in his visual outline, or plan of using media and technique, the cartographer need not double the point size in order to make a name twice as "important."

By far the most important aspect of type size at present is indicated by the simple question "Can the observer read it at all under the circumstances?" Frequently, cartographers are called upon to prepare presentations for groups. They must face such questions as "What is the minimum lettering size legible, under normal conditions, on a wall map or chart from the back or middle of a 40-foot room?" Or, "How large should the lettering be on a graph or map that is to be made into a slide and projected in an auditorium?" These are routine questions of considerable importance since they confront anyone who prepares or uses graphics.

Tables of equivalents are easy to use, but there are so many possibilities of changes in visibility and legibility due to other factors, such as variations of lettering design, lowering of background contrast, or confusing textural conflict, that simple tables must be used cautiously. Two types of tables are here presented, one for maps used in the original or in reduced form (Table 11), the other for maps enlarged by projection (Table 12).

Table 11 is based on the assumption that if a particular point size, at normal reading distance from the eye (18 inches), subtends a certain angle at the eye, then any size lettering if viewed at such a distance that it subtends the same angle is, for all practical purposes, the same size. Thus, 144-point lettering at 30 feet from the observer is the same as 8-point lettering at normal reading distance, since each circumstance results in the same angle subtended at the eye. It will be seen from the table that legibility diminishes rapidly with distance. For example, any lettering of 16-point size or smaller cannot be read even at 10 feet from the chart or map, and letters 1 inch high can be read from a distance of 40 feet only by a person with above average vision. To those with average (not normal) vision such letters are likely to be illegible from 25 feet.

Another type of table is required to answer the questions that arise when maps and diagrams are to be reproduced on slides and then projected. The problem in all its aspects becomes quite complicated, but the raw data concerning map size and results consequent upon magnification are helpful. It should be practicable in most cases to ascertain the actual size of a projected slide frame as well as the size of the lecture hall.

With such information and Tables 31–37 in Appendix G most lens and projector characteristics may be ignored.

Tables 31–37 in Appendix G give equivalent lettering values for projected maps that are magnified from 2 to 15 times their original size and viewed at various distances from the screen. An example will illustrate their use. Assume that a map is being prepared which measures *1 foot across* and is to be projected in an auditorium 70 feet long and, further, that the slide frame used in the projector equipment is *9 feet across* on the screen. From Table 12 (linear magnification, 9), repeated here for purposes of illustration, the following information may be derived:

A. The smallest lettering size which can be used on the original that can be read from any place in the lecture hall by a person with normal vision is 16 point.

B. Only the front half of the audience will be able to read 10-point type on the original drawing.

C. Lettering to be read only by the lecturer at the front as an aid in his presentation should be no larger than 6 point on the original.

It is wise to reemphasize the fact that the results obtained by using the tables here presented and those in Appendix G are subject to some unavoidable errors, for many other variables, in addition to size, establish relative or specific legibility. For example, if any lettering is to be on a colored background its legibility and visibility will be reduced (except if the background is yellow) roughly in proportion to the loss of value contrast. Differences in styles of type, and especially in the background patterns of shading or map data, may increase or reduce legibility. The photographic quality of the slides, the lens quality, and the amount of light from projectors frequently vary. Familiar word forms may

TABLE 11. APPROXIMATE EQUIVALENT SIZES OF LETTERING VIEWED FROM VARIOUS DISTANCES.

(Blank spaces indicate nonlegibility.)

Point size, at 18 inches	Letter height in inches	Equivalent size in points viewed at distance (feet) from observer									
		10	20	30	40	50	60	70	80	90	100
3–16											
18	0.25	3									
24	0.33	3									
30	0.41	4–5									
36	0.50	5	3								
42	0.58	6	3								
48	0.66	7	4								
54	0.75	8	4–5	3							
60	0.83	9	4–5	3							
72	1.00	10	5	4	3						
84	1.16	12	6	4–5	3						
96	1.33	14	7	4–5	3–4	3					
108	1.50	16	8	5	4	3					
120	1.66	18	9	6	4–5	3–4	3				
132	1.83	20	10	7	5	4	3–4				
144	2.00	22	11	8	5–6	4–5	4	3			
180	2.50	28	14	9	7	5–6	4–5	4	3		
216	3.00	32	16	10	8	6	5–6	5	4	3–4	3

TABLE 12. LINEAR MAGNIFICATION, 9.

(Blank spaces indicate nonlegibility.)

Point size on original	Approximate equivalent size in points viewed at distance (feet) from screen									
	10	20	30	40	50	60	70	80	90	100
6	8	4–5	3							
8	10	5	4							
10	12	6	4–5	3–4						
12	16	8	5	4	3					
14	18	9	6	5	4	3				
16	22	11	8	5–6	4–5	4	3			
18	24	12	8	6	5	4	3–4	3		
24	32	16	10	8	6	5–6	5	4	3–4	3
30	42	21	14	11	9	7	6	5–6	5	4–5
36	48	24	16	12	10	8	7	6	5–6	5

make undersize lettering recognizable. The tables of equivalent sizes have been calculated solely on the basis of angle subtended at the eye and do not take into account any of the less significant factors. Equivalent sizes are expressed to the nearest point in the smaller ranges with some clear intermediates noted, and in the larger they are approximate to the nearest even or common type size. Consequently, if any doubt arises as to the effect of any negative factors present, lettering sizes should be increased. Results obtained by following such a rule of thumb will rarely be unsatisfactory.

124 The Color of the Lettering and the Background

Legibility and perceptibility of lettering also depend considerably upon the color of the lettering and the background upon which it stands (see Fig. 120). Commonly, lettering of equal importance does not appear equal in various parts of the map because of background differences. Even when the same lettering is used everywhere because of other design requirements, the cartographer should be aware of the possible effects, and perhaps, within the limits of his design, he may be able to correct or at least alleviate the situation.

Stated in general terms, the legibility and perceptibility of lettering (other effects being equal) depend upon the amount of visual contrast between the lettering and its background. Putting aside such effects as might be due to texture of background, size of lettering, and so on, the basic variable is the degree of value contrast between the lettering and its background. Thus, black lettering on a white background would stand near the top of the scale, and as the value of the lettering approached the value of the background, visibility would diminish. This is of concern when either large regional names are "spread" over a considerable area composed of units colored or shaded differently or when names of equal rank must be placed on areas of different values. It makes no difference whether the value contrast is the result of color or of shading. The usual lettering in cartography is either black or white (reverse lettering), but occasionally lettering will be added to one of the color plates in the flat-color method of map reproduction. Regardless of the color of the print and of the background, if the value contrast is great the lettering will be legible.

White or reversed lettering on a dark or colored background is an effective and easy way to create contrast in the map lettering. It may be accomplished in a number of ways:

1. Lettering in white paint or ink.
2. Pasting a photostat negative of lettering on a black background.
3. Using a diapositive as a mask.
4. Using white preprinted lettering (see Article 127).

However reverse lettering is accomplished, it should be remembered that the rule of value contrast still obtains. In addition, white or open lettering appears

FIG. 120. Perceptibility and legibility depend upon lettering-background contrast.

smaller than black lettering of the same size (see Fig. 121). Consequently, if, for example, all names on oceans are to be white, it may be necessary to increase their size slightly in order to bring them in balance with the other lettering.

Kennerley—an upright Classic

Kennerley in the Italic form

Monsen Medium Gothic—upright

Monsen Medium Gothic Italic

Kennerley—an upright Classic

Kennerley in the Italic form

Monsen Medium Gothic—upright

Monsen Medium Gothic Italic

Fig. 121.   Reverse lettering appears slightly smaller than its opposite of the same size.

125   Freehand Lettering

The most versatile of all the forms of lettering is the freehand. With this method names may be inserted, oriented, and scaled as to size precisely as desired. Type and mechanical lettering have not been devised particularly for map use, and although they are relatively rapid and under many circumstances the desirable expedient, the best lettering for maps is the freehand; and well-designed lettering is as important to the quality of a map as any other element of design.

The learning of freehand lettering requires familiarity with and an ability to use the basic tools. It also requires a knowledge of the principles of letter formation and design. These elements require a much more thorough treatment than can be given in a book of this sort, and the reader is referred to the bibliog-

raphy for a listing of books treating these subjects.

The most important aspect for the beginner to appreciate is that lettering freehand requires planning. The planning includes, in addition to selecting the kind of letter (Gothic or Roman, slant or upright) and its sizes, the placing on the copy of guide lines which will aid in placing the letters and in making them conform to size. Guide lines may be drawn with a straightedge or a curve, but guide lines are better drawn with any of a number of patented devices designed for this purpose, such as the Ames lettering instrument or the Multi and Braddock-Rowe lettering angles. These devices have small holes in which a pencil point may be inserted. The device may then be moved along a drawing edge by moving the pencil. By placing the pencil in other holes, parallel lines may be

Fig. 122.   Guide lines.

drawn. Guide lines usually consist of three parallel lines as shown in Fig. 122. The bottom two determine the height of the lower-case letters. As a rule of thumb for the beginner, the spacing relationship between the lines should be one-third/two-thirds, with the larger space at the bottom. This is by no means a general rule, for the relationship is quite variable and depends upon the alphabet design. The upper guide line indicates the height of the capitals and the ascenders of such letters as b, d, f, etc.

After the guide lines have been placed, the lettering may be first drawn in lightly with pencil, in order that spacing and position problems may be solved. Spacing of the letters is important, for with poor spacing the words will appear ragged and uneven. Since letters are not the same shape the distance between them must be adjusted in order that the space will *appear* to be the same. The beginner will soon learn that there are different classes of letters according to their regular or irregular appearance and according to whether they are narrow, normal, or wide. They must be separated differently depending upon the combination in the word. Mechanical spacing should be avoided (see Fig. 123).

In order for the lettering pen or other tool to make the letter properly the letter should be stroked correctly. This depends

FIG. 123. Visual compared to mechanical spacing.

somewhat upon the pen and the paper, but obviously a sharp pen, such as a crow quill, cannot be moved up against the paper, for it will dig into the surface and then spatter. In general, strokes should be down or to the side (see Fig. 124).

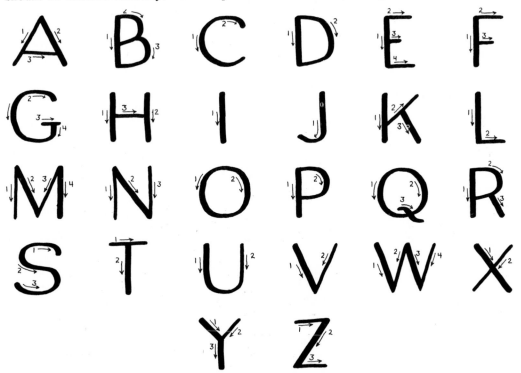

FIG. 124. Stroking the letters properly.

Fig. 125. The Leroy scriber and one template. Courtesy Keuffel and Esser Company.

TEMPLATE NO.	PEN NO.									
	00	0	1	2	3	4	5	6	7N	8N
80	A	B	C							
100	A	B	C	D						
120	A	B	C	D	E					
140	A	B	C	D	E	F				
175	A	B	C	D	E	F	G			
200	A	B	C	D	E	F	G	H		
240	A	B	C	D	E	F	G	H		
290	A	B	C	D	E	F	G	H	K	
350	A	B	C	D	E	F	G	H	K	L
425	A	B	C	D	E	F	G	H	K	L
500	A	B	C	D	E	F	G	H	K	L

Fig. 126. Sample of Leroy lettering. Courtesy Keuffel and Esser Company.

The greatest difficulty for the beginner to overcome is his probable mental attitude toward freehand lettering, for the chances are that he will approach the operation with trembling, which will be reflected in his lettering. He no doubt feels that the "pressure is on" when he puts ink to paper, and he is likely to complain that he can do much better with pencil. He probably can —because he is more relaxed. Smooth, easy lettering with a loose hand is not difficult, if the beginner will give himself a chance. As soon as he has mastered the basic stroking, he is ready to go on to letter design. Good design and good spacing are far more important than precise execution.

126 Mechanical Lettering

Mechanical lettering devices of several kinds are available for the person who cannot letter freehand acceptably and especially for the cartographic shop where a variety of draftsmen are employed and where uniformity is desired. These devices are a relatively expensive crutch for the person unwilling to learn freehand lettering. With their use acceptable, clean-cut appearing maps may be lettered, but it should be emphasized that the lettering produced by these devices appears, for the most part, mechanical and gives one the impression of looking at a building blueprint. Some of the complexities of good map lettering have been detailed in previous articles, and it is not to be expected that any mechanical device can approach their attainment without the expenditure of considerably more time and money than would be involved in doing the same thing freehand. Nevertheless, mechanical lettering devices have a place in cartography for the production of utility graphs, charts, and maps.

The best-known devices require a special pen, feeding through a small tube, while the pen is guided either mechanically or by hand with the aid of a template.

Leroy is the patented name of a lettering system involving templates, a scriber, and special Leroy pens (see Fig. 125). A different template is necessary for each size lettering. The template is moved along the T-square, and the scriber traces the depressed letters of the template and reproduces them with the pen beyond the

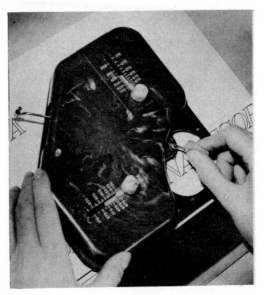

Fig. 127. Varigraph lettering instrument. The dials are for adjusting the height and width of the letter. Courtesy The Varigraph Company, Madison, Wisc.

template. Spacing is usually done by eye. (See Fig. 126.) A variety of letter weights and sizes in capitals and lower case are possible by interchanging templates and pens. In addition, templates with geological and mathematical symbols are available. The normal template of the Leroy is a simple Sans Serif or Gothic, but extended, condensed and outline forms are also available. A template carrying Cheltenham letters has been added to those available.

Varigraph is the patented name of a lettering device also involving a template with depressed letters and a stylus (see Fig. 127). The device is actually a sort of

FIG. 128. Sample of Varigraph lettering (Cartographic Roman) showing a few of the possible variations from a single template.

FIG. 129. Wrico lettering guide. Courtesy Wood-Regan Instrument Company, Nutley, N. J.

small, adjustable pantograph which fits over a template. The letters are traced from the template and are scribed with a pen at the other end of the pantograph-like assembly. Adjustments may be made to make large or small, extended or condensed lettering from a single template. Templates of a variety of letter styles are available ranging from a simple Gothic to a Sans Serif, and from a Cartographic Roman (see Fig. 128) to Old English Text.

Wrico is the patented name of a lettering system involving perforated templates or guides and special pens (see Figs. 129, 130, and 131). The lettering guides are placed directly over the area to be lettered and are moved back and forth to form the various parts of a letter. The pen is held in the hand and is moved around the stencil cut in the guide. The guide is held above the paper surface to prevent smearing. A considerable variety of letter forms are possible including condensed and extended. A different guide is necessary for each size, although width of line may be varied by changing the pen size.

Another method of applying lettering to the map mechanically is by means of an imprinter. This is a small form of a typographer's composing stick in which type may be placed and locked in position. It is then inked and pressed in place on the

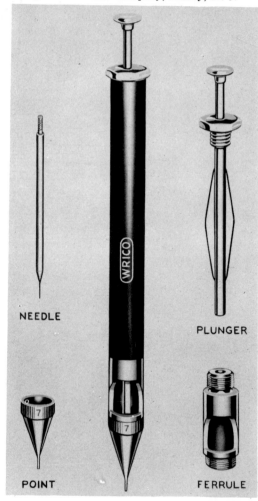

FIG. 130. Wrico lettering pen. The "point" is hollow for the ink feed. Courtesy Wood-Regan Instrument Company.

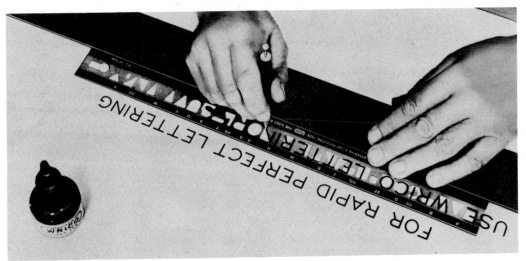

Fig. 131. Wrico pen and guide in operation. Courtesy Wood-Regan Instrument Company.

map. The type must then be cleaned and distributed before another name can be applied. Curved lettering is, of course, difficult to apply. The use of an imprinter is relatively slow compared to other methods. Essentially the same technique was formerly used in the wax-engraving process, where the names were pressed in wax which was then electroplated and used as the printing plate. The lettering on wax-engraved maps appears more mechanical than any other type of lettering, partly because of the poor letter forms and partly because of the tendency to overcrowd.

127 Preprinted Lettering

During the past ten or fifteen years a new technique of map lettering has become widely used. Known as stick-up lettering, this technique utilizes preprinted letters on some medium that can be made to adhere to the map. Stick-up lettering has a number of advantages over other methods of lettering which require the use of ink on the copy. Any of the thousands of type styles and sizes used in printing can be selected. The letters may be used as composed in a straight unit, or they may be cut

apart and applied separately to fit curves. If the position first selected for the name is not suitable, the name may be relocated with no attendant problem of erasing.

One disadvantage of stick-up is that, at present, it is necessary to use type faces originally designed for printing books. Such type faces have not been designed for any position except horizontal, neither have they been designed for any reduction. When such type is put in a curved position it is not so well designed as is good freehand lettering. Each font (one type face) contains letters of different sizes, and each size has been designed separately for use at that size. Consequently, when used on maps planned for reduction there is a tendency for the lettering to appear somewhat light, since 18-point lettering reduced one-half has thinner strokes than the 9-point size of the same font. It is generally necessary, when using stick-up lettering, to choose a somewhat larger point size than would ordinarily be warranted.

The preprinting may be done on a variety of surfaces, depending upon the printer's materials, such as gummed stock requiring only wetting, or thin tissue which can be "floated" into place with a thin adhesive or solvent, or Cellophane with an adhesive on the back. The last system combines the advantages of transparent backing and easy changing. The foremost commercial production of this kind of lettering for map use is by Monsen-Chicago, Inc., which uses the same technique that is used for Zip-a-tone, wax-backed Cellophane. Their Trans-Adhesive impressions are available on glossy acetate, matte-finish acetate, and flexible film (Vinylite) for

slight curves without cutting apart; and all have a wax backing. The same sort of material is available also in black ink on a white backing, which automatically masks the area around the letters, or in white ink for use over solid black to provide open or reverse lettering.

In use, stick-up lettering is merely cut from the printed sheet with a sharp, thin knife or needle and placed in position (see Fig. 132). It is then burnished tight, if wax-backed, or floated on with adhesive

FIG. 132. Preparing copy for the name plate of a map. Note the use of preprinted symbols in the lower portion of the illustration. Courtesy Rand McNally and Company.

solvent. There are several other types of stick-up used in cartography employing photographic techniques, but most of these are used exclusively by agencies or organizations owning the devices. However, in any stick-up procedure the technique is basically the same, preprinted lettering.

128 Positioning the Lettering

The manner in which the lettering is placed on the map in relation to the other map data is an important part of the lettering technique. The map usually has a grid or pattern of lines on it, and an incongruous appearance can easily result if the orientation of the basic lettering pattern is not carefully determined. For example, the projection grid may create one pattern, and if the lettering pattern is set at an angle the entire map may appear unstable.

Generally, the convention in cartography is to place the lettering parallel to the parallels, which requires curving the lettering on many projections. This is difficult to do with lettering devices. The problem may be lessened by indicating the grid only on the water, which carries few names, or by indicating the grid only as ticks near the border, and then placing the lettering horizontally. If the grid is necessary to the map purpose, then these expedients cannot be used. A particular problem is created by the "polar" and oblique forms of projections now so common. If the lettering is placed parallel to the parallels consistently, then that lettering at the side will be standing vertically; and if the lettering is oriented with north at the top, it will be upside down in the upper portion of the map. One method of preventing such predicaments is to change the orientation of the lettering at the horizontal grid line, so that it can be read with no more than a quarter turn of the head.

Names of features such as countries, mountain ranges, or oceans are usually spread so that the name includes the entire feature; but even if spread, the letters must be placed in a curve or line so that each letter follows the last normally. The letters also must be evenly spaced. This requires considerable planning in order to fit the individual letters in proper position without interfering with other lettering or lines on the map.

Names of rivers should "run" with the streams if possible. River names are normally not spread apart as are names of countries, but they should follow the curves of the adjacent portion of the stream. It is a good practice to curve them in a fashion concave to the streams, so that the upper portions of the letters are closer together. The upper part of lower-case letters have more clues to letter form than the lower.

Names of lakes, islands, swamps, peninsulas, and other relatively small features should be placed so that they are either contained entirely within the feature or are entirely outside it. This is especially necessary when the color or tint of the feature is different from its surroundings.

Titles and legend lettering should be balanced around a center line and positioned carefully. This may be most easily done by first planning each line on a separate strip of paper and then shifting their position on the map until the correct adjustment is obtained. If tracing paper or other translucent material is used, the shifting may be done beneath the paper and the final position traced on the worksheet or fair drawing.

Names of cities and other point locations should be placed to one side or the other of the symbol, and placed slightly above or below it. If put in line with the symbol, the symbol and lettering may interfere with one another.

129 Geographical Names

The cartographer frequently finds that the selection of styles and the application of the lettering is not nearly so knotty a problem as is the selection of the proper or appropriate spelling of the names he wishes to use. For example, does one name an important river in Europe *Donau* (German and Austrian), *Duna* (Hungarian), *Dunav* (Yugoslavian and Bulgarian), *Dunărea* (Rumanian), or does one spell it *Danube*, a form not used by any country through which it flows! Is it *Florence* or *Firenze*, *Rome* or *Roma*, *Wien* or *Vienna*, *Thessalonikē* or *Thessoloniki*, or *Salonika* or *Saloniki*, or any of a number of other variants? The problem is made even more difficult by the fact that names change because official languages change or because internal administrative changes occur. The problem of spelling is difficult indeed.

The problem is of sufficient moment that governments that produce many maps have established agencies whose sole job it is to formulate policy and to specify the spelling to be used for names on maps and in official documents. Such are the British Permanent Committee on Geographical Names (PCGN) and the United States Board on Geographical Names (BGN) of the Department of the Interior. The majority of such governmental agencies concern themselves only with domestic problems, but the two named above include the spelling of all geographical names as part of their function.

One of the major tasks of such an agency (and of every cartographer) is the determination of how a name that exists in its original form in a non-Latin alphabet shall be rendered in the Latin alphabet. Various systems of transliteration from one alphabet to another have been devised by experts, and the agencies have published the approved systems. The Board on Geographic Names has published numerous bulletins of place-name decisions and guides recommending treatment and sources of information for many foreign areas. These are available upon application. It is well for the cartographer to acquire, or at least to have available, such bulletins for he is frequently required to make decisions on matters of transliteration. Even more frequently he will find himself using map sources that contain other alphabets, characters, and ideographs.

The general rule is to use the conventional English form whenever such exists. Thus, *Finland* (instead of *Suomi*) and *Danube River* would be preferred. Names of places and features in countries using the Latin alphabet may, of course, be used in their local official form if the purpose of the map makes such treatment desirable or if there is no conventional English form.

The problem is much too complex to be treated in any detail in this book, but it is well for the student to be aware of it. His main worry, as a student, will be that of consistency in whatever general system he chooses. Above all, he must not let himself fall into toponymic blunders by placing on maps such names as the *Rio Grande River*, the *Sahara Desert*, or the *Sierra Nevada Mountains*.

9

Symbolization and Distribution Maps

130   The Map as a Symbol

The entire map is a symbol, as well as its parts, and it is not quite correct to designate only certain components as symbols. A coastline is actually a line of equal value (a contour), and has no existence at all, being but an imaginary line between water and land. Similarly, everything, from the lines used to represent the imaginary earth graticule to the marks employed to represent base or specialized data, cannot be shown as it actually is but must be symbolized. This is one of the major ways in which a map differs from an air photograph. The data on a map are selected and symbolized in order to tell a story, to make clear one or a series of relationships. A photograph of a portion of the earth is a record, unsymbolized and unselected, of what is "seen" by the camera. One of the major duties of the cartographer, then, is to understand the relations among symbols, their relative effectiveness, and their relative suitability for the purpose for which the map is being constructed.

The symbolism of cartography has developed over the centuries; consequently, traditions and conventions regarding symbolism have gained general acceptance. Symbols constitute a kind of code by which the cartographer can present the most ef-

fective story in the limited space available. In a sense, the symbolism of small-scale cartography has become standardized over the years, but the great possibilities of variation have, however, effectively prevented any rigid standardization, although in the case of large-scale maps standardization is more nearly approached. The cartographer who works with small-scale maps must of necessity be critical and imaginative, and adjust the representation and symbolism to the special purpose of his map.

Standardization of symbols can and must be accomplished for a set of maps at a given scale, such as a topographic set, but such standardization is likely to be useful only at that scale and in that combination. Special maps, such as those of the geographer or other social scientist, vary so widely in terms of scale and purpose that a large part of the cartographer's job is concerned with the effectiveness of the symbols he selects or designs. In the balance of this chapter the various kinds of symbols appropriate to represent facts other than base data are discussed, along with some of the fundamental principles underlying their use. Needless to say, all their possible variations or opportunities of employment cannot be touched upon

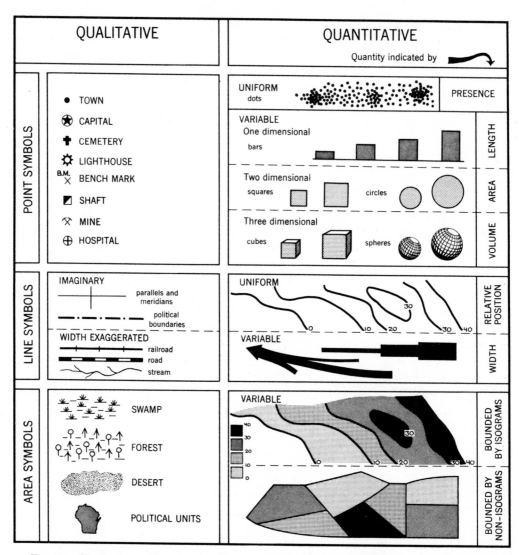

Fig. 133. Illustrative outline of point, line, and area symbols. Modified from John K. Wright by permission of *The Geographical Review,* published by the American Geographical Society of New York.

here. The reader is advised to examine closely the numerous examples of distribution maps appearing in books, periodicals, and newspapers in order to acquire a broader understanding of the manifold utility of cartographic symbolism.

131 Kinds of Symbols

Map symbols may be separated into two major categories, qualitative and quantitative, according to whether they represent kinds of phenomena, on the one hand, or amount as well as kind, on the other. Within each of those two major divisions the range of possible symbols falls into three subcategories, namely, point, line, and area symbols. Within each of these subcategories there are possible variations. The range is illustrated by representative examples in Fig. 133. Their characteristics and major utility will be separately considered in the following articles.

Almost as important as the inherent qualities of a symbol is its design, for, as has often been stated (but less often heeded), the map symbol that cannot be seen or read is wasted and is but a useless encumbrance. The appearance of a visual item may be varied by size, shape, and color contrasts. Dots may be large or small, regular or irregular, dark or light or colored. Lines may vary similarly. As was pointed out in Chapter 7, contrast of any of these qualities or combinations of them is the key to visibility. The possibilities of variation are large indeed, and the cartographer would do well to exercise his ingenuity and experiment with possibilites before settling upon any one design or kind of symbol.

132 Point Symbols

Point symbols such as dots, circles, spheres, cubes, or any of the other varieties may represent any phenomenon having territorial extent or simply location. A dot may represent a city; a triangle, a triangulation station; a circle, the population of a city or the production of an industrial plant. The variations and uses are legion. Thus, a point symbol may represent either simply *kind* as in the case of a capital city or both *kind* and *amount* as in the case of a circle representing the population of a city. The point symbol is not adaptable to showing directly a ratio or relationship.

Representation of *kind* by point symbols merely requires that the symbol design be characteristic enough to be seen and understood by the map reader.

Representation of *amount* by a point symbol may be accomplished either by repeating a uniform symbol, so that the aggregate number represents a total, or by varying the size (area or apparent volume) of each symbol in proportion to the amount at each location.

133 The Dot

The simplest of all maps using point symbols is the one wherein the data are presented by varying numbers of uniform dots, each representing the same amount. It is possible, of course, to substitute little drawings of men, or sheep, or cows (or whatever is being represented) for the simple dot. This generally reduces the amount of detail which may be presented, but it is sometimes desirable for rough distributions or for maps for children. This kind of map, called a dot map, is a great favorite among geographers, because, given the data, it is capable of showing more clearly than any other type of map the details of location of many phenomena. It provides a visual impression of relative density, easily comprehended by the reader, but it does not provide him with

Fig. 134. A dot map in which the dots are too small so that an unrevealing map is produced. One dot represents 40 acres.

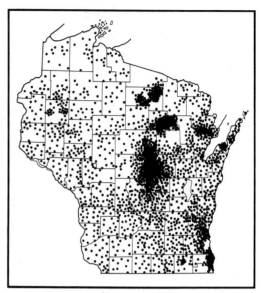

Fig. 135. A dot map in which the dots are too large so that an excessively "heavy" map is produced. An erroneous impression of excessive potato production is given. The same data and number of dots are used as in Fig. 134.

Fig. 136. A dot map in which the unit value of the dot is too large so that too few dots result; a barren map revealing little pattern is produced. Each dot in this example represents 150 acres.

Fig. 137. A dot map in which the unit value of the dot is too small so that too many dots result; an excessively detailed map is produced. The dots are the same size as those in Fig. 136. Each dot in this example represents 15 acres.

any absolute figures. Theoretically, it would be possible to count the dots and then multiply the number by the unit value of each dot to arrive at a total, but in practice it is almost never done.

A second advantage is the relative ease with which such maps may be made. No computation is ordinarily necessary beyond that of determining the number of dots required, which merely necessitates dividing the totals for each civil division by the number decided upon as the unit value of each dot.

Dot maps ordinarily show only one kind of data, for example, population or acres of cultivated land, but by using different-colored dots or different-shaped point symbols it is sometimes possible to include two different distributions on the same map. Of course, if there is no mixing of two types of data they both may be shown on the same map.

134 The Size and Value of the Dot

If the visual impression conveyed by a dot map is to be realistic the size of the dot and the unit value assigned must be carefully chosen. The five dot maps shown here have been prepared from the same data; only the size or number of dots used has been changed. The maps show potato acreage in Wisconsin in 1947.

If the dots are too small, as in Fig. 134, then the distribution will appear sparse and insignificant, and patterns will not be visible. If the dots are too large, then they will coalesce too much in the darker areas, as in Fig. 135, and give an overall impression of excessive density that is equally erroneous. It appears in Fig. 135 that there is little room for anything else in the region.

Equally important is the selection of the unit value of the dot. As a matter of fact the two problems (size and value of the

dot) are inseparable. The total number of dots should neither be so large that the map gives a greater impression of accuracy than is warranted nor should the total be so small that the distribution lacks any pattern or character. These unfortunate possibilities are illustrated in Figs. 136 and 137.

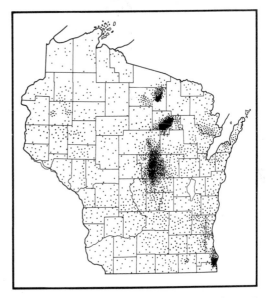

Fig. 138. A dot map in which the dot size and dot value have been more wisely chosen than in the preceding examples. Each dot in this example represents 40 acres.

The selection of unit value and size of dots should be made so that in the denser areas (of a dense distribution) the dots will just coalesce to form a dark area. Figure 138 is constructed from the same data as the preceding examples in this article but with a dot size and unit value more wisely chosen. Of course, if the distribution is a sparse one even in the relatively dense areas, as would be the case (to use an extreme example) with areas of marketable saw timber in South Dakota, then even the relatively dense areas should not appear dark.

Professor J. Ross Mackay has developed an ingenious graph to assist in determining the desirable dot size and unit value.* This graph, shown in Fig. 139, requires a knowledge of the sizes of dots that can be made by various kinds of pens. This information is presented in Table 13. By varying the relation between dot diameter and unit value, the cartographer can choose the relationship that will best present the picture of the actual distribution.

TABLE 13. DOT DIAMETERS OF VARIOUS PENS.

Pen type	Pen number	Dot diameter (line width) in inches
Barch-Payzant	8	0.012
	7	.018
	6	.025
	5	.036
	4	.046
	3	.059
	2	.073
	1	.086
Leroy	00	.013
	0	.017
	1	.021
	2	.026
	3	.035
	4	.043
	5	.055
	6	.067
	7	.083
Wrico	7	.018
	7A	.018
	6	.025
	6A	.025
	5	.027
	5A	.027
	4	.036
	4A	.036
	3	.048
	3A	.048
	2	.062
	2A	.062

Note: see Fig. 64 for width sizes of Pelican-Graphos nibs.

*J. Ross Mackay, "Dotting the Dot Map," *Surveying and Mapping*, 1949, Vol. 9, pp. 3–10.

The cartographer should remember that the visual relationships of black to white ratios and the complications introduced by the pattern of dots make it difficult, if not impossible, for a dot map to be visually perfect. The best approach is by experiment after narrowing the choices by use of the graph.

135 Locating the Dots

Theoretically the ideal dot map would be one with a large enough scale and with the data sufficiently well known so that each single unit could be precisely located. This is the case with large-scale topographic maps which show each house or each mine. They are the most accurate of dot maps. Ordinarily, however, it is desired that the map be of a small enough scale so that a larger area can be shown, in order to indicate more clearly the pattern of distribution. Sometimes, if the data are sparse enough, a unit value of one (e.g., paper mills) can still be used on a small-scale map and come close to presenting a true picture. If, however, it is necessary to make the unit value of the dot greater than one, the problem then arises of locating the one point symbol that represents several differently located units.

It is helpful to consider the several units to be represented as having a kind of center-of-gravity, and then to place the symbol as nearly as possible at that point. For example, an area of uneven distribution will have more dots in the dense and less in the sparse region, although all the cartographer knows from the original data is the total number of dots to place in the area. Consequently he must draw upon every available source of information to assist him in placing the dots as accurately as possible. Such aids as topographic maps, other distribution maps which he knows correlate well with the one being

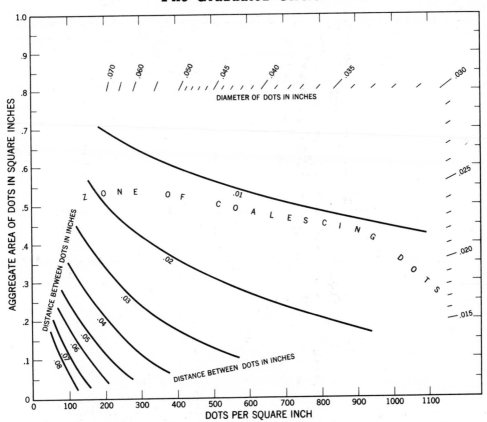

Fig. 139. Graph showing relation between dot size and dot density. Any relationship between numbers of dots and diameters of dots that falls in or beyond the "zone of coalescing dots" will produce dots on top of one another. Courtesy J. Ross Mackay and *Surveying and Mapping*.

prepared, soil maps, climatic maps, and many others, as well as a good knowledge of the area being mapped, are indispensable.

A dot map in which the dots are evenly spread over the unit areas, although numerically correct, could better use some other symbol than dots.

136 The Graduated Circle

The graduated dot or circle (or square) is used for presenting amounts when totals are of more interest than details of location. Thus, they are useful (1) when the units represented are close together but are large in number, such as in the population

of a city, or (2) for representing aggregate amounts for relatively large territories.

Representation is accomplished by varying the size of the circle so that the area covered by the circle is in each case proportional to the amount represented. Since the area of a circle is πr^2, and since π is constant, the method of construction is to extract the square roots of the data and then construct the circles with radii proportional to the *square roots*. The unit of measure applied to the square roots may be any desirable unit, such as tenths or hundredths of an inch, and should be selected so that the largest circle will not be

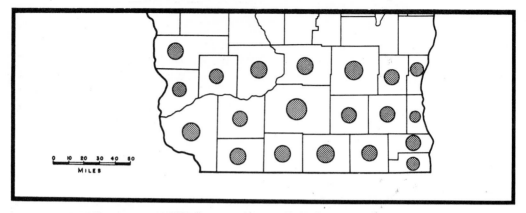

Fig. 140. Area available for crops by counties. The unit radius is too small.

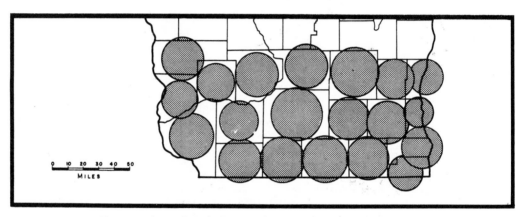

Fig. 141. Same data as Fig. 140 but the unit radius is too large.

too large, and the smallest, not too small. As long as the same unit is used for all circles, their areas will be proportional.

For example, Figs. 140 and 141 show the area of land available for crops in some counties. When too small a unit radius is chosen, then the circles are too small to show much, as is illustrated in Fig. 140. Also, the impression is given that there is practically no cultivated land in those counties. When too large a unit radius is chosen, then the circles are too large. Again, the representation does not reveal much, and the impression is given that practically all the land is cultivated, as in Fig. 141. A more reasonable presentation

would be obtained by selecting a unit that would provide each county with a circle more nearly the actual scale area of cultivated land. Actual size is not often desirable, however, for if this were done rectangular areas, largely cultivated, would require circles which would spill over the boundaries.

137 The Pie Chart

More than one kind of data can be shown with the same graduated circle by making it into a pie chart. Thus, to use the illustration of cultivated land in a county, any part of the cultivated-land total may be shown by segmenting the circle in the manner in which a pie is cut. Any relation of a part to the whole can be shown visually by the pie chart. For example, Figs. 142

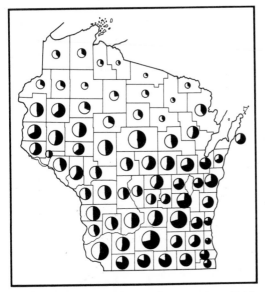

FIG. 142. Land in farms and per cent available for crops in Wisconsin by counties. The circle represents the land in farms. The per cent *available* for crops has been blacked in on each circle.

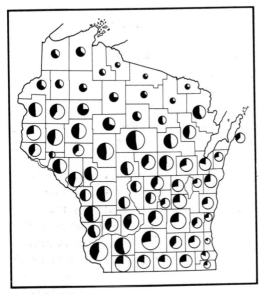

FIG. 143. Same data as in Fig. 142, but in this map the per cent *not available* for crops has been blacked in on each circle.

and 143 show the total amount of farm land in each county and at the same time show what percentage of that total is available for crops. The procedure merely requires that the percentage be determined and that, then, by using a "percentage protractor" the various values be marked off on each circle.

A "percentage protractor" may be constructed by drawing a circle and then subdividing the circumference according to percentage in the desired detail with dividers. A small hole at the center will make it possible to place the center of the protractor over the center of each graduated circle. The appropriate per cent can be marked off at the periphery.

It is important that the subdivision of each circle begin at the same point; otherwise, the reader will have difficulty in comparing the values. Also important is the selection of the portion to be shaded or colored. As is illustrated in Figs. 142 and 143, this can have considerable influence on the effect gained by the reader.

138   The Graduated Volume Symbol

Occasionally the cartographer is faced with a range of data that is so large that he cannot effectively show both ends of the range by graduated circles. If he makes the circles large enough to be differentiated clearly in the lower end of the scale, then those at the upper end will be too large. A solution, if the data *must* be presented on a map is to symbolize the data with apparent *volume* rather than area. This is done by making a comparable dimension of each proportional to the *cube roots* of the data, in the manner in which the two-dimensional graduated circles were made proportional to the square roots.

One kind of device used occasionally is the sphere-like symbol. An illustration of

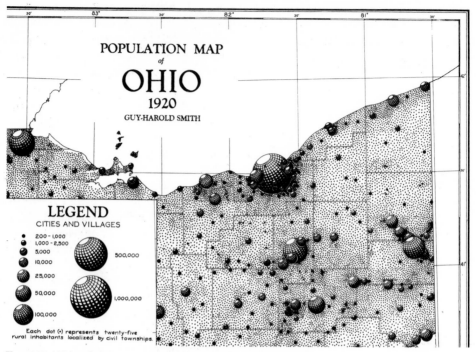

FIG. 144. Use of apparent three-dimensional symbols. From Population Map of Ohio by Guy-Harold Smith. Note that the legend has been relocated for purposes of illustration. Courtesy of Guy-Harold Smith and *The Geographical Review,* published by the American Geographical Society of New York.

its use is shown in Fig. 144. Another type of graduated volume symbol is the cube or the block pile, developed by Erwin Raisz, illustrated by Fig. 145. Volume symbols, being prepared so that their apparent values are proportional to the cube roots of the data, have the effect of actually lessening the plane area of the large symbols on the map. This, of course, is what makes it possible to map a larger range of data by this method. It has the marked disadvantage, however, that the smaller values cover a relatively larger map area, so that this portion of the data is magnified somewhat, unless the reader takes care to appreciate the volume aspect. Three-dimensional symbols such as sphere-like and cube-like symbols may be very graphic, especially if the visual impression is inten-

sified by good execution and design. This tends to offset somewhat the danger of the reader misinterpreting the relationship of these volumetric symbols.

139 Line Symbols

There are many kinds of line symbols. The most familiar are those that are qualitative in nature, that is to say, those that show a kind of feature, such as a river or a road. Although such line symbols are fundamentally alike in that they represent the qualitative nature of the feature without ordinarily indicating any quantitative value, they may be used for many kinds of purposes. For example, a line may represent a road and show exactly where it lies on a topographic map, whereas at a smaller scale it may be drawn merely to

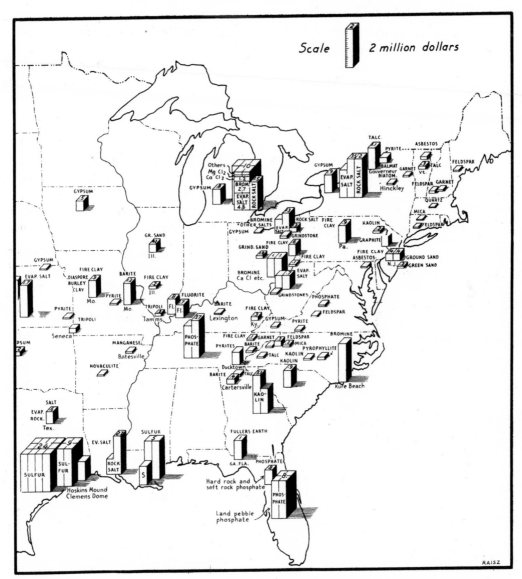

Fig. 145. Another form of three-dimensional symbols, called block piles, developed by Erwin Raisz. From a map by E. Raisz, taken from *Mining and Metallurgy*, AIME, March, 1941.

show that two places are connected by a road. Another line, for example a boundary, may be used merely to separate unlike areas. Thus, a line can be used qualitatively to join things, a line along which there is some constant quality; or it may be used to separate things, a line along which there is no constant quality.

Another kind of line is one along which there is some constant quantitative value such as a line of constant compass declination. There are many kinds of such quantitative lines, and they are extremely useful cartographic symbols. Because the value along them is assumed to be constant the prefix "iso" (equal) commonly precedes the term for the particular kind of value, e.g., isobar, equal barometric pressure.

Still another kind of line is one along which a specified quantitative value changes. Such lines are used to show movement and variable amount, separately or in combination. Traffic flow or commodity flow between areas is frequently represented in this fashion. An arrow alone may represent nothing but movement; but a line of varying width may show differences in capacity, without showing any movement, such as roadbed load limits. As a matter of fact, the tapering line of a river on a map is actually a flow line, although it is usually thought of as being a qualitative rather than a quantitative symbol.

As is true of all symbols, differentiation among the various kinds of lines depends upon contrasts of size, shape, and color.

140   The Isoline or Isogram

Isolines are lines of constant width along which there is either (1) an actual or (2) an assumed constant value. It is necessary for the cartographer and the map reader to understand fully the nature of each, because quite different concepts (and accuracy) underlie their employment.

Considerable confusion has obtained regarding the terminology of these kinds of quantitative lines, and they are variously called isorithm, isarithm, isopleth, and so on, in the literature. The simplest systematic terminology has been suggested by J. K. Wright who proposes the following outline:

Isoline, any line along which there is a constant value (sometimes called isogram).

1. *Isometric line,* a line of actual constant value, e.g., elevation above sea level.
2. *Isopleth,* a line of assumed constant value, e.g., population per square mile.

These terms will be employed in this book.

Isometric lines are common in cartography. The best-known example is the contour (isohypse or hypsometric line), all points of which are, at least theoretically, the same elevation above some datum. Such a line can truly be located, and, as a matter of fact, some contour lines have been accurately surveyed level lines. Most of them, however, have been located by simple linear interpolation and estimation. Nevertheless, such a line and all those like it (isotherm, isobath, isogone, etc.) show actual values capable of existing at points, and thus, by connecting points of equal value, along lines.

Isopleths, equally common in cartography, show concepts that cannot actually exist at points and thus cannot exist precisely along lines. For example, a density of population may be 50 persons per square mile for a specified area. Such a value cannot exist at a point, and the choice of locating a line connecting "points" of equal density becomes a matter of interpretation, rather than of fact as in the case of isometric lines.

Isopleths can be used to represent several types of ratios and proportions. These are discussed in Article 145.* Each of the two types of lines requires a different approach to the problem of their location and particularly to the selection of the intervals to be shown by the lines. In some cases the cartographer is interested in presenting the actual fact conveyed by his figures at points, whereas in others he is concerned with presenting the areal change from place to place.

141 The Isoline Interval

Probably the most important problem the cartographer must face in using isolines is the choice of the interval between the lines actually drawn. Theoretically, of course, an infinite number of lines is possible; in practice, a selection must be made.

In the case of isometric lines, such as contours, there is in fact a value at every point on the map, and there is no limit to the interval which may be chosen. It may be as small as desirable. There is, however, the matter of accuracy which acts as a brake against choosing too small an interval. Small intervals and numerous lines may give an impression of accuracy not warranted by the spread of the data. On the other hand, large intervals may not show sufficient detail. The cartographer must analyze the data and the purpose of the map, and select his interval accordingly.

Isometric lines, by their nature, are closed lines in the sense of a contour line, and shapes and form can be easily shown by them. A constant interval that does not change throughout the entire range is usually desirable. If the intervals decrease or increase, detail is emphasized in the

* The student is referred to the excellent discussion of this and other problems of isopleth mapping in J. Ross Mackay, "Some Problems and Techniques in Isopleth Mapping," *Economic Geography*, 1951, Vol. 27, pp. 1–9.

upper or lower portion of the range. This may be to the advantage of the map, as in the case of high mountains bordering an intensively utilized alluvial fringe, when both appear on the same map.

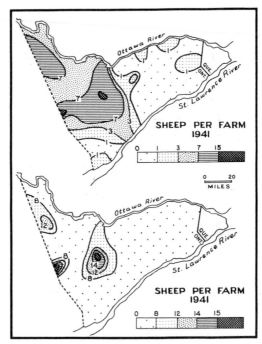

FIG. 146. These two maps have been prepared from the same ratios but employ different isopleth intervals. The intervals in the top map increase in steps of 1, 2, 4, and 8, whereas those in the bottom map increase in the reverse order, 8, 4, 2, and 1. The result is to provide detail and accentuate differences at the lower end of the scale in the top map and to reverse this relationship in the bottom map. Redrawn from Mackay, courtesy of *Economic Geography*.

Isopleths present a somewhat different problem. Since the concept is such that every point does not have a precise value, the selection of the interval is considerably more significant than it is with isometric lines. Figure 146 is an example of the variations that can result when different intervals are chosen.

On most maps containing isometric lines, one line is just as significant as any other.

In the case of isopleth mapping, however, it is frequently desirable to select lines and intervals which have some significance, either in themselves or in the areas they delimit. It is also desirable to select the interval in such a way that few isolated spots result on the map. A frequency graph, such as that illustrated in Fig. 147, in which the number of occurrences of each

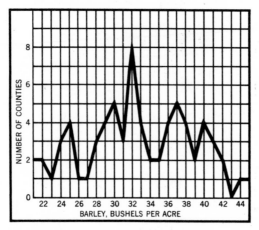

FIG. 147. An example of a frequency graph. The illustration is for barley production per acre per county in 1947 in Wisconsin.

ratio value is plotted on the vertical axis against the ratios on the horizontal axis, may be an aid to selecting class intervals. Generally, the low points on such a graph are the most desirable, since they come closer to satisfying the conditions mentioned above.

Although there is no theoretical limit to the number of intervals and their method of progression, there is a practical limit. If the interval or progression is confusing, the map will not serve its purpose. The most easily understood interval is a regular one (20, 40, 60, etc.; or 5, 10, 15, 20, 25, etc.), but the values are frequently meaningless as regards the data from which they are chosen. A compromise between the results of the frequency graph and

some sort of regularity of progression appears, at this writing, to be desirable. Before isopleth intervals and line values are chosen, it is imperative that some experimenting and testing be done on the map to see if the desired picture is presented.

It is apparent from the above that a high degree of professional integrity, as well as skill, is required of the cartographer who works with isopleths.

142 Locating the Isoline

Locating an isometric line is a matter of simple linear interpolation between known values or control points, combined with judgment of probable position under the circumstances. An isometric line is capable of having only one accurate position, and the cartographer's task is to come as close to that position as is possible in the particular instance.

This is not the case with isopleths, for they are not capable of having a single position; their location is a matter of interpretation. The values upon which isopleths are based are ratios, percentages, or proportions which are derived from two sets of data based on civil divisions, other units of area, or portions thereof. The resulting values, upon which the locations of the lines depend, refer to the whole areal unit employed, and each is "spread," so to speak, over the entire area of the unit. Therefore, unlike intrinsic values, there can be no *points* at which the values used in plotting the isopleths exist. Nevertheless, the lines must be located somewhere and upon some basis. In order to do this, control points are assumed. Two basic elements of interpretation thus exist. One involves the location of the *control points* between which interpolation is made, and the other is the choice of which *pairs* of control points are used when the isopleth value falls between a pair above and a pair below the selected value.

When the distribution is uniform over an area of regular shape the control point may be chosen as the center. If the distribution

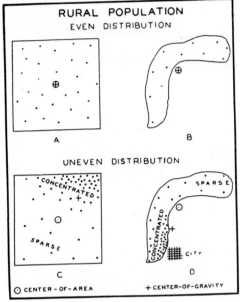

Fig. 148. Placing control points. From Mackay, courtesy of *Economic Geography*.

is known to be uneven the control point is shifted toward the concentration. Figure 148 illustrates the concept.*

* The following discussion is based largely on Mackay, *op. cit.*

The four diagrams of statistical divisions show possible locations of the center-of-gravity and center-of-area for uniform and variable distributions, with rural population used as an example.* They serve to illustrate the problem of locating the control point in regularly and irregularly shaped divisions. In *A*, which is rectangular, the center-of-gravity and center-of-area would, of course, coincide at the intersection of the diagonals. Because the distribution is even, the centers in *B* also coincide, but they lie outside the irregularly shaped area at some point that is more representative of the whole division than any point within it. The distributions are uneven in *C* and *D*, so the center-of-gravity is displaced away from the center-of-area. In each case, however, the center-of-gravity is probably the most accurate location for the control point.

Figure 149 illustrates the second problem of locating isopleths, that of choosing between pairs of control points when the one pair provides a value above and the other a value below the chosen isopleth value.

* Center-of-area may be considered as the balance point of the area without the distribution taken into account, whereas the center-of-gravity takes into account any unevenness of the distribution.

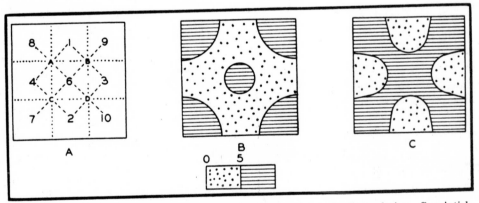

Fig. 149. The problem of selecting pairs of control points to use in interpolation. See Article 142 for explanation. From Mackay, courtesy of *Economic Geography*.

The nine control numbers in diagram *A* have been chosen so that certain pairs of control numbers are above 5 and others are below 5. When the value of a number intermediate between four control points is being interpolated, it may be considered

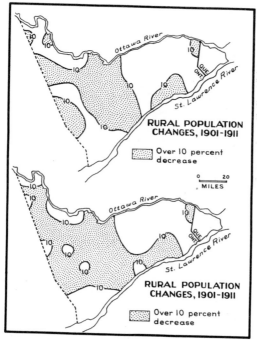

FIG. 150. Two maps of rural population change in Ontario. The problem illustrated in Fig. 149 is shown by two practical examples in these two maps which have been prepared from the same census data. See Article **142** for explanation. Redrawn from Mackay, courtesy of *Economic Geography*.

as above or below 5, depending upon the pairs of control points used in determining its value. Diagram *B* has been drawn on the assumption that the values of the numbers lying between control points are below 5, and diagram *C* with the numbers above 5. Since in this case there is no supplementary information which may be used in making a choice, the matter is not capable of solution. Diagram *B* is just as accurate as diagram *C*. Figure 150 illus-

trates the differences that can result when this problem is handled in two different ways. Wherever a number could be considered as either above or below 10, it was chosen as below 10 in the top map and above 10 in the bottom map. In this particular example, supplementary information gained by studying rural population changes in the preceding and following decades would probably have provided a fairly accurate basis for accepting or rejecting the values.

In order to locate the isopleths as accurately as is possible, considering their limitations, it is necessary, just as when making dot maps, for the cartographer to draw upon all his knowledge of the area and upon all the aids available. A thorough knowledge of the character of the distribution being mapped is, of course, indispensable.

143   Flow Lines

Flow lines are lines, usually of variable width, showing movement along the route of the line or between the terminal points connected by the line. The width of the line is usually proportional (linear) to the number represented at each point. Figure 151 is an example of a flow-line map.

Lines can increase or decrease in width as values are added or subtracted. There are many types of flow maps, differing from one another in the manner in which the movement is shown. Actual movement along the route may be represented, or, as in origin and destination maps, the terminal points may simply be connected. Arrowheads are often used to show the direction of movement, although the varying thickness and angle with which "tributaries" enter frequently show flow adequately. Tributaries should, of course, enter smoothly in order to enhance the visual concept of movement. In some instances the range of the data is so large

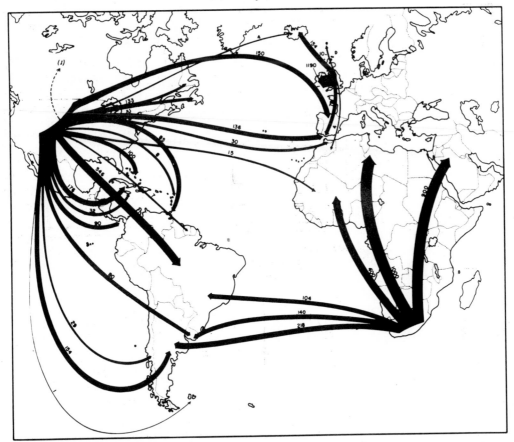

F<small>IG</small>. 151. A portion of a map using one form of simple flow lines. Map, prepared in the Office of Economic Warfare, showing coal exports of United States, United Kingdom, and Union of South Africa in 1944. Widths of lines are not in proportion to amounts; numbers show thousands of metric tons.

that a unit width value capable of allowing differentiation among the small lines would render the large ones much too large. It is, consequently, sometimes necessary to symbolize the smaller lines in some way, such as by dots or dashes. Volume flow lines are also possible. Numbers may be placed alongside the lines to convey more exact information.

144 Area Symbols

Area symbols, like line and point symbols, may be used to represent either qualitative or quantitative data. Qualitative area symbols are those such as simulated

grass for marshes, patterns to show vegetation, soil, or terrain types, and a host of others. They differentiate kind, and each symbol used should be sufficiently varied from the others so that no confusion can result. Many qualitative symbols have become conventional through long use.

Quantitative area symbols are employed to convey data in two ways. Either they may consist of the application of some coloring or shading to make the positions of isolines clearer, as in the case of the familiar relief map, or they may be used to symbolize different values in areas the boundaries of which have no actual numerical

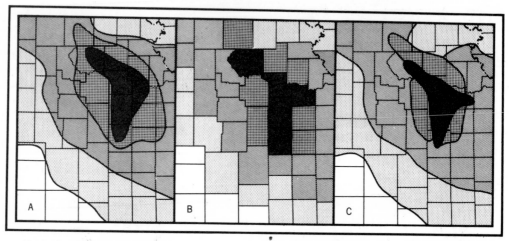

FIG. 152. Three ways of using area symbols. A hypothetical distribution. See Article 144 for explanation. Note the unconscious application, by the reader, of greater value to the darker areas.

value. Figure 152 shows the results of three different ways of using area symbols to show amount. Map *A* is a shaded isopleth map. Map *B* is a map whereon the shading has been applied to the statistical unit used in compilation. It is obvious that the boundaries of the shading have no significance beyond showing the units used. The third map, *C*, uses lines simply to separate areas containing similar values. In this map, although the lines have no constant numerical value, they do represent zones of change.

There is a wide range of prepared area symbols available, and the ultimate range is limited only by the imagination of the cartographer. Basically, area symbols may vary either in terms of pattern (lines, dots, etc.) or in terms of value, that is to say, their relative darkness or lightness. Parallel lines tend to cause the viewer to have disturbing eye movements, as was illustrated in Article 113, and it is generally good practice to use parallel lines sparingly. Dot patterns are more stable and differentiate areas more clearly. Naturally, when a large number of patterns is required, parallel lines must occasionally be utilized. They should be surrounded by other kinds of patterns as often as possible.

Qualitative area symbolization should be accomplished by variation in pattern, whereas quantitative variation should utilize value changes. The range from dark to light automatically gives the impression of varying amount, with the darker standing for the greater amount. The visual values selected for categories on a map of graded intensities are extremely important. The same map with the same data may be made to appear quite different by changing the spread of values, as is illustrated in Fig. 153. The range appears much greater in map *B* than in map *A*.

The general tendency is for one to assume that, within any gradation, black is "complete" and white is "empty." Consequently, the positions on the value scale should be chosen to bear a reasonable relation to the spread of the data. If the visual range is great the reader cannot help but infer a great data range.

The eye cannot accommodate much more than six or eight steps from black to white,

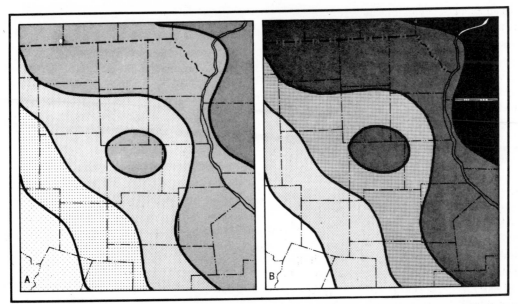

FIG. 153. The same data are used in maps *A* and *B* but symbolized with different spreads of visual values. A hypothetical distribution.

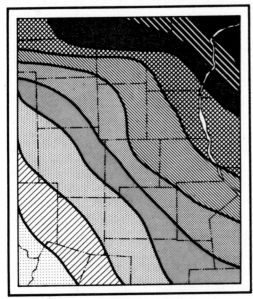

FIG. 154. Pattern aids when values are too close together. A hypothetical distribution.

out in Article 112. Consequently, if the grading requires that the value steps be too close together on the gray scale, the cartographer may introduce numbers or patterns to aid in differentiation, as is illustrated in Fig. 154.

145 Distribution Maps

In a general sense, any map is a distribution map, for it is impossible to present relative location without showing distribution. Nevertheless, a large group of maps containing point, line, or area symbols are commonly termed distribution maps, in contrast to atlas maps, topographic maps, historical maps, and the other categories in the commonly employed, loose, and overlapping classification of kinds of maps. Many distribution maps employ statistical data; but distributions may be nonnumerical in the statistical sense, so it would not be proper to call them statistical maps. These are the kinds of maps that show, for example, areas predominantly inhabited by

and even in this limited range considerable confusion can result from the juxtaposition of different values, as was pointed

Moslems or the distribution of important fishing grounds.

Maps showing quantitative distributions are one of the cartographer's stock in trade. They are capable of surprising variety and can be used to present almost any kind of data. Few maps can be made that do not in some way present quantitative information, even if the amounts involved result from so simple an operation as grading the symbols for cities of different size for an atlas map. Column after column of numbers in tables frequently are excessively forbidding, and the statistical map often can present the same material in a more understandable and interesting manner. Tabular materials of various kinds, ranging from a federal census to reports of commissions (e.g., Interstate Commerce) and from the reports of industrial concerns to the results of one's own tabulation, exist in staggering variety. With such a wealth of material, it is to be expected that the cartographer finds a large percentage of his effort is devoted to preparing this type of map.

It is necessary for the student to have well in mind that figures *can* lie, cartographically at least, if they are not properly presented. Hasty evaluation of data, or the selection of data to support conclusions unwarranted in the first place, results in intellectually questionable maps. Their production is vicious for they may be, and unfortunately sometimes are, used by their authors or others to support the very conclusions from which they were drawn in the first place. The exhortation, occasionally implied or stated in this book, "to make the map tell the story desired by the author" is not contradictory to the preceding. The question is a matter of integrity. Another great danger is that of providing an impression of precision greater than can be justified by the facts. To

keep from doing this the cartographer is often forced to invent symbols such as dashed lines or patterns of question marks, which may detract from the appearance of the map but which will serve the more important purpose of preventing the map reader from falling into the common trap of "believing everything he sees."

The examples of kinds of distribution maps in the balance of this chapter by no means complete the list, for the number of possibilities of combination and presentation are almost infinite. Included, however, are the major types of presentation commonly used by geographers and other social scientists. For the purpose of considering some of their characteristics and some aspects of their preparation, they may be divided in two classes. In one group we may put those maps that treat one or more classes of data which are expressed on the map in absolute or intrinsic terms. The information presented by this type of map may be either quantitative or qualitative such as numbers of people or predominant races. Many combinations are possible, and two or more kinds of data may be presented at once; but in no case are the data expressed as a relationship, except by visual implication.

In the other group we may put those maps that show related values (e.g., ratios, averages, proportions, etc.) and on which the mapped values are derived from some sort of comparison of two kinds of data. There are three kinds of relationships, the characteristics of which are presented in Table 14.* Most of these kinds of maps present information that results from simple calculation, in which one element of the data is a dividend and the other a divisor.

* Adapted from Mackay, "Some Problems and Techniques in Isopleth Mapping," *Economic Geography*, 1951, Vol. 27, pp. 1–9.

TABLE 14. EXAMPLES OF KINDS OF MAPPABLE RELATIONSHIPS.

Mapped values	Calculation characteristics	Example
A. General ratios, averages, yields, etc.	Dividend and divisor different	$\dfrac{75,000 \text{ acres in farms}}{750 \text{ farms}}$ = average size farm of 100 acres
		$\dfrac{75,000 \text{ bushels of corn}}{2,500 \text{ acres in corn}}$ = yield of 30 bushels of corn per acre
B. Density	Dividend and divisor different. Divisor is total or significant part of the area of the statistical division	$\dfrac{5,000 \text{ persons}}{100 \text{ square miles}}$ = density of 50 persons per square mile
		$\dfrac{5,000 \text{ persons}}{50 \text{ square miles cultivated land}}$ = density of 100 persons per square mile of cultivated land
C. Proportions (percentages)	1. Dividend and divisor in same units	1. $\dfrac{4,000 \text{ beef cattle}}{2,000 \text{ dairy cattle}}$ = proportion of 2 to 1 of beef cattle over dairy cattle
	2. Dividend a portion of the divisor	2. $\dfrac{4,000 \text{ beef cattle}}{6,000 \text{ cattle (all kinds)}} \times 100 = 66\%$ of cattle are beef cattle

146 Processing Data

The basic approach to processing data for statistical maps is by way of the kinds of symbols or techniques that may properly be used to convey the information. The range of symbols was discussed in the preceding portion of this chapter, and it is only necessary here to reiterate the fact that the cartographer has a wide choice indeed. Consequently, his first action, after selecting or preparing the map base, is to decide upon the mode of presentation. He must decide if it is to be a static (all the data as of one period or place) or a dynamic (change of time or place) map, and he must select the symbolism (point, line, or areal, or combination). The next step is to process the crude statistics in such fashion that they become usable for the system of presentation that has been selected.

When data are obtained from a variety of sources it usually is necessary to equate them so that they provide comparable values. For example, different countries use different units of measure such as long tons or short tons, U.S. gallons or Imperial gallons, hectares or acres, and so on. Frequently the units must be further equated to bring them into strict conformity. If, for example, one were preparing a map of fuel reserves, it would not be sufficient only to change the tonnage units to comparable values, but it would also be necessary to bring the tonnage figures into conformity on the basis of their BTU rating. It is also frequently necessary to process the statistics so that unwanted aspects are removed. A simple illustration is provided by the mechanics of preparing a density map of rural population (persons per square mile) based on county data. The populations and areas of minor civil divisions and the totals for counties may be available. If that is the situation, the areas and populations of incorporated divisions must be subtracted from the county totals. Another illustration is provided by the well-known regional isothermal map. If the relationships between temperatures, latitudes, air masses, etc., are desired the effects of elevation must be removed from the reported figures. This involves ascertaining the altitudes of each station and the reduction of each temperature value to its sea-level equivalent.

After the statistical data have been made comparable the next step is to convert them to mappable data. This may, of course, not be necessary for many maps such as the isothermal map referred to above, because in that case the data need merely be plotted and isolines drawn. On the other hand, ratios, per acre yields, densities, percentages, and indices must be calculated before plotting. Some kinds of symbols, such as graduated circles or spheres, require determination of square roots or cube roots. Many of these operations may be

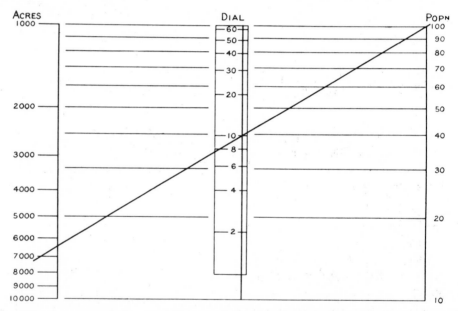

FIG. 155. A nomograph for calculating population density per square mile from acres and population. Logarithmic paper is used. On the one margin is plotted *area in acres,* the plotting being done on a strip of logarithmic graph paper pasted upside down so that the smaller quantity appears at the top. On the opposite margin is plotted *population,* with the smallest quantity at the bottom. Halfway between these scales and parallel to them is pasted the dial, a strip of two-cycle logarithmic paper that is labeled and scaled (beginning at the bottom) to indicate *density per square mile.* To determine how far up the sheet to paste this dial, a thread is stretched between 6,400 on the area scale and 100 on the population scale. As an area of 6,400 acres (10 square miles) with 100 people would have a density of 10 people per square mile, the middle strip should be adjusted so that the thread crosses it at 10. Calculations can then be made by merely stretching the thread between a point on the area scale and one on the population scale, the point where the thread crosses the dial being the density per square mile. From Alexander and Zahorchak, courtesy *The Geographical Review,* published by the American Geographical Society of New York.

most efficiently handled by various kinds of calculating aids.

Perhaps the most useful aid for this purpose is the slide rule. Quite acceptable accuracy can be attained with the slide rule, and percentages, ratios, division, and multiplication can be computed almost as fast

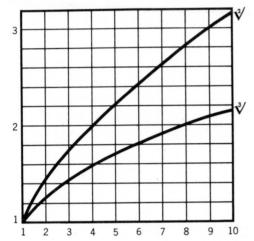

Fig. 156. A nomograph to provide plotting values. The nomograph is constructed to show the square or cube roots of the plotting range on the horizontal axis. Of course, the range may extend to any limit. The vertical scale is determined by the actual drawing scale. Thus, all that is necessary is to place the compass on the graph at the appropriate point on the horizontal scale and set it at the line of square or cube roots.

as the cartographer can read the figures. The manipulation of the slide rule for these purposes can be learned in a short time. Square roots and cube roots can also be derived from the slide rule, or can be determined from mathematical tables such as those in Appendix B.

If a large number of calculations involves the same kinds of units on a variable scale, it is frequently a saving of time to prepare a *nomograph*. Nomographs should be reserved for calculations involving two or more variables, as, for example, when data are (1) population and (2) acres, and the desired result is persons per square

mile. Figure 155 illustrates a nomograph of this type. Another type is used to derive plotting values from data such as are shown in Fig. 156.

Figure 139 in Article 134 is a more complex kind of nomograph. Practically any kind of calculation involving variables can be set up on a nomograph, and the student may refer to any standard work on nomography for ideas.

147 Qualitative and Quantitative Distribution Maps

One of the major tasks of the cartographer is to select ways of presenting qualitative data. The types of data he may need to present run a long gamut, from such qualitative facts as religions, dominant livelihoods, or racial characteristics to settlement forms, vegetation characteristics, or dominant agricultural practices. These maps present kinds of things but do not show amount.

Qualitative maps generally utilize area symbols, and are distinguished by presenting the cartographer with a problem for which there is no easy solution. When the distribution of qualities is mapped in its entirety, it is immediately evident that qualitative areas are generally not mutually exclusive. Consequently, the cartographer is forced to devise a means of showing overlap. This may be done in a number of ways, as suggested in Fig. 157, none of which is suited to all circumstances.

If the map is a color map it is possible to choose colors that give the impression of mixture. For example, a red and a blue when superposed appear purple, and that color looks like a mixture. On the other hand, a color produced by mixing red and green does not look like a mixture of its components.

The selection of area symbols for qualitative maps poses the problem, common to all qualitative distribution maps, of sym-

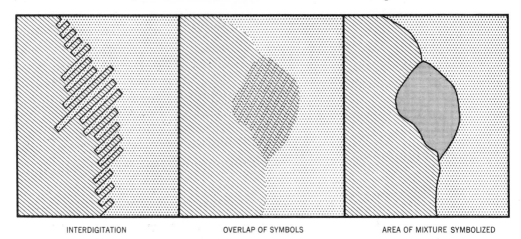

INTERDIGITATION   OVERLAP OF SYMBOLS   AREA OF MIXTURE SYMBOLIZED

Fɪɢ. 157. Methods of showing mixture and overlap.

bolizing without much value contrast. As was pointed out earlier, clarity and visibility are the result of contrast, and, of the various kinds of contrast, value (degree of darkness) is probably the most important. Value changes are, however, inappropriate on a qualitative map because of the universal tendency to assign quantitative meaning to value differences. Thus a darker area symbol looks more "important" to the map reader. Of course, such emphasis could be used to advantage, if the cartographer were desirous of drawing attention to one or more of the various qualitative elements he is mapping. The use of color complicates the problem even further.

Quantitative information may be combined with the qualitative to present details of distribution. This may be accomplished in two ways: (1) by showing ratios or a proportion of the whole and (2) by symbolizing totals and showing percentages thereof. Figure 158 shows the ratio between two components. It should be noted that the presentation gives no indication of the total numbers involved. The total amount may be included in the presentation by using pie charts in which the area of the circle represents the total, and each

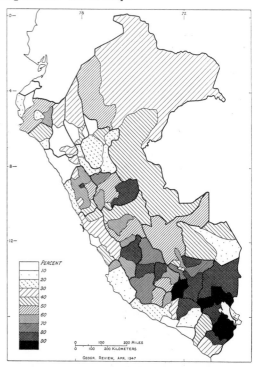

Fɪɢ. 158. Quantitative-qualitative population map showing the percentage of "Indians" to total population of Peru by provinces. Courtesy *The Geographical Review,* published by the American Geographical Society of New York.

circle is subdivided to show the relative amount of each component of the total. Such a map is illustrated in Fig. 142.

Distribution maps are limited in the detail they can convey by the size of the areal units for which data are available. There is no question that, in the large majority of instances, qualitative and quantitative changes rarely coincide with administrative districts, but it is often necessary to use their boundaries as lines of change on maps. If more nearly correct impressions of distribution are desirable the dot map may be employed. This type of map is useful for showing distribution details, and the level of quality and completeness depends upon the ability of the cartographer to bring all the pertinent evidence to bear on the problem of where to put the dots.

Considerable detail can be introduced in the map if the map is made on the basis of the smallest civil divisions and then greatly reduced. Placing the dots with reference to minor civil divisions can be easily done by using tracing paper, cloth, or plastic for the map and putting under

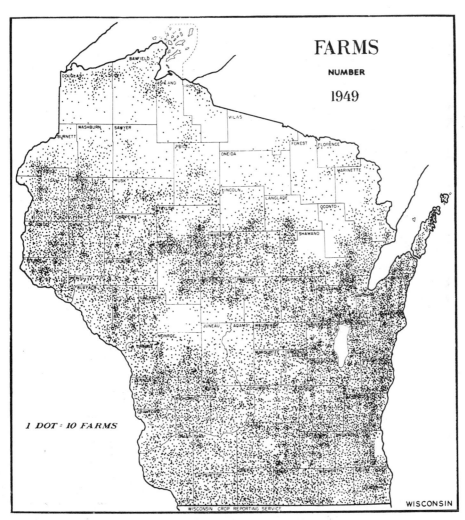

Fig. 159. An undesirable pattern on a dot map. See text for explanation. Courtesy Wisconsin Crop Reporting Service.

it a map of the minor civil divisions as a guide. Only the larger administrative units need then be shown on the map. Care must be exercised so as not to leave the guiding boundary areas blank, for they will show up markedly in the final map as white lines. Care must also be taken that the dotting does not inadvertently produce lines and clusters of dots that do not occur in actuality. Such regularity can easily occur and is quite noticeable by contrast to its amorphous surroundings. Figures

159 and 160 were made in the same office and present nearly the same dot distributions. Figure 159 was prepared by a relatively inexperienced cartographer who placed the dots a bit too evenly within the the minor civil divisions. An undesirable overall pattern of regularity resulted. Figure 160 was made by a more experienced cartographer who, by "looking ahead," placed the dots in the minor civil divisions so that a more desirable, smoother pattern resulted.

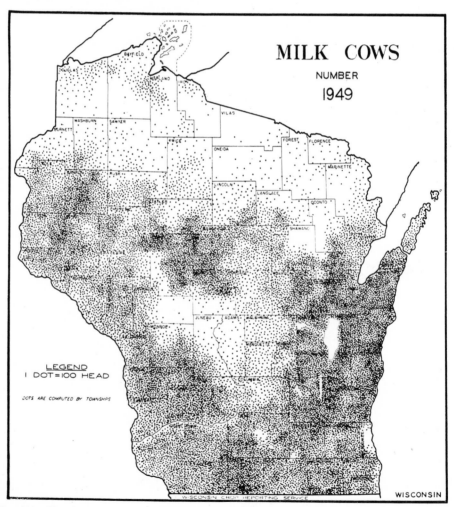

Fig. 160. Nearly the same distribution as that shown on Fig. 159 but prepared by a more experienced cartographer. See text for explanation. Courtesy Wisconsin Crop Reporting Service.

The preparation of dot maps for distributions wherein there are areas of extreme concentration poses a difficult problem. The difficulty is frequently encountered when preparing population maps. Dot maps are easily constructed for rural populations where an appropriate unit value and dot size have been chosen. It is more difficult to map total population, for in urban areas with their large totals and small area the dots simply fall on top of one another. One solution is to symbolize the city population with graduated circles, which may be lightly shaded or merely left as open circles.

The distribution of intrinsic or absolute numbers presented on dot maps is a particularly useful device, not only because a good visual impression of the distribution and its pattern can be presented, but also because such maps can be useful as a step in understanding correlations of distribution. The dot map lends itself well to the superposition of other kinds of data, and the areal relations between the two may be quickly apparent on the map. The preparation of dot maps of population or other types of distributions and the placing on them of boundaries such as those indicating soils or landforms may show up areal coincidences or correlations not previously suspected.

Density maps differ from other distribution maps in that they show relative values, rather than absolute. The raw data are made relative to the total area (or to a significant part) of the divisions for which the distribution data are available. The specific value that results is a kind of density index, and it requires some mental calculation on the part of the reader to appreciate it.

The most common density map is that which shows the number of things per square mile, or some other unit such as square kilometer. For example, the mapping values for a population density map are obtained by dividing the population by the number of areal units in the civil divisions for which the data are available. Such a map provides a detailed representation from which specific values are available. To proceed with the same example, the relation of population to productive area is frequently more important in predominately agricultural societies than is a simple population to total area ratio. If the data are available an interesting distribution can be shown by relating population to cultivated land or to productive area defined in some other way. Figure 161 illustrates a map of this kind.

Other kinds of information can be derived from area and related to population. For example, one can easily compute the average distance between spaced units. If A is the area, and n the number of units in the area, and D is the average distance between them, then

$$D = 1.0746 \sqrt{A \div n}$$

The values of D can be plotted and isopleths can be drawn, or area symbols can be used to differentiate the unit categories.

Observation of supplementary data frequently shows that one part of a unit area has a higher density than another, yet only the density for the whole area may be available directly from the statistics. John K. Wright has presented a relatively simple system for calculating the densities of parts; his explanation follows: * "Assume, for example, a township with a known average density of 100 persons to the square mile. Assume, further, that

* John K. Wright, "A Method of Mapping Densities of Population with Cape Cod as an Example," *The Geographical Review*, 1936, Vol. 26, pp. 103–110.

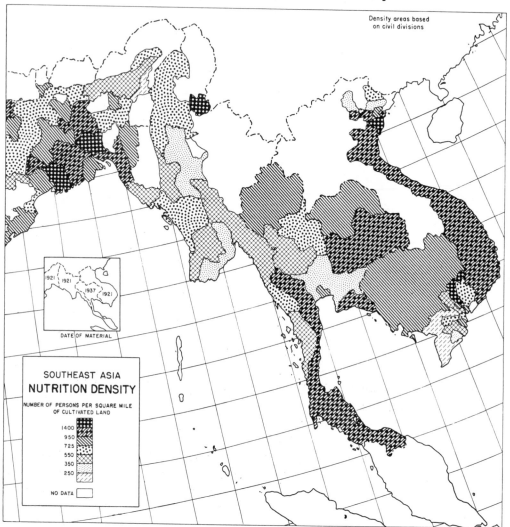

Fɪɢ. 161. A "nutrition" map. Note the inclusion by the cartographer of the helpful index to the date of the information. Note also the unconventional orientation in order to conserve scale. Map by W. Zelinsky, courtesy of the *Far Eastern Quarterly*.

examination of topographic maps and consideration of other evidence have shown that this township may be divided into two parts, m, comprising 0.8 of the entire area of the township and having a relatively sparse population, and n, comprising the remaining 0.2 of the township and having a relatively dense population. If, then, we estimate that the density of population in m is 10 persons to the square mile, a density of 460 to the square mile must be assigned to n in order that the estimated densities m and n may be consistent with 100, the average density for the township as a whole.

"The figure 460 for the density in n was obtained by solving the following fundamental equation:

$$\frac{D - (D_m a_m)}{1 - a_m} = D_n$$

or

$$\frac{100 - (10 \times 0.8)}{0.2} = 460$$

where D is the average density of population of the township as a whole, D_m the estimated density in m, a_m the fraction of the total area of the township comprised in m, $1 - a_m$ the fraction comprised in n, and D_n the density that must accordingly be assigned to n.

"D_m and a_m are estimated approximately. It is not necessary to measure a_m accurately, since the margin of error in a rough estimate is likely to be less than the margin of error in the best possible estimate of D_m.

"Study of neighboring townships sometimes gives a clue to a value that may reasonably be assigned to D_m. For example, the topographic map may show what would appear to be similar types of population distribution prevailing over T_m, or part of one township, and over the whole of S, an adjacent township. It would be reasonable, therefore, to assign to T_m a density comparable with the average density in S.

"Having assigned estimated but consistent densities to two parts [of an area], one may then divide each (or one) of these parts into two subdivisions and work out densities for the latter in the same manner; and the process may be repeated within each subdivision.

"The method is merely an aid to consistency in apportioning estimated densities, either of population or of other phenomena, within the limits of . . . territorial units for whose subdivisions no statistical data are available. Obviously it should not be applied in mapping densities of population within counties in the United States, since census figures are published

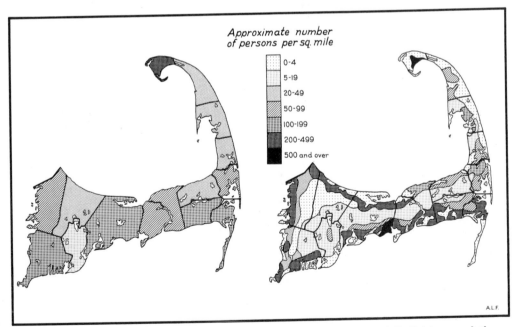

Fig. 162. The left-hand map shows the density according to whole civil divisions, and the right-hand map shows the refinement that can be developed by this system. Redrawn from *The Geographical Review*, published by the American Geographical Society of New York.

for the townships and other minor civil divisions within the counties. On the other hand, it might well be applied in mapping various phenomena for which statistics are available by counties but not by minor civil divisions."

Table 38 in Appendix H enables one to solve the fundamental equation without either multiplication or division. Figure 162 shows the refinement that can be made. The bounding lines of the area symbols on the right-hand map are neither civil boundaries nor isograms in the strict sense. They have been called *dasymetric* lines and are useful where the mapped data do not change gradually.

10

Representing the Terrain

148 Representing the Terrain

In the preceding chapter various techniques of symbolism were discussed according to the principles underlying their utility. Another approach to the same problem would be to consider separately the various categories of information commonly presented on maps and then to discuss the various techniques by which each can be symbolized. The difficulty with such an approach is that there is considerable similarity in the methods of representing such phenomena as population data, agricultural data, manufacturing data, and so on, which would necessarily result in a great deal of repetition. There is, however, one category of geographical data that is so different from the others as to make it almost imperative that it be treated separately. This is the category concerning the surface of the land. The data in this category also may be represented by point, line, or area symbols, or by combinations of them.

The representation of the three dimensions of the earth's surface has always been of special concern to cartographers, but the earliest maps and even those of the Middle Ages showed little of this probably because of the paucity of knowledge about land forms. To be sure, mountains were shown as piles of crags, and ranges appeared as "so many sugar loaves"; but until precise surveying provided some foundations upon which the cartographer could base his drawings, land forms could not be well represented. As soon as surveying did provide the basic information, the representation of terrain became almost of primary concern.

There is something about the three-dimensional surface that intrigues cartographers, and sets it a little apart from the other symbolization techniques. First, it requires a bit more skill. Moreover, it is a continuous phenomenon; that is, all portions of the earth above the sea have a three-dimensional form, and as soon as the land is represented all of it must be represented, at least by implication. It is also the one phenomenon the cartographer works with that exists as an impression in the minds of most map readers, and the reader is therefore relatively critical in his approach to its representation on the map.

Because of its universal spread, and because of the relative importance to man of minor land forms, the representation of terrain has also been a great problem to the cartographer. If he shows the surface in sufficient detail to satisfy the local significance of the land forms, then the problem arises of how to present the other map data. If he shows with relative thoroughness the nonland-form data, which perhaps are more important to the purpose of the map, he may be reduced merely to suggesting the land surface, an expedient not

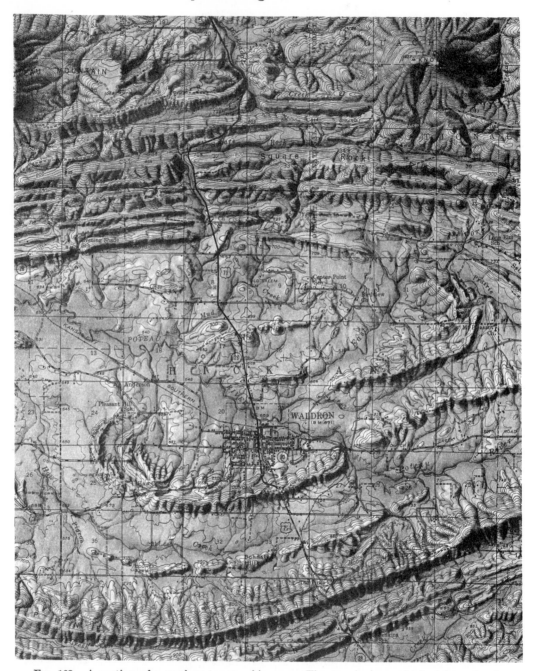

Fig. 163. A portion of a modern topographic map. The terrain is emphasized by colored shading which is overprinted on contours. The black halftone cannot do justice to the excellence of the original. Waldron Quadrangle, Arkansas, United States Geological Survey, 1949.

F<small>IG</small>. 164. Drawing land forms for a modern atlas. Drawn in black on a blue-line base plate, the surface representation is printed in brown on the final map. Courtesy Rand McNally and Company.

likely to please either the map maker or the map reader. And, to make matters worse (or better, depending on how one looks at it), the development of aviation has made the effective and precise representation of terrain a most important task. The pilot must be able to recognize the area beneath him, and the passenger has naturally become more interested than he formerly was in the general nature of that surface, for he may now see it. His height above it provides a reduction similar to that of a map.

The story of the development of land-

Fig. 165. A much reduced portion of a modern wall map emphasizing surface. The detailed terrain is derived from photographing a carefully made, three-dimensional model. The map is reproduced by complex color printing analogous to process color. Map by Wenschow (Germany), courtesy Denoyer-Geppert Company, Chicago, Ill.

form representation is a recital of the search for symbolizations suitable to a variety of purposes and scales. On large-scale maps the desirable symbolization is one that appears natural and at the same time is capable of exact measurement of such elements of the land surface as slope, altitude, volume, and shape. The major problem arises from the fact that, generally speaking, the most effective visual presentation is the least commensurable, whereas the most commensurable is the least effective visually. One of the major decisions of every survey has been in what manner to balance these opposing conditions. Although it is somewhat early as yet to judge, there is some indication that advances in color printing have enabled the cartographer to reach a relatively effective combination, without undue sacrifice of either desirable end. The new, shaded relief, contour maps of the United States Geological Survey are a case in point (see Fig. 163).

Perhaps even more of a problem has been that of depicting land forms on smaller-scale maps. If we reserve for the geographer and geomorphologist the specialized techniques of terrain appreciation and analysis, small-scale land-form representation is a major problem for atlas maps, wall maps, and other general-purpose reference maps, as well as for those special-purpose maps in which regional terrain is an important element of the base data. The smaller scale requires considerable generalization of the land forms, which is no simple task, as well as the balancing of the surface representation with the other map data, so that neither one overshadows the other. (See Fig. 164.) No less a problem is the representation, in bolder strokes, of the land forms for wall maps, so that such important elements as major regional slopes, elevations, or degrees of dissection are clearly visible from a distance (see Fig. 165). Practically every conceivable technique, from brilliant coloring to the artists' shading, has been tried.

For many years to come the representation of land forms will be an interesting and challenging problem, for it is unlikely that convention, tradition, or the paralysis of standardization will take any great hold on this aspect of cartography. Particu-

larly will this probably be true of the terrain representation on special-purpose maps, for each such map will be a new challenge.

149 The History of Representing the Terrain

If we restrict the notion of the cartographic representation of the terrain to those undulations of some magnitude, we

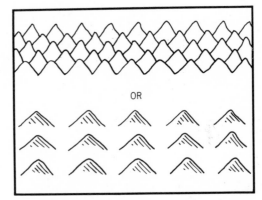

Fig. 166. Crude symbolization of hills and mountains.

find that the first symbols were crude drawings of hills and mountains as they might be seen from the side, such as those depicted in Fig. 166. This constituted a more or less standard form until the latter part of the eighteenth century (1799), when a flow-line symbol, called the *hachure*, was advocated by an Austrian army officer. Each individual hachure is a line of varying width that follows the direction of greatest slope. By varying the widths of the lines according to the steepness of the slopes on which they lie, the steepness of the rise may be indicated. When many of them are drawn close together, they collectively show the slopes and "ups and downs" of the surface. This turned out to be particularly useful on the then recently initiated, large-scale, topographic military maps; and, for nearly a century, the ha-

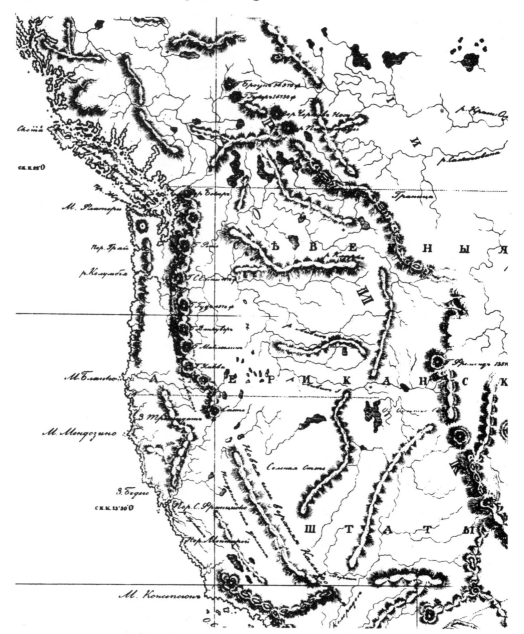

Fig. 167. Genus *hachure,* species *woolly worm.* From an old Russian atlas.

chure was widely employed. Figures 173 and 174 are examples of hachured maps. On small-scale maps or maps of poorly known areas, hachuring degenerated into the familiar "hairy caterpillars," an ex-ample of which is shown in Fig. 167. These worms are not yet extinct, and they still may occasionally be encountered.

Another line symbol, the *contour,* had been invented in the first half of the eighteenth century (1730), before the advent of the hachure. A Dutchman named Cruquius, being called upon to represent the bottom configuration of the Merwede River, did so by using isolines of equal depth. Others, perhaps independently, seized upon the idea of representing dry-land surface with a similar type of line symbol; but it was not until relatively late in the nineteenth century that contours became a common method of depicting the terrain on survey maps. One development, which grew out of the use of contours on large-scale maps, was their extreme generalization on small-scale maps, resulting in the familiar "relief map," together with its layer coloring according to altitude, originally developed more than a century ago (1842). The colors, of course, are area symbols between isolines.

After the development of lithography in the first half of the nineteenth century, it became possible easily to produce continuous tonal variation or shading. It was not until after about 1870, however, that this type of area symbol was utilized for the representation of the terrain, the shading applied being a function of the slope. Not long after, color gradations were combined with shading, and some truly "visual" maps of the land surface were forthcoming. Various techniques of shading and coloring were tried, but the general aim was to achieve the impression on the flat map of an actual third dimension. Warm and cool colors (yellow-red as opposed to blue-green) were combined with various kinds of shadows, so that the visual effect of the third dimension was most strikingly achieved.

By the beginning of the present century the basic methods of presenting terrain on large-scale topographic maps (contouring, hachuring, and shading) had been discovered, and the essential incompatibility be-

tween commensurability on the one hand and visual effectiveness on the other was readily apparent. For the last several decades the problem has been one of how to combine the techniques to achieve both ends. The newer topographic maps are the most effective yet produced.

The representation of the land surface at large scales is concerned essentially with the three major elements of configuration, the slope, the height, and the shape of the surface formed by elevations and angles. The various methods outlined above, and their combinations and derivatives, seem to provide the answer, more or less, for the problem at large scales; but the representation of land surface at smaller scales is another matter. Here the generalization required is so great that only the higher orders of elevation and slope may be presented by contours or hachures, whereas detail, if shown, becomes so intricate that the map is useful for little else. To be sure, the exceptionally skillful cartographic artist can apply shading or hachuring effectively, but such skill is not easy to develop. As knowledge of the land surface of the earth has grown, so also has the need for some method of presenting effectively that surface at smaller scales.

The problem has not been solved. There have been many attempts at solution, but, to the present, each has been found wanting. Layer coloring between selected and generalized contours has been the technique most often employed, mainly because of its relative simplicity; but it leaves much to be desired. Character of surface is presented only by implications of elevation; the generalized contours show little except regional elevations, which are not very significant; and the problems of color gradation and multiple printing plates are difficult. The larger the scale, of course, the more efficient the system becomes.

Hachures at small scales are likely to revert to the woolly worm, and the shading technique, without expensive multiple color plates, tends to become little else than a background color, which serves only to reduce the visibility of the other map data.

In lieu of layering, hachuring, and shading at small scales, some other techniques have been suggested and tried. One of the more common, and more effective, devices is that of drawing the terrain pictorially, as a kind of bird's-eye view. This may be done as a black line drawing, or as a continuous tone line drawing on Ross or Coquille board, or it may be rendered in wash or crayon for halftone reproduction. Figure 180 is an example of pictorial terrain. Many variations of technique have been employed involving combinations of layer coloring, shading, shadowing, and pictorial representation. Excellent examples are the interesting perspectives of Richard Edes Harrison that have appeared in *Fortune* magazine and elsewhere.

The other systems of land-form representation that have been tried or suggested ·either require more effort and expense than the results seem to warrant or they are so complex and intellectually involved that their use is limited to the professional geographer and geomorphologist, whose knowledge of land forms is sufficient to interpret them. In the former class would fall the interesting "orthographical relief" and "relief contour" work of Professor Tanaka of Japan. In the latter would fall the landform unit-area technique, the nonpictorial morphographic technique, the average-slope technique, the relative-relief technique, and so on. Some of these techniques will be considered below.

150 Contours

Representation of the form of the land by means of contours is the most commensurable system yet devised. A contour is an isometric line of equal elevation above sea level, and the characteristics of contours as they lie on the land are not difficult to visualize. It is well, however, for the student to bear in mind one fact of utmost significance, namely, that a contour map (and most other maps, for that matter) assume a vertical view at every portion of the map. That is to say, the reader is directly above each point and is looking down along a line perpendicular to the assumed sea-level surface.

The assumed sea-level surface is called the *datum plane*, which is the surface projected beneath the land of a particular earth spheroid. This surface is essentially

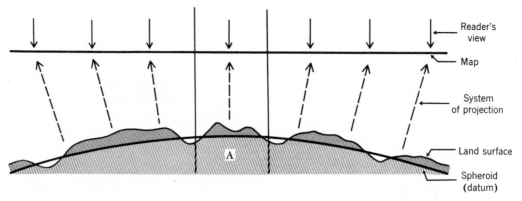

FIG. 168. The building of a contour map. The section outlined and designated as *A* is enlarged in Fig. 169. The curvatures are, of course, greatly exaggerated.

that which would be assumed by a world-wide ocean that was not modified by variations in density and gravity.* It is apparent that the spheroid surface is not a flat surface but is curved in every direction. It is the problem of the mapper to establish the horizontal position on, and the elevation above, this surface of a large number of points on the land. When enough positions are known and the curved datum surface has been transformed into a plane surface by means of a projection system, such as the polyconic, the map may then be made. The map reader *sees* the represented land surface orthographically. Figure 168 illustrates these important relationships.

Figure 169 is an enlargement of a portion of Fig. 168 to show the system of representing the land surface by means of isometric lines of equal elevation above sea level, i.e., the datum. The various elevations above sea level may be considered as imaginary curved surfaces parallel to the

* This concept is an expedient, for it is now well known that the surface that would be assumed by a continuous ocean, with the present surface density and gravity differences retained, would not be that of a spheroid. Rather, it would have local undulations, and would instead be a *geoid* surface. It is the establishment of this surface that is one of the problems of geodesy. Although considerable is known about the nature of the geoid surface in some parts of the world, not enough is known for it to be used as a datum.

datum. The system of projection flattens them. Lines are drawn along the imaginary contact between the elevation planes and the land surface. Everywhere along each line the same elevation above the datum obtains. These lines are the contour lines.

Figure 170 is a pictorial view and a map view of the same hypothetical land form shown in section in Fig. 169. In a sense, the contours are the shorelines that would result if sea level were to be raised by successive 20-foot intervals. This illustrates one especially important feature of contours that is not necessarily true of other isolines, namely, that all the land inside a contour *must* be higher than the land outside it. In places where a depression exists such as a kettle, sink, or crater, it is shown by a contour with small ticks on the inner side. This shows that the land inside that particular line is lower than the land outside it.

Contours on a topographic map are remarkably expressive symbols, if they have been correctly drawn and if the interval between them is relatively small. The most obvious expression is that of elevation. The elevation of all points on a map may be determined within one-half the contour interval. For example, if the interval between contours is 20 feet, and if any point not on a contour must necessarily

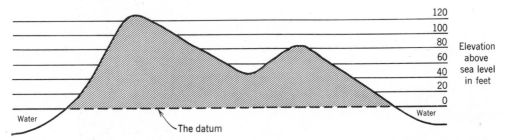

Fig. 169. Surfaces of equal elevation above sea level, successively spaced, are the basis of contour lines. The curved datum and elevational surfaces have here been made into true planes as by means of projection and are seen in cross section.

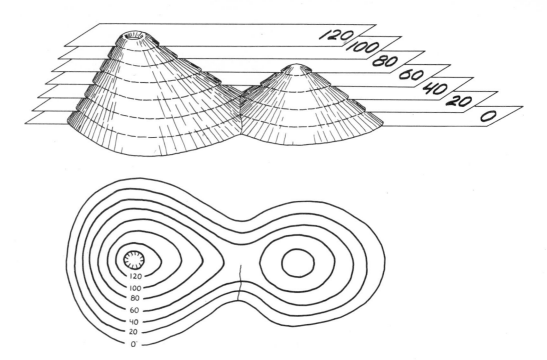

FIG. 170. Pictorial and map view of contours on the hypothetical island seen in profile in Fig. 169. In the upper drawing the flattened elevational planes are shown cutting part way through the island. In the lower drawing the traces of the intersections of the planes with the surface become contours. Note the depression contour.

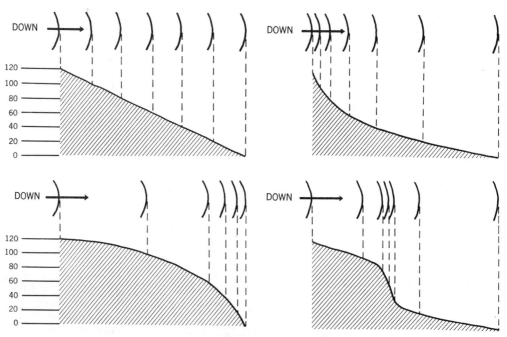

FIG. 171. Some examples of characteristic contour patterns and the profiles of the shapes on which they lie.

e above the lower and below the higher
the two contours between which it is lo-
ed, then a point can be reckoned to the
rest 10 feet. One must, however, bear
mind that not all contour maps are of
e same order of accuracy. Before the
cceptance of the air photograph as a device from which to derive contours, the
lines were drawn in the field with the aid
of a scattering of "spot heights" or elevations. Consequently, often they were by
no means precisely located.

The shapes of undulations of the land
surface are well indicated by the pattern
of spacing of the contours. Smooth, steep,
gentle, concave, convex, and other simple
shapes are all readily apparent on contour
maps as indicated in Fig. 171. Contours
always bend upstream when they lie
athwart a valley; they always bend down
slope when crossing a spur (see Fig. 172).
The angle of slope of the land is shown
by the spacing of the contours, and procedures have been worked out whereby
even the average slope of areas may be determined from the spacings of the contours.
Profiles of the land along a traverse, or
along a road or railroad, can easily be constructed from a contour map by working
backwards from the map (Fig. 170) to the
profile (Fig. 169). The recognition of topographic forms, structural details, and even
rock types may often be derived from the
contour patterns on topographic maps.
Although contours do not present quite so
clear a visual picture of the surface as
does shading, the immense amount of information that may be obtained by careful
and experienced interpretation makes the
contour by far the most useful device for
presenting the land on topographic maps.

It is apparent that much of the utility
of contours depends upon their spacing,
and the choice of a contour interval is not
an easy task. In areas of high relief the

interval must necessarily be large, and as
the interval is increased the amount of surface detail lost between the contours becomes correspondingly greater. If, owing

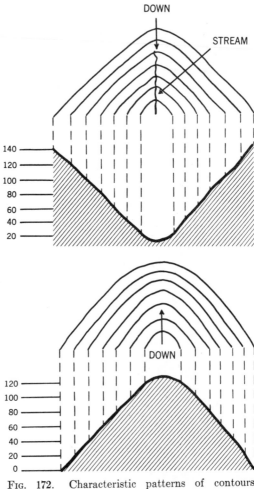

Fig. 172. Characteristic patterns of contours
crossing a valley or spur.

to lack of data or scale, the contour interval must be excessive, other methods of
presentation, such as hachures or shading,
are likely to be preferable. In some cases,
lack of data results in *form lines* being employed in place of contours. These are dis-
continuous lines which, by their orientation, suggest shapes but from which precise elevations are not to be read.

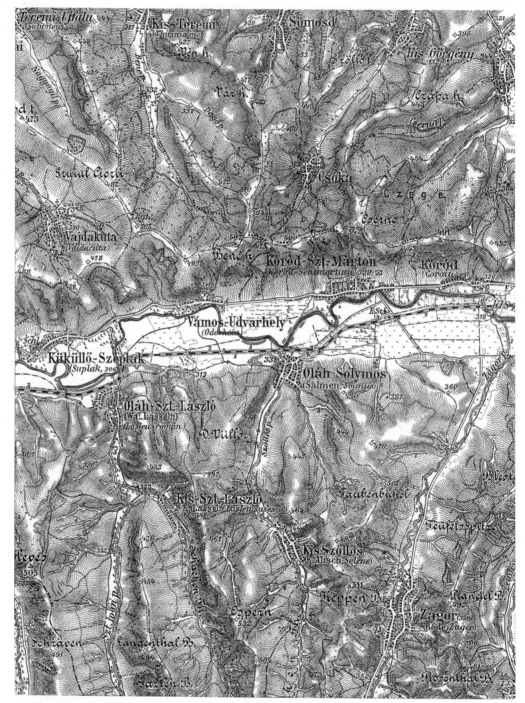

Fig. 173. A section of a hachured topographic map with vertical illumination. Austria-Hungary, 1:75,000.

151 Hachures

Hachures are not commensurable as contours are, but for many purposes, especially at smaller scales, they provide a more readily visible picture of the land. The hachure is a line symbol drawn down the slope, and it is varied in width or spacing with the slope of the land on which it lies. The steeper the surface, the darker the representation. The original form of hachures was based on the assumption of a light source directly over each portion of the map in line with the reader. As the light shone upon the assumed three-dimensional land surface it would be reflected in the direction of origin (to the reader) in some proportion to the angle of the slope (see Fig. 173). A number of different slope-darkness relationships have been used. For example, the originator, Lehmann, established a system wherein any slope 45° or more would appear black on the map.

The varying amounts of light and dark may be produced either by thickening lines, as in the Lehmann system, or by decreasing the spaces between lines of the same thickness. Many different combinations have been tried, but they all are based on the same general idea—a change of slope changes the amount of light reflected. Other variations have been incorporated in the system, such as having the light come from some angle other than vertical. Oblique lighting produced a more realistic picture, and some of the shaded hachure maps produced in this fashion are remarkably effective, as for example the Dufour map illustrated in Fig. 174.

The major difficulty experienced with hachures is that, although slope is their basis, it cannot practically be measured from the map, regardless of the precision underlying the representation. Flat areas, whether they are on the tops of uplands or in valleys, appear the same, and only streams or spot heights strategically placed make it possible for the reader to tell them apart. Another difficulty of hachuring is that its effectiveness, when printed in one color, is dependent in large degree upon the darkness of the ink. Thus, a considerable problem is created, for as darker inks are used to make the terrain more effective the other map detail becomes correspondingly obscured.

It is interesting to note that precise, effective hachuring depends upon a considerable knowledge of the terrain. In actual practice, contours were often drawn on the field sheets of a survey, and the final map was hachured in the office from the contours. Thus the original French survey for the 1:80,000 map had contoured field sheets but was published only in the hachured form. In modern times hachures have been little used on topographic maps. They are still employed in smaller scales in atlases and on occasional special maps.

152 Shading

Shading is the representation of the land surface by means of variations in light and dark. In the outline of symbolism presented in the preceding chapter, shading occupies a place in the area-symbol category. The variations of light and dark, as in a chiaroscuro drawing, are applied according to a number of different systems. For example, the shading may vary according to the slope of the land as seen from above, in a fashion similar to vertically lighted hachuring, or it may be applied according to the angles of light reflection that might occur if the light source were at some particular angle. In its simplest form, shading attempts to create the impression, appropriately exaggerated, one might gain from viewing a carefully lighted model of the land, as is illustrated in Fig.

FIG. 174. A section of the Dufour map of Switzerland in which obliquely lighted hachure shading is employed. Sheet 19, 1858, Switzerland, 1:100,000.

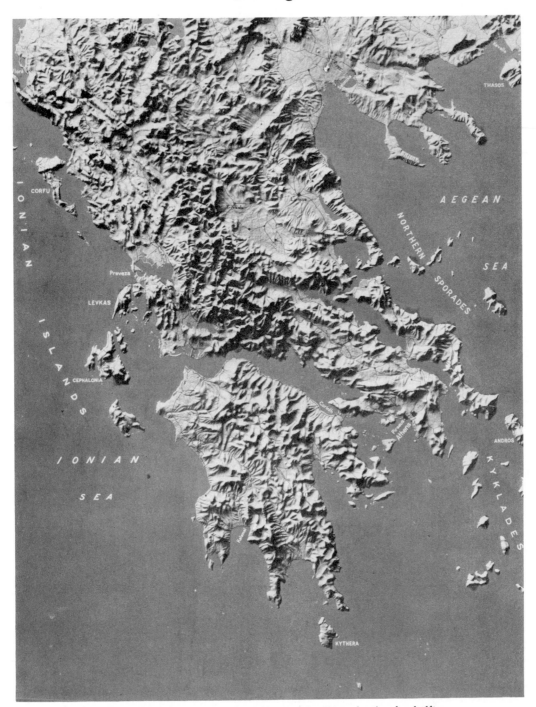

Fig. 175. A portion of a topographic model. Reproduction by halftone.

175. Of course, the usual shaded map is not quite the same as an area seen from above, for the observer is, in theory, directly above all parts of the map; there is no perspective.

Not long after hachuring with vertical lighting was employed on topographic maps, it was discovered that a more realistic effect could be attained by varying the line widths to give the effect of light coming from the side. The Dufour map of Switzerland, started in 1833 and completed in 1866, and illustrated in the previous article, is an outstanding example. This method was followed in other surveys as well. In such maps the graphic quality took precedence over the desire to indicate precise slope, although attempts to combine them were extensively investigated.

The versatility of lithography gave the cartographer of the nineteenth century a medium previously lacking, and he was quick to take advantage of it. Lithography allowed smoother and easier application of shading with a crayon, which was considerably faster than the tedious drawing of hachures, even if the hachures were not graded precisely according to slope categories. After the use of stone for lithography declined, the gradation of light and dark (continuous tone) was accomplished by halftoning. The "terrain plate" is usually prepared separately and is halftoned; the line work of the map is then either combined with it and printed as a combination line and halftone, with one press plate, or it is printed separately, as two impressions with different inks. Continuous-tone drawing is generally decidedly preferable to photographing a model when the reproduction is to be a monochrome, because much more contrast and sharper detail can be attained in the drawing. The continuous-tone monochrome drawing may be done in wash (painted with a brush), by airbrush, by carbon pencil, charcoal, or crayon; in any case it must be reproduced by halftone, since it employs continuous tone. (See Fig. 176.)

The drawing or the photograph of the model may also be reproduced in color, and various other effects are thus possible. For example, several identical halftones may be separated during the retouching stage; portions of them may then be printed in different colors, so as to achieve an effect of elevational layer tints, in addition to the realistic terrain. The coloring need not conform strictly to elevational lines, but may be employed simply to distinguish lowlands from uplands in any particular region.

It is, of course, not necessary that the vertically viewed terrain drawing be drawn in such a way that its reproduction requires the halftone process. The obliquely illuminated hachure map, exemplified by the Dufour map (Fig. 174), is one example of the kind of copy that could be reproduced by a line cut. Ross board and Coquille board may also be employed to the same end. (See Fig. 177.) The line-cut method reduces the cost considerably, but does not allow quite as much contrast or detail.

One of the problems facing the cartographer, when he plans to employ vertically viewed shaded terrain, is the direction from which the apparent illumination is to come. A curious and not completely understood phenomenon is that under different directional illumination, depressions and rises will appear reversed. Consequently, the illumination direction must be chosen so that the proper effect will be obtained. Generally, when the light comes from the upper right, elevations appear "up" and depressions, "down." In addition to providing the correct impression of relief, the direction of lighting is important in illuminating effectively the terrain being presented. Many areas have a "grain" or

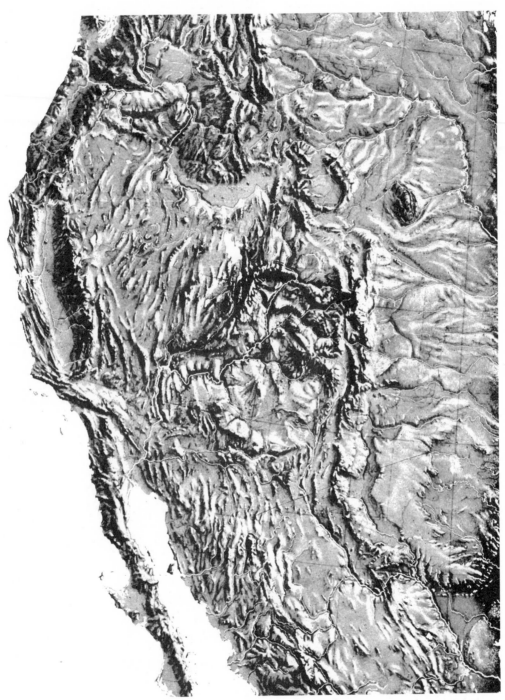

FIG. **176.** A chiaroscuro (light and shade) drawing of a portion of the terrain of western North America by Richard Edes Harrison. Reproduction by halftone. The terrain is vertically viewed with the light source at the side. The white rivers were masked out with the dia-positive of the drainage drawing. Shading done with crayon on drawing paper.

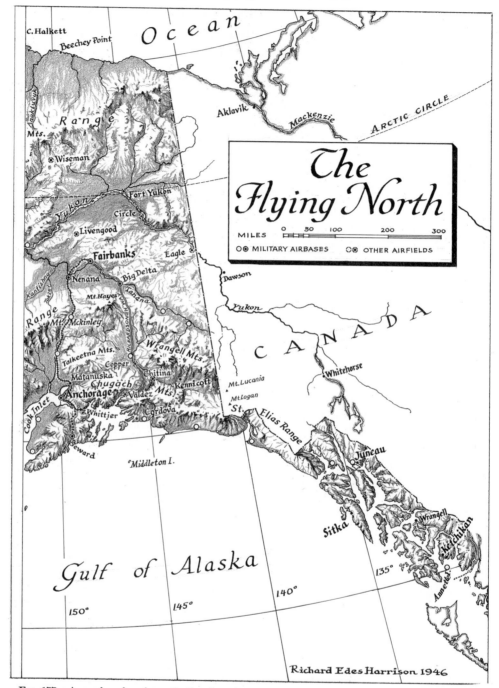

FIG. 177. A much reduced, vertically viewed terrain drawing, done with No. 60 Castell pencil and India ink on Ross board; reproduction by line cut. The lighting is from an angle, but the shading is also a function of elevation, as lowlands are systematically darkened. This is a portion of one-half of a split drawing used 'for the end paper of a book. From *The Flying North*, by Jean Potter, copyright **1947**, courtesy The Macmillan Company, publishers.

pattern of terrain alignment that would not show effectively if the illumination were from a direction parallel to it. For example, a smooth ridge with a northwest-southeast trend would require the same illumination on both sides, if the light were to come from the northwest. Finally, the cartographer must select the direction of lighting so that the items of significance will not all be in the dark shadow areas.

The utility of shading as a visual vehicle for presenting land form has long been appreciated. It was to be expected that there would be attempts to make it in some way commensurable as well as visually effective. The first such attempt was the hachure. A number of other possibilities have been suggested, but none of them have been tried beyond the experimental stage.

The late Max Eckert, one of Europe's foremost cartographers, attempted to use point symbols in the hachure-slope manner.* By using more carefully controlled dot sizes graded according to slope, he hoped to produce a map in which the amount of light that would be reflected from a vertical source would be accurately represented. The author also presented a suggestion combining point symbols with the unit-area technique in which the darkness was a function of the average slope of uniform small areas.†

* Max Eckert, *Die Kartenwissenschaft,* Berlin and Leipzig, 1921, Bd. 1, pp. 585–590.
† Arthur H. Robinson, "A Method for Producing Shaded Relief from Areal Slope Data," *Annals of the Association of American Geographers,* 1946, Vol. 36, pp. 248–252.

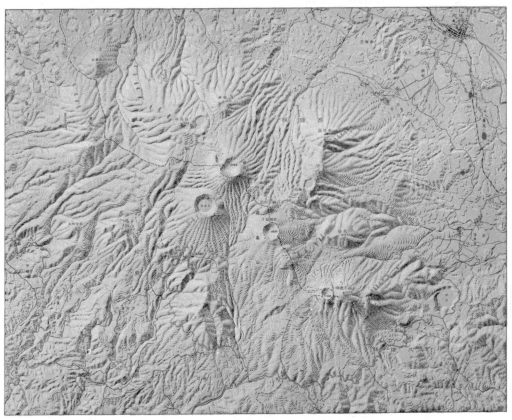

Fig. 178. An example of Professor Tanaka's illuminated contour method. Courtesy of *The Geographical Review,* published by the American Geographical Society of New York.

Two interesting suggestions having to do with contours and profiles have been made by Professor Tanaka of Japan.* His latest suggestion is to illuminate contours systematically so that they provide an impression of shading with oblique illumination, as well as being commensurable. Figure 178 is an example.

153 Pictorial Terrain

Almost as soon as maps were drawn, the major terrain features were represented pictorially in crude fashion. As artistic abilities have increased and as knowledge of the earth's surface has expanded, the pictorial representation has become increasingly effective. Within the past fifty years this method of presenting the land features has made great strides. One reason for this has been the advent of the airplane; the airplane has made us more conscious of the appearance of terrain, and the air photograph has provided a source of information hitherto unavailable.

Pictorial terrain on maps ranges from the schematic terrain commonly seen in newspaper maps to the scientifically accurate diagrammatic physiographic, or land-type, drawing; it may be line cut or halftone; and it may be monochrome or multicolor. Whatever its use and its form, pictorial terrain drawings may be grouped in two general categories: (1) the perspective drawing and (2) the pictorial map.

This arbitrary grouping places in the first category those drawings that essay to show a portion of the earth, as seen from some distant point; the second category

* K. Tanaka, "The Orthographical Relief Method of Representing Hill Features on a Topographical Map," *Geographical Journal,* 1932, Vol. 79, pp. 213–219; K. Tanaka, "The Relief Contour Method of Representing Topography on Maps," *The Geographical Review,* 1950, Vol. 40, pp. 444–456.

includes those maps that show terrain by means of pictorial symbols on a base map. The grouping is by no means a classification, for who is to say that terrain sketched

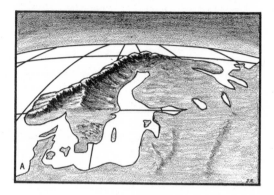

Fig. 179. Sketches showing the difference between the perspective-drawing type (at top) and the pictorial-map type (at bottom).

on an orthographic or near orthographic projection is not a map? Nevertheless, in the first category terrain is shown more realistically with more or less "true" perspective, whereas in the second terrain is shown more diagrammatically and the perspective of the whole is not correct. The relationship between them is shown by Fig. 179.

FIG. 180. A much reduced worksheet or "scrub sheet" of a perspective land-form drawing by Richard Edes Harrison. The map, for which this was the preliminary study, appeared in final form in *Fortune* magazine, 1942.

The perspective drawing has become popular in recent decades (see Fig. 180). Drawings of this type are usually done on an orthographic projection, or a near-orthographic, such as a photograph of the globe. The terrain is then modeled so that the earth's curvature is simulated and so that the entire drawing provides the impression of a view of the earth as seen from a point far above. Remarkably graphic (but not realistic) effects can be created with this method of terrain representation. They are particularly useful as illustrations of national viewpoints and of strategic concepts in a world that is growing smaller each year.

The student should have clearly in mind why pictorial terrain cannot be realistic but must exaggerate to a tremendous degree. Actual departures of the earth's surface up or down from the spheroid are very small, relative to horizontal distances, and

they can hardly be shown at all at most medium and small scales. For example, the highest mountain on the earth, Everest, is a bit over 29,000 feet above sea level, or only about 5½ miles. If the terrain of the continent of Asia were represented pictorially and accurately on a map with a scale of 1:10,000,000, Mount Everest would be only about ⅟₃₀ inch high! Consequently, almost all pictorial-terrain representation must greatly exaggerate and simplify the terrain. This introduces problems of selection and generalization, which make it absolutely necessary that the cartographer be relatively competent in the field of land-form geography.

One of the more distinctive contributions of American cartography is the pictorial map in which the terrain is represented schematically on a base map. Although this type of map is not limited to cartographers in the United States, it has reached

FIG. 181. A portion of a small-scale physiographic diagram by A. K. Lobeck. Courtesy of
the Geographical Press, Columbia University, New York.

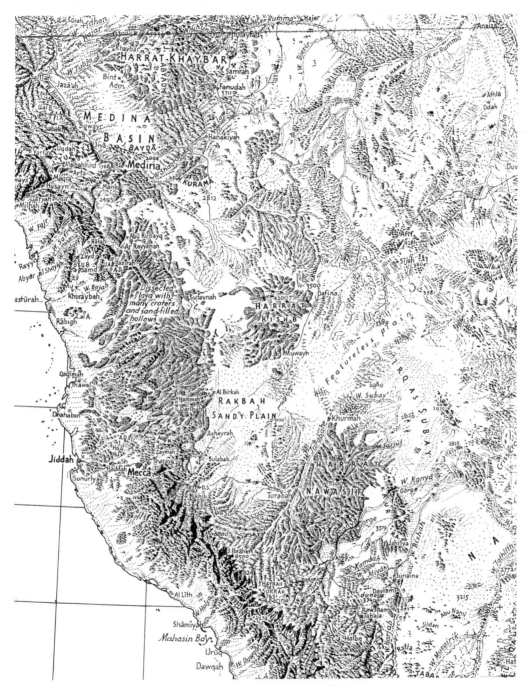

FIG. 182. A portion of a small-scale land-form map. From Landforms of Arabia by Erwin Raisz.

its highest development through the efforts of A. K. Lobeck, Erwin Raisz, Guy-Harold Smith, and a few others. Its origin is related to the earlier work of W. M. Davis, who developed terrain sketching and block diagramming to a high art.

The pictorial map of terrain is known by many names, depending upon the purpose of the map. Some are called physiographic diagrams, wherein the main aim is to present the surface forms in some relation to their genesis. The maps of A. K. Lobeck are of this type. In his maps he suggests by varying darkness and texture the major structural and rock-type differences having expression in the surface forms (see Fig 181).

Land-form, or land-type, maps are those in which more emphasis is given to the surface forms and less to their genesis. This type of map is exemplified by those of Erwin Raisz, who has developed a set of schematic symbols to represent the basic varieties of land forms and land types* (see Fig. 182).

There is, of course, no sharp distinction between the physiographic diagram and the land-form map. All possible combinations of emphasis on underlying structure, rock type, and process may be employed. Whatever the combination, the terrain is positioned on the map without perspective, but the terrain symbols are derived from their oblique appearance.

No treatment of pictorial terrain in cartography would be complete without mention of the block diagram from which the physiographic diagram stemmed. The block diagram has had a profound influence on terrain representation, and the cartographer can expect to be called upon to draw one occasionally. The block dia-

* See E. Raisz, "The Physiographic Method of Representing Scenery on Maps," *The Geographical Review*, 1931, Vol. 21, pp. 297–304; E. Raisz, *General Cartography*, 2nd Ed., McGraw-Hill Book Company, New York, 1948, pp. 120–121.

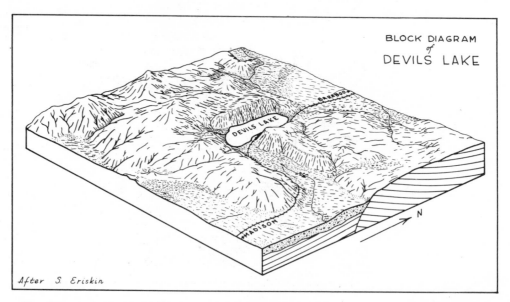

Fig. 183. A simple block diagram prepared for student field-trip use. The natural appearance of the surface forms on a perspective block makes the concepts easily understandable to anyone.

gram may be thought of as a small portion of a large perspective drawing of the earth, which has been removed as a block and enlarged to exhibit the detail. Commonly the underlying structure is placed on one face of the block in correct visual relation to the overlying topography, so that the relation between them is obvious. Almost any degree of elaborateness may be incorporated in a block diagram, ranging from the successive stages in the development of an area to multiple cross sections of the structure (see Fig. 183). For examples of these the reader is referred to the many works of W. M. Davis and A. K. Lobeck. The latter has produced a text which is required reading for anyone interested in developing his skill along this line.*

154 Other Methods of Depicting Land Surface

Perhaps the most widely used method of presenting land-surface information on wall maps, in atlases, and on other "physical" maps is that called by various names such as layer tinting, hypsometric coloring, or altitude tinting. This is the application of different area symbols (hue, pattern, or value) to the areas between the isometric lines (contours). On small-scale maps the simplification of the chosen contours must, of necessity, be large. Consequently, the "contour" lines on such maps are not particularly meaningful, and the system degenerates, so to speak, into a mere presentation of categories of surface elevation. It is an obvious fact that surface elevation is, in itself, of little consequence with regard to the character of third-order land forms. For example, much of the great plains of the United States lies at an elevation between 2,000 and 5,000 feet, yet a considerable proportion of it is as flat as any coastal plain. In contrast, most of

* A. K. Lobeck, *Block Diagrams*, John Wiley & Sons, New York, 1924.

mountainous Norway lies at an elevation of less than 5,000 feet. The conclusion is inescapable, namely, that layer tinting at small scales portrays little about the land surface except elevation zones. Such information is of value to an airplane pilot and to a number of others concerned with subjects, such as meteorology, wherein altitude is of some consequence. It is, however, of little value in presenting the significant differences or similarities of the land surface. It should be emphasized that the larger the scale, assuming a reasonable degree of contour simplification, the more useful the layer system. When the scale has been increased to the point at which the character of the isolines themselves and their relationships become meaningful, then the representation graduates to being a contour map, which is a most useful map.

The one concept, besides elevation, that the relief map does help to portray for large areas is that of the second-order, three-dimensional structure of a region. Thus, a relief map of South America shows clearly a ridge of high land near and paralleling the western coast. This may be useful to one who is familiar with geographic interrelationships, for he can speculate with some certainty regarding the climate, vegetation, drainage, occupance, and other possible consequences. To the uninitiated, however, simple layer tinting may well be meaningless.

Colored layer tints at small scales, when combined with pictorial terrain or shading, nearly satisfy most of the land-form requirements of the general map reader. It gives him the major structure as well as the detail. On the other hand, to do this is expensive, and it demands a skill not generally enjoyed by most cartographers. The Wenschow wall maps, previously mentioned, and the works of Richard Edes Harrison are outstanding examples of such combinations. Their reproduction is neces-

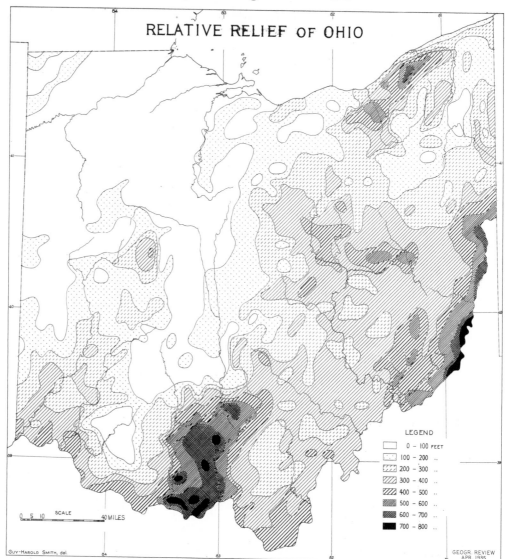

RELATIVE RELIEF OF OHIO

LEGEND

	0 – 100 FEET
	100 – 200 ..
	200 – 300 ..
	300 – 400 ..
	400 – 500 ..
	500 – 600 ..
	600 – 700 ..
	700 – 800 ..

SCALE
0 5 10   40 MILES

Guy-Harold Smith, del.

GEOGR. REVIEW
APR. 1935

FIG. 184. A relative- or local-relief map. The values were obtained for each 5′ quadrangle. The lines are isopleths. Drawn by Guy-Harold Smith, and reproduced by courtesy of *The Geographical Review*, published by the American Geographical Society of New York.

sarily by color process, or some equally expensive method, and their reproduction cost effectively removes them from the endeavors of the average cartographer. Even the inclusion of a sample in this book is out of the question.

Because of the relative inadequacy of the layer-tinting method for showing de-

tail, geographers have been searching for ways to present a more useful representation of the land surface. Several methods have been suggested:

1. Terrain unit or descriptive land-form-category method.
2. Relative-relief method.
3. Slope-value method.

With the possible exception of the first named, none has attained an acceptance that even approaches hachuring, shading, or layer tinting. The method of symbolization and presentation, which is the cartographer's major role, is straightforward; area symbols are used to reinforce either isograms or dasymetric lines. The major problem, inherent in these methods, is the determination of what to present, not how to present it. Consequently, to utilize these methods himself the cartographer must be essentially a geomorphologist, or he must simply present the work of others.

The terrain-unit method employs descriptive terms that range from the simple "mountains," "hills," or "plains" designations to complex, structural, topographic descriptions such as "maturely dissected hill land, developed on gently tilted sediments." The lines bounding the area symbols have no meaning other than being zones of change from one kind of area to another. This method of presenting land forms has been found useful in textbooks and in regional descriptions for a variety of purposes, ranging from military terrain analysis to regional planning. Its basic limitations are the regional knowledge of the maker and the geographical competence of the map reader.

In both Europe and the United States the concept of relative relief, as opposed to elevation above sea level, has been tried.* Relative, or local, relief is the difference between the highest and lowest elevations in a limited area, e.g., 5′ quadrangle (see Fig. 184). These values are then plotted on a map and isopleths drawn. Area sym-

bols, as in layer tinting, may also be applied. The method is of value when applied to areas of considerable size, for basic land form and physiographic divisions are emphasized; but it seems to be unsuited for differentiating important terrain details too small to extend beyond the confines of the unit area chosen for statistical purposes. It is best adapted to relatively small-scale representation.

From the time the hachure became popular, the cartographer and geographer have been concerned with the representation of the slope of the land. Hachuring and shading, although not particularly commensurable, provide a graphic account of slopes on medium- and large-scale maps. The problem of presenting actual slope values on small-scale maps is not easily solved. One technique, suggested by Raisz and Henry, is the slope-category method.* In this method, areas of similar slope are outlined and presented by means of area symbols (see Fig. 185). The system emphasizes detail, and the relationships between slopes and important minor topographic features are well presented, at the expense, however, of the major topographic features. In this respect it is somewhat the opposite of the relative-relief technique. Other slope techniques, such as per cent of flat land per unit area have been tried, but, except for specialized teaching or research purposes, they have not been widely used.

* See Guy-Harold Smith, "The Relative Relief of Ohio," *The Geographical Review*, 1935, Vol. 25, pp. 272–284.

* E. Raisz and J. Henry, "An Average Slope Map of Southern New England," *The Geographical Review*, 1937, Vol. 27, pp. 467–472. See also Glenn T. Trewartha and Guy-Harold Smith, "Surface Configuration of the Driftless Cuestaform Hill Land," *Annals of the Association of American Geographers*, Vol. 31, 1941, pp. 25–45; see map of average slope, p. 27.

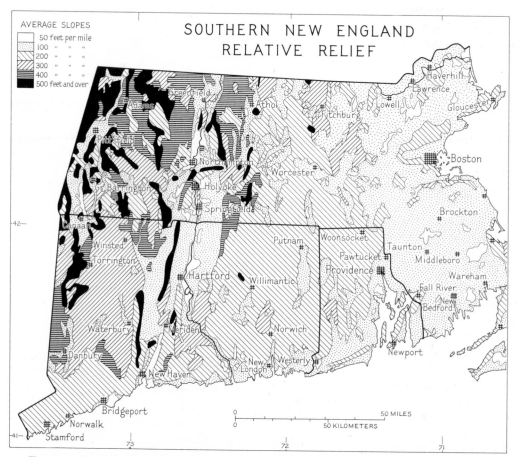

FIG. 185. A portion of a slope-value map by Raisz and Henry. The areas of similar slope were outlined on topographic maps by noting areas of consistent contour spacing. Courtesy of *The Geographical Review,* published by the American Geographical Society of New York.

Natural Trigonometric Functions

The following table gives the values of the *sine, cosine, tangent,* and *cotangent* of degrees from 0° to 90°. For degrees at the left use the column headings at the top; for degrees at the right use column headings at the bottom.

For fractions of degrees an appropriate amount of the difference between adjacent values may be used. For precise calculations, however, one should employ a more complete table and especially one showing the logarithms of the trigonometric functions.

The values of the *secant* and *cosecant* may be derived as follows: secant = 1 ÷ cos; cosecant = 1 ÷ sin.

TABLE 15. NATURAL TRIGONOMETRIC FUNCTIONS.

°	Sin	Tan	Cot	Cos	°	°	Sin	Tan	Cot	Cos	°
0	.0000	.0000	—	1.0000	90	23	.3907	.4245	2.356	.9205	67
1	.0174	.0175	57.290	.9998	89	24	.4067	.4452	2.246	.9135	66
2	.0349	.0349	28.636	.9994	88	25	.4226	.4663	2.144	.9063	65
3	.0523	.0524	19.081	.9986	87	26	.4384	.4877	2.050	.8988	64
4	.0698	.0699	14.301	.9976	86	27	.4540	.5095	1.963	.8910	63
5	.0872	.0875	11.430	.9962	85	28	.4695	.5317	1.881	.8829	62
6	.1045	.1051	9.514	.9945	84	29	.4848	.5543	1.804	.8746	61
7	.1219	.1228	8.144	.9925	83						
8	.1392	.1405	7.115	.9903	82	30	.5000	.5773	1.732	.8660	60
9	.1564	.1584	6.314	.9877	81	31	.5150	.6009	1.664	.8572	59
						32	.5299	.6249	1.600	.8480	58
10	.1736	.1763	5.671	.9848	80	33	.5446	.6494	1.540	.8387	57
11	.1908	.1944	5.145	.9816	79	34	.5592	.6745	1.483	.8290	56
12	.2079	.2126	4.705	.9781	78	35	.5736	.7002	1.428	.8191	55
13	.2249	.2309	4.331	.9744	77	36	.5878	.7265	1.376	.8090	54
14	.2419	.2493	4.011	.9703	76	37	.6018	.7535	1.327	.7986	53
15	.2588	.2679	3.732	.9659	75	38	.6157	.7813	1.280	.7880	52
16	.2756	.2867	3.487	.9613	74	39	.6293	.8098	1.235	.7771	51
17	.2924	.3057	3.271	.9563	73						
18	.3090	.3249	3.078	.9511	72	40	.6428	.8391	1.192	.7660	50
19	.3256	.3443	2.904	.9455	71	41	.6561	.8693	1.150	.7547	49
						42	.6691	.9004	1.111	.7431	48
20	.3420	.3640	2.747	.9397	70	43	.6820	.9325	1.072	.7313	47
21	.3584	.3839	2.605	.9336	69	44	.6947	.9657	1.035	.7193	46
22	.3746	.4040	2.475	.9272	68	45	.7071	1.0000	1.000	.7071	45
°	Cos	Cot	Tan	Sin	°	°	Cos	Cot	Tan	Sin	°

Appendix B

Squares, Cubes, and Roots

TABLE 16. SQUARES, CUBES, AND ROOTS.

n	n^2	$\sqrt{n}$	$\sqrt{10n}$	n^3	$\sqrt[3]{n}$	$\sqrt[3]{10n}$
1	1	1.000	3.162	1	1.000	2.154
2	4	1.414	4.472	8	1.260	2.714
3	9	1.732	5.477	27	1.442	3.107
4	16	2.000	6.325	64	1.587	3.420
5	25	2.236	7.071	125	1.710	3.684
6	36	2.449	7.746	216	1.817	3.915
7	49	2.646	8.367	343	1.913	4.121
8	64	2.828	8.944	512	2.000	4.309
9	81	3.000	9.487	729	2.080	4.481
10	100	3.162	10.000	1 000	2.154	4.642
11	121	3.317	10.488	1 331	2.224	4.791
12	144	3.464	10.954	1 728	2.289	4.932
13	169	3.606	11.402	2 197	2.351	5.066
14	196	3.742	11.832	2 744	2.410	5.192
15	225	3.873	12.247	3 375	2.466	5.313
16	256	4.000	12.649	4 096	2.520	5.429
17	289	4.123	13.038	4 913	2.571	5.540
18	324	4.243	13.416	5 832	2.621	5.646
19	361	4.359	13.784	6 859	2.668	5.749
20	400	4.472	14.142	8 000	2.714	5.848
21	441	4.583	14.491	9 261	2.759	5.944
22	484	4.690	14.832	10 648	2.802	6.037
23	529	4.796	15.166	12 167	2.844	6.127
24	576	4.899	15.492	13 824	2.884	6.214
25	625	5.000	15.811	15 625	2.924	6.300
26	676	5.099	16.125	17 576	2.962	6.383
27	729	5.196	16.432	19 683	3.000	6.463
28	784	5.292	16.733	21 952	3.037	6.542
29	841	5.385	17.029	24 389	3.072	6.619
30	900	5.477	17.321	27 000	3.107	6.694
31	961	5.568	17.607	29 791	3.141	6.768
32	1 024	5.657	17.889	32 768	3.175	6.840
33	1 089	5.745	18.166	35 937	3.208	6.910
34	1 156	5.831	18.439	39 304	3.240	6.980
35	1 225	5.916	18.708	42 875	3.271	7.047
36	1 296	6.000	18.974	46 656	3.302	7.114

TABLE 16. SQUARES, CUBES, AND ROOTS (*Continued*).

n	n^2	$\sqrt{n}$	$\sqrt{10n}$	n^3	$\sqrt[3]{n}$	$\sqrt[3]{10n}$
37	1 369	6.083	19.235	50 653	3.332	7.179
38	1 444	6.164	19.494	54 872	3.362	7.243
39	1 521	6.245	19.748	59 319	3.391	7.306
40	1 600	6.325	20.000	64 000	3.420	7.368
41	1 681	6.403	20.248	68 921	3.448	7.429
42	1 764	6.481	20.494	74 088	3.476	7.489
43	1 849	6.557	20.736	79 507	3.503	7.548
44	1 936	6.633	20.976	85 184	3.530	7.606
45	2 025	6.708	21.213	91 125	3.557	7.663
46	2 116	6.782	21.448	97 336	3.583	7.719
47	2 209	6.856	21.679	103 823	3.609	7.775
48	2 304	6.928	21.909	110 592	3.634	7.830
49	2 401	7.000	22.136	117 649	3.659	7.884
50	2 500	7.071	22.361	125 000	3.684	7.937
51	2 601	7.141	22.583	132 651	3.708	7.990
52	2 704	7.211	22.804	140 608	3.733	8.041
53	2 809	7.280	23.022	148 877	3.756	8.093
54	2 916	7.348	23.238	157 464	3.780	8.143
55	3 025	7.416	23.452	166 375	3.803	8.193
56	3 136	7.483	23.664	175 616	3.826	8.243
57	3 249	7.550	23.875	185 193	3.849	8.291
58	3 364	7.616	24.083	195 112	3.871	8.340
59	3 481	7.681	24.290	205 379	3.893	8.387
60	3 600	7.746	24.495	216 000	3.915	8.434
61	3 721	7.810	24.698	226 981	3.936	8.481
62	3 844	7.874	24.900	238 328	3.958	8.527
63	3 969	7.937	25.100	250 047	3.979	8.573
64	4 096	8.000	25.298	262 144	4.000	8.618
65	4 225	8.062	25.495	274 625	4.021	8.662
66	4 356	8.124	25.690	287 496	4.041	8.707
67	4 489	8.185	25.884	300 763	4.062	8.750
68	4 624	8.246	26.077	314 432	4.082	8.794
69	4 761	8.307	26.268	328 509	4.102	8.837
70	4 900	8.367	26.458	343 000	4.121	8.879
71	5 041	8.426	26.646	357 911	4.141	8.921
72	5 184	8.485	26.833	373 248	4.160	8.963
73	5 329	8.544	27.019	389 017	4.179	9.004
74	5 476	8.602	27.203	405 224	4.198	9.045
75	5 625	8.660	27.386	421 875	4.217	9.086
76	5 776	8.718	27.568	438 976	4.236	9.126
77	5 929	8.775	27.749	456 533	4.254	9.166
78	6 084	8.832	27.928	474 552	4.273	9.205
79	6 241	8.888	28.107	493 039	4.291	9.244
80	6 400	8.944	28.284	512 000	4.309	9.283

TABLE 16.   SQUARES, CUBES, AND ROOTS (*Continued*).

n	n^2	$\sqrt{n}$	$\sqrt{10n}$	n^3	$\sqrt[3]{n}$	$\sqrt[3]{10n}$
81	6 561	9.000	28.461	531 441	4.327	9.322
82	6 724	9.055	28.636	551 368	4.344	9.360
83	6 889	9.110	28.810	571 787	4.362	9.398
84	7 056	9.165	28.983	592 704	4.380	9.435
85	7 225	9.220	29.155	614 125	4.397	9.473
86	7 396	9.274	29.326	636 056	4.414	9.510
87	7 569	9.327	29.496	658 503	4.431	9.546
88	7 744	9.381	29.665	681 472	4.448	9.583
89	7 921	9.434	29.833	704 969	4.465	9.619
90	8 100	9.487	30.000	729 000	4.481	9.655
91	8 281	9.539	30.166	753 571	4.498	9.691
92	8 464	9.592	30.332	778 688	4.514	9.726
93	8 649	9.644	30.496	804 357	4.531	9.761
94	8 836	9.695	30.659	830 584	4.547	9.796
95	9 025	9.747	30.822	857 375	4.563	9.830
96	9 216	9.798	30.984	884 736	4.579	9.865
97	9 409	9.849	31.145	912 673	4.595	9.899
98	9 604	9.899	31.305	941 192	4.610	9.933
99	9 801	9.950	31.464	970 299	4.626	9.967
100	10 000	10.000	31.623	1 000 000	4.642	10.000

Appendix C

Geographical Tables*

TABLE 17. LENGTHS OF DEGREES OF THE PARALLEL.

Lat.	Meters	Statute miles	Lat.	Meters	Statute miles	Lat.	Meters	Statute miles
° ′			° ′			° ′		
0 00	111 321	69.172	30 00	96 488	59.956	60 00	55 802	34.674
1 00	111 304	69.162	31 00	95 506	59.345	61 00	54 110	33.623
2 00	111 253	69.130	32 00	94 495	58.716	62 00	52 400	32.560
3 00	111 169	69.078	33 00	93 455	58.071	63 00	50 675	31.488
4 00	111 051	69.005	34 00	92 387	57.407	64 00	48 934	30.406
5 00	110 900	68.911	35 00	91 290	56.725	65 00	47 177	29.315
6 00	110 715	68.795	36 00	90 166	56.027	66 00	45 407	28.215
7 00	110 497	68.660	37 00	89 014	55.311	67 00	43 622	27.106
8 00	110 245	68.504	38 00	87 835	54.579	68 00	41 823	25.988
9 00	109 959	68.326	39 00	86 629	53.829	69 00	40 012	24.862
10 00	109 641	68.129	40 00	85 396	53.063	70 00	38 188	23.729
11 00	109 289	67.910	41 00	84 137	52.281	71 00	36 353	22.589
12 00	108 904	67.670	42 00	82 853	51.483	72 00	34 506	21.441
13 00	108 486	67.410	43 00	81 543	50.669	73 00	32 648	20.287
14 00	108 036	67.131	44 00	80 208	49.840	74 00	30 781	19.127
15 00	107 553	66.830	45 00	78 849	48.995	75 00	28 903	17.960
16 00	107 036	66.510	46 00	77 466	48.136	76 00	27 017	16.788
17 00	106 487	66.169	47 00	76 058	47.261	77 00	25 123	15.611
18 00	105 906	65.808	48 00	74 628	46.372	78 00	23 220	14.428
19 00	105 294	65.427	49 00	73 174	45.469	79 00	21 311	13.242
20 00	104 649	65.026	50 00	71 698	44.552	80 00	19 394	12.051
21 00	103 972	64.606	51 00	70 200	43.621	81 00	17 472	10.857
22 00	103 264	64.166	52 00	68 680	42.676	82 00	15 545	9.659
23 00	102 524	63.706	53 00	67 140	41.719	83 00	13 612	8.458
24 00	101 754	63.228	54 00	65 578	40.749	84 00	11 675	7.255
25 00	100 952	62.729	55 00	63 996	39.766	85 00	9 735	6.049
26 00	100 119	62.212	56 00	62 395	38.771	86 00	7 792	4.842
27 00	99 257	61.676	57 00	60 774	37.764	87 00	5 846	3.632
28 00	98 364	61.122	58 00	59 135	36.745	88 00	3 898	2.422
29 00	97 441	60.548	59 00	57 478	35.716	89 00	1 949	1.211
						90 00	0	0

*Tables 17 and 18 are from U.S. Coast and Geodetic Survey; Table 19 is from *Smithsonian Geographical Tables*.

TABLE 18.   LENGTHS OF DEGREES OF THE MERIDIAN.

Lat.	Meters	Statute miles	Lat.	Meters	Statute miles	Lat.	Meters	Statute miles
°			°			°		
0–1	110 567.3	68.703	30–31	110 857.0	68.883	60–61	111 423.1	69.235
1–2	110 568.0	68.704	31–32	110 874.4	68.894	61–62	111 439.9	69.246
2–3	110 569.4	68.705	32–33	110 892.1	68.905	62–63	111 456.4	69.256
3–4	110 571.4	68.706	33–34	110 910.1	68.916	63–64	111 472.4	69.266
4–5	110 574.1	68.707	34–35	110 928.3	68.928	64–65	111 488.1	69.275
5–6	110 577.6	68.710	35–36	110 946.9	68.939	65–66	111 503.3	69.285
6–7	110 581.6	68.712	36–37	110 965.6	68.951	66–67	111 518.0	69.294
7–8	110 586.4	68.715	37–38	110 984.5	68.962	67–68	111 532.3	69.303
8–9	110 591.8	68.718	38–39	111 003.7	68.974	68–69	111 546.2	69.311
9–10	110 597.8	68.722	39–40	111 023.0	68.986	69–70	111 559.5	69.320
10–11	110 604.5	68.726	40–41	111 042.4	68.998	70–71	111 572.2	69.328
11–12	110 611.9	68.731	41–42	111 061.9	69.011	71–72	111 584.5	69.335
12–13	110 619.8	68.736	42–43	111 081.6	69.023	72–73	111 596.2	69.343
13–14	110 628.4	68.741	43–44	111 101.3	69.035	73–74	111 607.3	69.349
14–15	110 637.6	68.747	44–45	111 121.0	69.047	74–75	111 617.9	69.356
15–16	110 647.5	68.753	45–46	111 140.8	69.060	75–76	111 627.8	69.362
16–17	110 657.8	68.759	46–47	111 160.5	69.072	76–77	111 637.1	69.368
17–18	110 668.8	68.766	47–48	111 180.2	69.084	77–78	111 645.9	69.373
18–19	110 680.4	68.773	48–49	111 199.9	69.096	78–79	111 653.9	69.378
19–20	110 692.4	68.781	49–50	111 219.5	69.108	79–80	111 661.4	69.383
20–21	110 705.1	68.789	50–51	111 239.0	69.121	80–81	111 668.2	69.387
21–22	110 718.2	68.797	51–52	111 258.3	69.133	81–82	111 674.4	69.391
22–23	110 731.8	68.805	52–53	111 277.6	69.145	82–83	111 679.9	69.395
23–24	110 746.0	68.814	53–54	111 296.6	69.156	83–84	111 684.7	69.398
24–25	110 760.6	68.823	54–55	111 315.4	69.168	84–85	111 688.9	69.400
25–26	110 775.6	68.833	55–56	111 334.0	69.180	85–86	111 692.3	69.402
26–27	110 791.1	68.842	56–57	111 352.4	69.191	86–87	111 695.1	69.404
27–28	110 807.0	68.852	57–58	111 370.5	69.202	87–88	111 697.2	69.405
28–29	110 823.3	68.862	58–59	111 388.4	69.213	88–89	111 698.6	69.406
29–30	110 840.0	68.873	59–60	111 405.9	69.224	89–90	111 699.3	69.407

TABLE 19.   AREAS OF QUADRILATERALS OF EARTH'S SURFACE OF 1° EXTENT IN LATITUDE AND LONGITUDE.

Lower latitude of quadrilateral °	Area in square miles	Lower latitude of quadrilateral °	Area in square miles
0	4 752.16	45	3 354.01
1	4 750.75	46	3 294.71
2	4 747.93	47	3 234.39
3	4 743.71	48	3 173.04
4	4 738.08	49	3 110.69
5	4 731.04		
6	4 722.61	50	3 047.37
7	4 712.76	51	2 983.08
8	4 701.52	52	2 917.85
9	4 688.89	53	2 851.68
		54	2 784.62
10	4 674.86	55	2 716.67
11	4 659.43	56	2 647.85
12	4 642.63	57	2 578.19
13	4 624.44	58	2 507.70
14	4 604.87	59	2 436.42
15	4 583.92		
16	4 561.61	60	2 364.34
17	4 537.93	61	2 291.51
18	4 512.90	62	2 217.94
19	4 486.51	63	2 143.66
		64	2 068.68
20	4 458.78	65	1 993.04
21	4 429.71	66	1 916.75
22	4 399.30	67	1 839.84
23	4 367.57	68	1 762.33
24	4 334.52	69	1 684.24
25	4 300.17		
26	4 264.51	70	1 605.62
27	4 227.56	71	1 526.46
28	4 189.33	72	1 446.81
29	4 149.83	73	1 366.69
		74	1 286.12
30	4 109.06	75	1 205.13
31	4 067.05	76	1 123.75
32	4 023.79	77	1 041.99
33	3 979.30	78	959.90
34	3 933.59	79	877.49
35	3 886.67		
36	3 838.56	80	794.79
37	3 789.26	81	711.83
38	3 738.80	82	628.64
39	3 687.18	83	545.24
		84	461.66
40	3 634.42	85	377.93
41	3 580.54	86	294.08
42	3 525.54	87	210.12
43	3 469.44	88	126.10
44	3 412.26	89	42.04

Appendix D

Tissot's Indicatrix

The law of deformation was developed by M. A. Tissot, and appears in full in his *Mémoire sur la représentation des surfaces et les projections des cartes géographiques*, Paris, 1881, which includes 60 pages of deformation tables for various projections. An account of it appears in English in Oscar S. Adams, "General Theory of Polyconic Projections," U.S. Coast and Geodetic Survey *Special Publication 57*, Washington, D. C. 1934, pp. 153–163. The following account is based in the main on the explanation by F. J. Marschner and is used by permission of the *Annals of the Association of American Geographers*.

The Law of Deformation

Tissot demonstrated that when a spherical surface is transformed into a plane surface there occurs more or less transformation of the angles and surface areas around each point. On the sphere there are at each point on the surface an infinite number of tangents each of which, of course, represents a direction on the sphere. The law of deformation states that, whatever the system of representation, *there are at each point of the spherical surface at least two tangents perpendicular to each other which will reappear at right angles to each other on the projection*, although all the other angles at that point are altered from their original position. An infinitely small circle, the center of which is the intersecting point of the tangents on the spherical surface, will be deformed on the projection and become an ellipse. The two perpendicular diameters of the circle, which retain their relative positions on the projection, constitute then the major and minor axes of the ellipse. The function of the ellipse is that of an indicator in that it provides comparable values with reference to the original circle. The ellipse is on that account referred to as the indicatory ellipse or the indicatrix.

For the purpose of comparing alterations in the linear and angular elements on different projections, only the maximums for each point are needed. The semimajor and semiminor axes of the indicatrix denote the maximum changes in scale, and at the same time provide the necessary data for determining the angular deformation and the areal exaggeration. The semimajor axis, $OA = a$ (Fig. 186), and the semiminor axis, $OB = b$, are expressed numerically in terms proportionate to unity, this being the radius of the original circle, $r = OM = 1$.

All points in the circumference of the circle necessarily have their counterparts in the periphery of the ellipse, but only one point within a quadrant is subjected to the maximum angular deflection from its original position with reference to the coordinates of the quadrant. The point subjected to the greatest deflection is identified in the circumference of the circle with M, and has its counterpart in the periphery of the ellipse in point M'. As a consequence, the original angle $MOA = U$ is altered to $M'OA = U'$, and the difference of these two angles, $U - U' = \omega$, denotes the maximum possible angular deflection within one quadrant.

If an angle were to have its sides located in two quadrants and if they were to occupy the position of maximum change in both directions, then the angle in question would incur the maximum deflection for one quadrant on both sides, so that 2ω denotes the possible maximum angular change that may occur at a point.

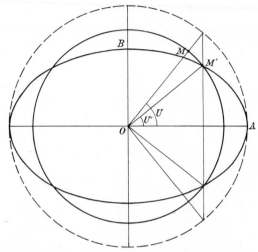

Fig. 186. The indicatrix in the above illustration has been constructed as an equal-area representation of the circle to which the following indices apply: $OM = r = 1$; $OA = a = 1.25$; $OB = b = 0.80$; $MOA = U = 51° 21' 40''$; $M'OA = U' = 38° 39' 35''$; $U - U' = \omega = 12° 40' 50''$; $2\omega = 25° 21' 40''$; $ab = S = 1.25 \times 0.80 = 1$. From Marschner.

Changes in the surface area may or may not be a corollary to the transformation of the circle into an ellipse. If there has been a change in the surface area its magnitude can be readily established by comparing the areal contents of the original circle with that of the indicatrix. The area of the circle is $r^2\pi$, while the area of the ellipse is $ab\pi$. Therefore, since the axes of the indicatrix are based on the unit circle in which $r = 1$ and since π is a constant, the product of $ab = S$ fully expresses the areal relationship between the ellipse and the circle. For the purpose of comparing map projections only a, b, 2ω, and S are needed as indices, and if the condition of equivalence is satisfied even S can be omitted.

In the preceding, the discussion of the indicatrix has been based on the supposition that the original circle always appears in the representation in the standard form of an ellipse; this is not necessarily true. On conformal projections the scale, by definition, is the same in every direction at a point. The scale differs, however, from point to point. It will be equal to unity at some points; it will be greater or less at others; but it will always be the same in every direction around a point. That is to say, $a = b$. Hence, the angular relations around a point will be the same on a conformal projection as they are on the sphere. On conformal projections the indicatrix thus appears in the form of a circle, but the indicatrix will differ in size from the original circle. Only on standard lines or at standard points represented without exaggeration is the original size retained in the representation. Under these circumstances, the indicatrix can be considered as a special case of the ellipse in which a equals b, but does not equal 1. With a and b being equal, the index of areal change is derived from the square of the radius of the indicatrix, $S = a^2$.

Appendix E

Lambert Projection Tables

TABLE 20. TABLE FOR THE CONSTRUCTION OF A LAMBERT AZIMUTHAL EQUAL-AREA PROJECTION CENTERED ON THE EQUATOR. COORDINATES IN UNITS OF THE EARTH'S RADIUS ($R = 1$). (From Deetz and Adams.)

Lat.	Long. 0° x	Long. 0° y	Long. 10° x	Long. 10° y	Long. 20° x	Long. 20° y	Long. 30° x	Long. 30° y	Long. 40° x	Long. 40° y
0°	0	0.000	0.174	0.000	0.347	0.000	0.518	0.000	0.684	0.000
10°	0	0.174	0.172	0.175	0.343	0.177	0.512	0.180	0.676	0.185
20°	0	0.347	0.166	0.349	0.331	0.352	0.493	0.359	0.651	0.369
30°	0	0.518	0.156	0.519	0.311	0.525	0.463	0.535	0.610	0.548
40°	0	0.684	0.142	0.686	0.283	0.693	0.420	0.705	0.553	0.722
50°	0	0.845	0.124	0.848	0.245	0.855	0.364	0.868	0.478	0.887
60°	0	1.000	0.101	1.003	0.199	1.010	0.295	1.023	0.386	1.041
70°	0	1.147	0.073	1.149	0.144	1.156	0.212	1.167	0.277	1.183
80°	0	1.286	0.039	1.287	0.078	1.291	0.114	1.299	0.148	1.308
90°	0	1.414	0.000	1.414	0.000	1.414	0.000	1.414	0.000	1.414

Lat.	Long. 50° x	Long. 50° y	Long. 60° x	Long. 60° y	Long. 70° x	Long. 70° y	Long. 80° x	Long. 80° y	Long. 90° x	Long. 90° y
0°	0.845	0.000	1.000	0.000	1.147	0.000	1.286	0.000	1.414	0.000
10°	0.835	0.192	0.987	0.201	1.132	0.212	1.267	0.227	1.393	0.246
20°	0.804	0.382	0.949	0.399	1.086	0.421	1.213	0.448	1.329	0.484
30°	0.752	0.567	0.886	0.591	1.011	0.621	1.125	0.659	1.225	0.707
40°	0.679	0.744	0.798	0.773	0.906	0.809	1.002	0.854	1.083	0.909
50°	0.586	0.911	0.685	0.942	0.773	0.981	0.849	1.028	0.909	1.083
60°	0.471	1.065	0.548	1.095	0.614	1.132	0.668	1.175	0.707	1.225
70°	0.335	1.203	0.387	1.228	0.430	1.257	0.463	1.291	0.484	1.329
80°	0.178	1.321	0.204	1.336	0.224	1.353	0.238	1.372	0.246	1.393
90°	0.000	1.414	0.000	1.414	0.000	1.414	0.000	1.414	0.000	1.414

TABLE 21. TABLE FOR THE CONSTRUCTION OF A LAMBERT EQUAL-AREA PROJECTION CENTERED AT LATITUDE 40°. COORDINATES IN UNITS OF THE EARTH'S RADIUS ($R = 1$). (Adapted from Deetz and Adams.)

Lat.	Long. 0° x	Long. 0° y	Long. 10° x	Long. 10° y	Long. 20° x	Long. 20° y	Long. 30° x	Long. 30° y	Long. 40° x	Long. 40° y
90°	0	+0.845	0.000	+0.845	0.000	+0.845	0.000	+0.845	0.000	+0.845
80°	0	+0.684	0.032	+0.686	0.063	+0.692	0.093	+0.704	0.120	+0.718
70°	0	+0.518	0.062	+0.521	0.121	+0.533	0.175	+0.553	0.231	+0.580
60°	0	+0.347	0.082	+0.352	0.174	+0.369	0.257	+0.396	0.334	+0.434
50°	0	+0.174	0.112	+0.181	0.222	+0.200	0.328	+0.234	0.427	+0.280
40°	0	0.000	0.133	+0.007	0.264	+0.029	0.391	+0.067	0.510	+0.120
30°	0	−0.174	0.151	−0.166	0.300	−0.142	0.445	−0.102	0.582	−0.045
20°	0	−0.347	0.166	−0.338	0.329	−0.313	0.489	−0.272	0.642	−0.214
10°	0	−0.518	0.177	−0.509	0.353	−0.484	0.524	−0.442	0.689	−0.383
0°	0	−0.684	0.185	−0.675	0.369	−0.651	0.548	−0.610	0.722	−0.553
−10°	0	−0.845	—	—	—	—	—	—	—	—

Lat.	Long. 50° x	Long. 50° y	Long. 60° x	Long. 60° y	Long. 70° x	Long. 70° y	Long. 80° x	Long. 80° y	Long. 90° x	Long. 90° y	Long. 100° x	Long. 100° y
90°	0.000	+0.845	0.000	+0.845	0.000	+0.845	0.000	+0.845	0.000	+0.845	0.000	+0.845
80°	0.143	+0.736	0.163	+0.758	0.178	+0.782	0.188	+0.808	0.192	+0.834	—	—
70°	0.278	+0.613	0.318	+0.646	0.349	+0.701	0.371	+0.751	0.382	+0.804	—	—
60°	0.403	+0.481	0.463	+0.538	0.511	+0.602	0.547	+0.674	0.567	+0.752	0.570	+0.833
50°	0.518	+0.338	0.583	+0.408	0.663	+0.489	0.713	+0.580	0.744	+0.679	0.755	+0.785
40°	0.620	+0.186	0.702	+0.267	0.801	+0.361	—	—	—	—	—	—
30°	0.710	−0.027	0.825	+0.115	—	—	—	—	—	—	—	—
20°	0.785	−0.138	—	—	—	—	—	—	—	—	—	—
10°	0.844	−0.307	—	—	—	—	—	—	—	—	—	—
0°	0.887	−0.478	—	—	—	—	—	—	—	—	—	—

Appendix F

Stereographic Projection Tables

Professor James A. Barnes has worked out a simplified method of calculating tables for constructing the stereographic projection. Anyone who can read values from a table of logarithms of the trigonometric functions can compute values for a projection centered on any point on the sphere. The formulas originally appeared in *Surveying and Mapping*. The symbols are:

α = angle of tilt (position of center).
ϕ = latitude.
λ = longitude.
U = upper intersection of parallel with central meridian.
L = lower intersection of parallel with central meridian.
Q = intersection of homolatitude of center point and central meridian.
N = intersection of meridian and homolatitude.
M = center of meridian arc on homolatitude.

Calculation of the position of the parallels:

For north latitudes and equator: $U = + \tan \frac{1}{2}(180° - \phi - \alpha)$.
For south latitudes less than α: $U = + \tan \frac{1}{2}(180° + \phi - \alpha)$.
For south latitudes greater than α: $U = - \tan \frac{1}{2}(\phi + \alpha)$.
For north latitudes greater than α: $L = + \tan \frac{1}{2}(\phi - \alpha)$.
For north latitudes less than α and equator: $L = - \tan \frac{1}{2}(\alpha - \phi)$.

For south latitudes less than α: $L = - \tan \frac{1}{2}(\phi + \alpha)$.
For south latitudes greater than α: $L = - \tan \frac{1}{2}(180° + \alpha - \phi)$.

Note: Plus and minus signs indicate whether the value is above or below the center of the projection. The center of any parallel is midway between U and L.

Calculation of the position of the meridians:

$Q = - \tan \alpha$.
$N = \sec \alpha \cdot \tan \frac{1}{2}\lambda$.
$M = \sec \alpha \cdot \cot \lambda$.

Note: N and M correspond to *Bow* and *Center* values in the following tables.

The following tables have been computed (by J. A. Barnes) for projections centered at 10°-latitude intervals (the table for 40° appears in Article 66), and will be sufficient for most purposes of small-scale maps, where the stereographic is desired as an end, or as a means to an end as suggested in Articles 69 and 70. For large-scale and precision work the formulas above should be used to compute values for the exact center.

Values in the tables and those resulting from the above formulas are for a globe with a diameter of unity ($D = 1$). To determine figures to scale multiply each calculation by the diameter of the generating globe of chosen scale.

Directions for the use of the tables appear in Article 66.

TABLE 22. TABLE FOR CONSTRUCTING THE STEREOGRAPHIC PROJECTION CENTERED ON $0°$.

TABLE 23. TABLE FOR CONSTRUCTING THE STEREOGRAPHIC PROJECTION CENTERED ON $10°$.

$D = 1$

$D = 1$

Parallels	Upper		Lower	Parallels	Upper		Lower
North pole		1.00000		North pole		0.83910	
80°	1.19175		0.83910	80°	1.00000		0.70021
70°	1.42815		0.70021	70°	1.19175		0.57735
60°	1.73205		0.57735	60°	1.42815		0.46631
50°	2.14451		0.46631	50°	1.73205		0.36397
40°	2.74748		0.36397	40°	2.14451		0.26795
30°	3.73205		0.26795	30°	2.74748		0.17633
20°	5.67128		0.17633	20°	3.73205		0.08749
10°	11.43005		0.08749	10°	5.67128		0.00000
0°	0.00000	0.00000	0.00000	0°	11.43005		−0.08749
10°	−0.08749		−11.43005	10°	−0.17633	−0.17633	−0.17633
20°	−0.17633		−5.67128	20°	−0.26795		−11.43005
30°	−0.26795		−3.73205	30°	−0.36397		−5.67128
40°	−0.36397		−2.74748	40°	−0.46631		−3.73205
50°	−0.46631		−2.14451	50°	−0.57735		−2.74748
60°	−0.57735		−1.73205	60°	−0.70021		−2.14451
70°	−0.70021		−1.42815	70°	−0.83910		−1.73205
80°	−0.83910		−1.19175	80°	−1.00000		−1.42815
South pole		−1.00000		South pole		−1.19175	

$H = 0.00000$

$H = -0.17633$

Meridians	Bow	Center	Meridians	Bow	Center
10°	0.08749	5.67128	10°	0.08884	5.75876
20°	0.17633	2.74748	20°	0.17905	2.78986
30°	0.26795	1.73205	30°	0.27208	1.75877
40°	0.36397	1.19175	40°	0.36958	1.21014
50°	0.46631	0.83910	50°	0.47350	0.85204
60°	0.57735	0.57735	60°	0.58626	0.58626
70°	0.70021	0.36397	70°	0.71101	0.36958
80°	0.83910	0.17633	80°	0.85204	0.17905
90°	1.00000	0.00000	90°	1.01543	0.00000

TABLE 24. TABLE FOR CONSTRUCTING THE STERE-
OGRAPHIC PROJECTION CENTERED ON 20°.

TABLE 25. TABLE FOR CONSTRUCTING THE STERE-
OGRAPHIC PROJECTION CENTERED ON 30°.

$D = 1$

$D = 1$

Parallels	Upper		Lower	Parallels	Upper		Lower
North pole		0.70021		North pole		0.57735	
80°	0.83910		0.57735	80°	0.70021		0.46631
70°	1.00000		0.46631	70°	0.83910		0.36397
60°	1.19175		0.36397	60°	1.00000		0.26795
50°	1.42815		0.26795	50°	1.19175		0.17633
40°	1.73205		0.17633	40°	1.42815		0.08749
30°	2.14451		0.08749	30°	1.73205		0.00000
20°	2.74748		0.00000	20°	2.14451		−0.08749
10°	3.73205		−0.08749	10°	2.74748		−0.17633
0°	5.67128		−0.17633	0°	3.73205		−0.26795
10°	11.43005		−0.26795	10°	5.67128		−0.36397
20°	−0.36397	−0.36397	−0.36397	20°	11.43005		−0.46631
30°	−0.46631		−11.43005	30°	−0.57735	−0.57735	−0.57735
40°	−0.57735		−5.67128	40°	−0.70021		−11.43005
50°	−0.70021		−3.73205	50°	−0.83910		−5.67128
60°	−0.83910		−2.74748	60°	−1.00000		−3.73205
70°	−1.00000		−2.14451	70°	−1.19175		−2.74748
80°	−1.19175		−1.73205	80°	−1.42815		−2.14451
South pole		−1.42815		South pole		−1.73205	

$H = -0.36397$

$H = -0.57735$

Meridians	Bow	Center	Meridians	Bow	Center
10°	0.09310	6.03526	10°	0.10103	6.54863
20°	0.18764	2.92381	20°	0.20360	3.17251
30°	0.28515	1.84321	30°	0.30940	2.00000
40°	0.38733	1.26824	40°	0.42028	1.37295
50°	0.49624	0.89295	50°	0.53845	0.96891
60°	0.61440	0.61440	60°	0.66667	0.66667
70°	0.74515	0.38733	70°	0.80853	0.42028
80°	0.89295	0.18764	80°	0.96891	0.20360
90°	1.06418	0.00000	90°	1.15470	0.00000

TABLE 26. TABLE FOR CONSTRUCTING THE STERE-
OGRAPHIC PROJECTION CENTERED ON 50°.

$D = 1$

Parallels	Upper		Lower
North pole		0.36397	
80°	0.46631		0.26795
70°	0.57735		0.17633
60°	0.70021		0.08749
50°	0.83910		0.00000
40°	1.00000		−0.08749
30°	1.19175		−0.17633
20°	1.42815		−0.26795
10°	1.73205		−0.36397
0°	2.14451		−0.46631
10°	2.74748		−0.57735
20°	3.73205		−0.70021
30°	5.67128		−0.83910
40°	11.43005		−1.00000
50°	−1.19175	−1.19175	−1.19175
60°	−1.42815		−11.43005
70°	−1.73205		−5.67128
80°	−2.14451		−3.73205
South pole		−2.74748	

$H = -1.19175$

Meridians	Bow	Center
10°	0.13611	8.82296
20°	0.27432	4.27432
30°	0.41686	2.69460
40°	0.56624	1.85404
50°	0.72545	1.30541
60°	0.89820	0.89820
70°	1.08933	0.56624
80°	1.30541	0.27432
90°	1.55572	0.00000

TABLE 27. TABLE FOR CONSTRUCTING THE STERE-
OGRAPHIC PROJECTION CENTERED ON 60°.

$D = 1$

Parallels	Upper		Lower
North pole		0.26795	
80°	0.36397		0.17633
70°	0.46631		0.08749
60°	0.57735		0.00000
50°	0.70021		−0.08749
40°	0.83910		−0.17633
30°	1.00000		−0.26795
20°	1.19175		−0.36397
10°	1.42815		−0.46631
0°	1.73205		−0.57735
10°	2.14451		−0.70021
20°	2.74748		−0.83910
30°	3.73205		−1.00000
40°	5.67128		−1.19175
50°	11.43005		−1.42815
60°	−1.73205	−1.73205	−1.73205
70°	−2.14451		−11.43005
80°	−2.74748		−5.67128
South pole		−3.73205	

$H = -1.73205$

Meridians	Bow	Center
10°	0.17498	11.34230
20°	0.35265	5.49495
30°	0.53590	3.46410
40°	0.72794	2.38351
50°	0.93262	1.67820
60°	1.15470	1.15470
70°	1.40042	0.72794
80°	1.67820	0.35265
90°	2.00000	0.00000

TABLE 28. TABLE FOR CONSTRUCTING THE STEREOGRAPHIC PROJECTION CENTERED ON 70°.

$D = 1$

Parallels	Upper		Lower
North pole		0.17633	
80°	0.26795		0.08749
70°	0.36397		0.00000
60°	0.46631		−0.08749
50°	0.57735		−0.17633
40°	0.70021		−0.26795
30°	0.83910		−0.36397
20°	1.00000		−0.46631
10°	1.19175		−0.57735
0°	1.42815		−0.70021
10°	1.73205		−0.83910
20°	2.14451		−1.00000
30°	2.74748		−1.19175
40°	3.73205		−1.42815
50°	5.67128		−1.73205
60°	11.43005		−2.14451
70°	−2.74748	−2.74748	−2.74748
80°	−3.73205		−11.43005
South pole		−5.67128	

$H = -2.74748$

Meridians	Bow	Center
10°	0.25580	16.58172
20°	0.51555	8.03309
30°	0.78343	5.06418
40°	1.06418	3.48446
50°	1.36339	2.45336
60°	1.68806	1.68806
70°	2.04727	1.06418
80°	2.45336	0.51555
90°	2.92381	0.00000

TABLE 29. TABLE FOR CONSTRUCTING THE STEREOGRAPHIC PROJECTION CENTERED ON 80°.

$D = 1$

Parallels	Upper		Lower
North pole		0.08749	
80°	0.17633		0.00000
70°	0.26795		−0.08749
60°	0.36397		−0.17633
50°	0.46631		−0.26795
40°	0.57735		−0.36397
30°	0.70021		−0.46631
20°	0.83910		−0.57735
10°	1.00000		−0.70021
0°	1.19175		−0.83910
10°	1.42815		−1.00000
20°	1.73205		−1.19175
30°	2.14451		−1.42815
40°	2.74748		−1.73205
50°	3.73205		−2.14451
60°	5.67128		−2.74748
70°	11.43005		−3.73205
80°	−5.67128	−5.67128	−5.67128
South pole		−11.43005	

$H = -5.67128$

Meridians	Bow	Center
10°	0.50383	32.65958
20°	1.01543	15.82208
30°	1.54306	9.97447
40°	2.09602	6.86303
50°	2.68536	4.83228
60°	3.32483	3.32483
70°	4.03233	2.09602
80°	4.83228	1.01543
90°	5.75877	0.00000

TABLE 30. TABLE FOR CONSTRUCTING THE STEREOGRAPHIC PROJECTION CENTERED ON 90°.

$D = 1$

Parallels	Upper		Lower	Parallels	Upper	Lower
North pole		0		30°	1.73205	−1.73205
80°	0.08749		−0.08749	40°	2.14451	−2.14451
70°	0.17633		−0.17633	50°	2.74748	−2.74748
60°	0.26795		−0.26795	60°	3.73205	−3.73205
50°	0.36397		−0.36397	70°	5.67128	−5.67128
40°	0.46631		−0.46631	80°	11.43005	−11.43005
30°	0.57735		−0.57735	South pole	∞	∞
20°	0.70021		−0.70021			
10°	0.83910		−0.83910			
0°	1.00000		−1.00000			
10°	1.19175		−1.19175			
20°	1.42815		−1.42815			

$H = \infty$

Meridians are straight lines through the center with equal angles between them.

Appendix G

Lettering Magnification Tables

Tables 31–37 provide equivalent lettering sizes for projected maps that are magnified from 2 to 15 times their original size and are viewed at various distances from a screen. Equivalent sizes are expressed to the nearest even or common point size in the smaller ranges, with some clear intermediates noted, and in the larger sizes they are approximate to the nearest even or common point size.

The tables are used by permission of *Surveying and Mapping*, in which they originally appeared.

Notes: (1) Approximate equivalent letter heights *in inches* of point sizes appear in Table 11, Article 123. (2) For magnifications intermediate to those shown in the tables the data may be determined for all practical purposes by a linear interpolation.

TABLE 31.   LINEAR MAGNIFICATION, 2.

(Blank spaces indicate nonlegibility.)

Point size on original	Approximate equivalent size in points viewed at distance (feet) from screen									
	10	20	30	40	50	60	70	80	90	100
6										
8										
10										
12	3									
14	4									
16	4–5									
18	5									
24	7	4								
30	9	4–5	3							
36	10	5	4							

TABLE 32. LINEAR MAGNIFICATION, 3.

(Blank spaces indicate nonlegibility.)

Point size on original	Approximate equivalent size in points viewed at distance (feet) from screen									
	10	20	30	40	50	60	70	80	90	100
6										
8	3									
10	4–5									
12	5									
14	6	3								
16	7	4								
18	8	4–5								
24	10	5	4							
30	12	6	4–5	3–4						
36	16	8	5	4	3					

TABLE 33. LINEAR MAGNIFICATION, 4.

(Blank spaces indicate nonlegibility.)

Point size on original	Approximate equivalent size in points viewed at distance (feet) from screen									
	10	20	30	40	50	60	70	80	90	100
6	3									
8	4–5									
10	6	3								
12	7	4								
14	8	4–5								
16	9	4–5	3							
18	10	5	4							
24	14	7	4–5	3–4						
30	18	9	6	4–5	3–4	3				
36	22	11	8	5–6	4–5	4	3			

TABLE 34. LINEAR MAGNIFICATION, 6.

(Blank spaces indicate nonlegibility.)

Point size on original	Approximate equivalent size in points viewed at distance (feet) from screen									
	10	20	30	40	50	60	70	80	90	100
6	5									
8	7	4								
10	9	4–5	3							
12	10	5	4							
14	12	6	4–5	3						
16	14	7	4–5	3–4						
18	16	8	5	4	3					
24	22	11	8	5–6	4–5	4	3			
30	28	14	9	7	5–6	4–5	4	3		
36	33	16	10	8	6	5–6	5	4	3–4	3

TABLE 35. LINEAR MAGNIFICATION, 9.

(Blank spaces indicate nonlegibility.)

Point size on original	Approximate equivalent size in points viewed at distance (feet) from screen									
	10	20	30	40	50	60	70	80	90	100
6	8	4–5	3							
8	10	5	4							
10	12	6	4–5	3–4						
12	16	8	5	4	3					
14	18	9	6	5	4	3				
16	22	11	8	5–6	4–5	4	3			
18	24	12	8	6	5	4	3–4	3		
24	32	16	10	8	6	5–6	5	4	3–4	3
30	42	21	14	11	9	7	6	5–6	5	4–5
36	48	24	16	12	10	8	7	6	5–6	5

Appendix G

TABLE 36. LINEAR MAGNIFICATION, 12.

(Blank spaces indicate nonlegibility.)

Point size on original	Approximate equivalent size in points viewed at distance (feet) from screen									
	10	20	30	40	50	60	70	80	90	100
6	10	5	4							
8	14	7	4–5	3–4						
10	18	9	6	4–5	3–4	3				
12	22	11	8	5–6	4–5	4	3			
14	24	12	8	6	5	4	3–4	3		
16	30	14	10	8	6	5	4	3–4		
18	32	16	10	8	6	5–6	5	4	3–4	3
24	42	21	14	11	9	7	6	5–6	5	4–5
30	54	27	18	14	12	9	8	7	6	5–6
36	68	34	24	16	13	11	9	8	7	6

TABLE 37. LINEAR MAGNIFICATION, 15.

(Blank spaces indicate nonlegibility.)

Point size on original	Approximate equivalent size in points viewed at distance (feet) from screen									
	10	20	30	40	50	60	70	80	90	100
6	13	6–7	4–5	3						
8	18	9	6	4–5	3–4	3				
10	24	12	8	6	5	4	3			
12	28	14	9	7	5–6	4–5	4	3		
14	32	16	10	8	6	5	4–5	4	3–4	3
16	36	18	12	9	8	6	5	4–5	4	3–4
18	42	21	14	11	9	7	6	5–6	5	4–5
24	54	27	18	14	12	9	8	7	6	5–6
30	68	34	23	17	13	12	10	9	8	7
36	80	40	27	20	16	14	12	10	9	8

Appendix H

Estimating Densities of Fractional Areas

The table below, devised by John K. Wright, enables one to solve without multiplication or division the fundamental equation required to estimate densities of fractional areas referred to in Article 147. The explanation and tables are here presented by permission of *The Geographical Review*, published by the American Geographical Society of New York.

The basic equation is

$$D_n = \frac{D}{1 - a_m} - \frac{D_m a_m}{1 - a_m}$$

in which D_n = the density in area n.

D = average density of the area as a whole (number of units ÷ area).

D_m = estimated density in part m of area.

a_m = the fraction (0.1 to 0.9) of the total area comprised in m.

$1 - a_m$ = the fraction (0.1 to 0.9) of the total area comprised in n.

Values of $\dfrac{D}{1 - a_m}$ and $\dfrac{D_m a_m}{1 - a_m}$ may be extracted from the table as follows. The table is entered at the top with a_m and entered at the side with D or D_m as arguments. When D is the argument, the left-hand column under the particular value of a_m gives values of $\dfrac{D}{1 - a_m}$. When D_m is the argument, the right-hand column under the particular value of a_m gives values of $\dfrac{D_m a_m}{1 - a_m}$.

In order to obtain D_n, subtract the value obtained from entering the table with D_m as argument from the value obtained from entering the table with D as argument. (If this value is a minus quantity, then the value of D_m is too large to be consistent with the values of D and of a_m.)

For example: $D = 100$, $D_m = 10$, $a_m = 0.8$. From row 100 and the left-hand column under 0.8 extract value 500; from row 10 and the right-hand column under 0.8 extract value 40; $500 - 40 = 460 = D_n$.

TABLE 38. TABULAR AID TO CONSISTENCY IN ESTIMATING DENSITIES OF POPULATION.

a_m

D or D_m	0.9 $D_m a_m$, $1-a_m$	0.9 D, $1-a_m$	0.8 $D_m a_m$, $1-a_m$	0.8 D, $1-a_m$	0.7 $D_m a_m$, $1-a_m$	0.7 D, $1-a_m$	0.6 $D_m a_m$, $1-a_m$	0.6 D, $1-a_m$	0.5 $D_m a_m$, $1-a_m$	0.5 D, $1-a_m$	0.4 $D_m a_m$, $1-a_m$	0.4 D, $1-a_m$	0.3 $D_m a_m$, $1-a_m$	0.3 D, $1-a_m$	0.2 $D_m a_m$, $1-a_m$	0.2 D, $1-a_m$	0.1 $D_m a_m$, $1-a_m$	0.1 D, $1-a_m$	D or D_m
1	9	10	4	5	2.3	3	1.5	2	1	2	0.7	2	0.4	1	0.3	1	0.1	1	1
2	18	20	8	10	4.7	7	3.0	5	2	4	1.3	3	0.9	3	0.5	3	0.2	2	2
3	27	30	12	15	7.0	10	4.5	7	3	6	2.0	5	1.3	4	0.8	4	0.3	3	3
4	36	40	16	20	9.3	13	6.0	10	4	8	2.7	7	1.8	6	1.0	5	0.4	4	4
5	45	50	20	25	11.7	17	7.5	12	5	10	3.3	8	2.2	7	1.3	6	0.6	5	5
6	54	60	24	30	14.0	20	9.0	15	6	12	4.0	10	2.7	9	1.5	8	0.7	6	6
7	63	70	28	35	16.3	23	10.5	17	7	14	4.7	12	3.1	10	1.8	9	0.8	7	7
8	72	80	32	40	18.6	27	12.0	20	8	16	5.3	13	3.6	12	2.0	10	0.9	8	8
9	81	90	36	45	21.0	30	13.5	22	9	18	6.0	15	4.0	13	2.3	11	1.0	9	9
10	90	100	40	50	23.3	33	15.0	25	10	20	6.7	17	4.4	14	2.5	13	1.1	11	10
11	99	110	44	55	25.6	37	16.5	27	11	22	7.3	18	4.9	16	2.8	14	1.2	12	11
12	108	120	48	60	28.0	40	18.0	30	12	24	8.0	20	5.3	17	3.0	15	1.3	13	12
13	117	130	52	65	30.3	43	19.5	32	13	26	8.7	22	5.8	19	3.3	16	1.4	14	13
14	126	140	56	70	32.6	47	21.0	35	14	28	9.3	23	6.2	20	3.5	18	1.6	16	14
15	135	150	60	75	35.0	50	22.5	37	15	30	10.0	25	6.7	22	3.8	19	1.7	17	15
16	144	160	64	80	37.3	53	24.0	40	16	32	10.7	27	7.1	23	4.0	20	1.8	18	16
17	153	170	68	85	39.6	57	25.5	42	17	34	11.3	28	7.5	24	4.3	21	1.9	19	17
18	162	180	72	90	41.9	60	27.0	45	18	36	12.0	30	8.0	26	4.5	23	2.0	20	18
19	171	190	76	95	44.3	63	28.5	47	19	38	12.7	32	8.4	27	4.8	24	2.1	21	19
20	180	200	80	100	46.6	67	30.0	50	20	40	13.3	33	8.9	29	5.0	25	2.2	22	20
21	189	210	84	105	48.9	70	31.5	52	21	42	14.0	35	9.3	30	5.3	26	2.3	23	21
22	198	220	88	110	51.3	73	33.0	55	22	44	14.7	37	9.8	32	5.5	28	2.4	24	22
23	207	230	92	115	53.6	77	34.5	57	23	46	15.3	38	10.2	33	5.8	29	2.6	26	23
24	216	240	96	120	55.9	80	36.0	60	24	48	16.0	40	10.7	35	6.0	30	2.7	27	24
25	225	250	100	125	58.3	83	37.5	62	25	50	16.7	42	11.1	36	6.3	31	2.8	28	25
26	234	260	104	130	60.6	87	39.0	65	26	52	17.3	43	11.5	37	6.5	33	2.9	29	26
27	243	270	108	135	62.9	90	40.5	67	27	54	18.0	45	12.0	39	6.8	34	3.0	30	27
28	252	280	112	140	65.2	93	42.0	70	28	56	18.6	46	12.4	40	7.0	35	3.1	31	28
29	261	290	116	145	67.6	97	43.5	72	29	58	19.3	48	12.9	42	7.3	36	3.2	32	29
30	270	300	120	150	69.9	100	45.0	75	30	60	20.0	50	13.3	43	7.5	38	3.3	33	30
31	279	310	124	155	72.2	103	46.5	77	31	62	20.6	51	13.8	45	7.8	39	3.4	34	31
32	288	320	128	160	74.6	107	48.0	80	32	64	21.3	53	14.2	46	8.0	40	3.6	36	32
33	297	330	132	165	76.9	110	49.5	82	33	66	22.0	55	14.7	48	8.3	41	3.7	37	33
34	306	340	136	170	79.2	113	51.0	85	34	68	22.6	56	15.1	49	8.5	43	3.8	38	34
35	315	350	140	175	81.6	117	52.5	87	35	70	23.3	58	15.5	50	8.8	44	3.9	39	35
36	324	360	144	180	83.9	120	54.0	90	36	72	24.0	60	16.0	52	9.0	45	4.0	40	36
37	333	370	148	185	86.2	123	55.5	92	37	74	24.6	61	16.4	53	9.3	46	4.1	41	37
38	342	380	152	190	88.5	127	57.0	95	38	76	25.3	63	16.9	55	9.5	48	4.2	42	38
39	351	390	156	195	90.9	130	58.5	97	39	78	26.0	65	17.3	56	9.8	49	4.3	43	39
40	360	400	160	200	93.2	133	60.0	100	40	80	26.6	66	17.8	58	10.0	50	4.4	44	40
41	369	410	164	205	95.5	137	61.5	102	41	82	27.3	68	18.2	59	10.3	51	4.6	46	41
42	378	420	168	210	97.9	140	63.0	105	42	84	28.0	70	18.6	60	10.5	53	4.7	47	42
43	387	430	172	215	100.2	143	64.5	107	43	86	28.6	71	19.1	62	10.8	54	4.8	48	43
44	396	440	176	220	102.5	147	66.0	110	44	88	29.3	73	19.5	63	11.0	55	4.9	49	44
45	405	450	180	225	104.9	150	67.5	112	45	90	30.0	75	20.0	65	11.3	56	5.0	50	45
46	414	460	184	230	107.2	153	69.0	115	46	92	30.6	76	20.4	66	11.5	58	5.1	51	46
47	423	470	188	235	109.5	157	70.5	117	47	94	31.3	78	20.9	68	11.8	59	5.2	52	47
48	432	480	192	240	111.8	160	72.0	120	48	96	32.0	80	21.3	69	12.0	60	5.3	53	48
49	441	490	196	245	114.2	163	73.5	122	49	98	32.6	81	21.8	71	12.3	61	5.4	54	49

50	450	500	200	250	116.5	167	75.0	125	50	100	33.3	83	22.2	72	12.5	63	5.6	56	50
51	459	510	204	255	118.8	170	76.5	127	51	102	34.0	85	22.6	73	12.8	64	5.7	57	51
52	468	520	208	260	121.2	173	78.0	130	52	104	34.6	86	23.1	75	13.0	65	5.8	58	52
53	477	530	212	265	123.5	177	79.5	132	53	106	35.3	88	23.5	76	13.3	66	5.9	59	53
54	486	540	216	270	125.8	180	81.0	135	54	108	36.0	90	24.0	78	13.5	68	6.0	60	54
55	495	550	220	275	128.2	183	82.5	137	55	110	36.6	91	24.4	79	13.8	69	6.1	61	55
56	504	560	224	280	130.5	187	84.0	140	56	112	37.3	93	24.9	81	14.0	70	6.2	62	56
57	513	570	228	285	132.8	190	85.5	142	57	114	38.0	95	25.3	82	14.3	71	6.3	63	57
58	522	580	232	290	135.1	193	87.0	145	58	116	38.6	96	25.8	84	14.5	73	6.4	64	58
59	531	590	236	295	137.5	197	88.5	147	59	118	39.3	98	26.2	85	14.8	74	6.6	66	59
60	540	600	240	300	139.8	200	90.0	150	60	120	40.0	100	26.6	86	15.0	75	6.7	67	60
61	549	610	244	305	142.1	203	91.5	152	61	122	40.6	101	27.1	88	15.3	76	6.8	68	61
62	558	620	248	310	144.5	207	93.0	155	62	124	41.3	103	27.5	89	15.5	78	6.9	69	62
63	567	630	252	315	146.8	210	94.5	157	63	126	42.0	105	28.0	91	15.8	79	7.0	70	63
64	576	640	256	320	149.1	213	96.0	160	64	128	42.6	106	28.4	92	16.0	80	7.1	71	64
65	585	650	260	325	151.5	217	97.5	162	65	130	43.3	108	28.9	94	16.3	81	7.2	72	65
66	594	660	264	330	153.8	220	99.0	165	66	132	44.0	110	29.3	95	16.5	83	7.3	73	66
67	603	670	268	335	156.1	223	100.5	167	67	134	44.6	111	29.7	96	16.8	84	7.4	74	67
68	612	680	272	340	158.4	227	102.0	170	68	136	45.3	113	30.2	98	17.0	85	7.6	76	68
69	621	690	276	345	160.8	230	103.5	172	69	138	46.0	115	30.6	99	17.3	86	7.7	77	69
70	630	700	280	350	163.1	233	105.0	175	70	140	46.6	116	31.1	101	17.5	88	7.8	78	70
71	639	710	284	355	165.4	237	106.5	177	71	142	47.3	118	31.5	102	17.8	89	7.9	79	71
72	648	720	288	360	167.8	240	108.0	180	72	144	48.0	120	32.0	104	18.0	90	8.0	80	72
73	657	730	292	365	170.1	243	109.5	182	73	146	48.6	121	32.4	105	18.3	91	8.1	81	73
74	666	740	296	370	172.4	247	111.0	185	74	148	49.3	123	32.9	107	18.5	93	8.2	82	74
75	675	750	300	375	174.8	250	112.5	187	75	150	50.0	125	33.3	108	18.8	94	8.3	83	75
76	684	760	304	380	177.1	253	114.0	190	76	152	50.6	126	33.7	109	19.0	95	8.4	84	76
77	693	770	308	385	179.4	257	115.5	192	77	154	51.3	128	34.2	111	19.3	96	8.6	86	77
78	702	780	312	390	181.7	260	117.0	195	78	156	51.9	129	34.6	112	19.5	98	8.7	87	78
79	711	790	316	395	184.1	263	118.5	197	79	158	52.6	131	35.1	114	19.8	99	8.8	88	79
80	720	800	320	400	186.4	267	120.0	200	80	160	53.3	133	35.5	115	20.0	100	8.9	89	80
81	729	810	324	405	188.7	270	121.5	202	81	162	53.9	134	36.0	117	20.3	101	9.0	90	81
82	738	820	328	410	191.1	273	123.0	205	82	164	54.6	136	36.4	118	20.5	103	9.1	91	82
83	747	830	332	415	193.4	277	124.5	207	83	166	55.3	138	36.9	120	20.8	104	9.2	92	83
84	756	840	336	420	195.7	280	126.0	210	84	168	55.9	139	37.3	121	21.0	105	9.3	93	84
85	765	850	340	425	198.1	283	127.5	212	85	170	56.6	141	37.7	122	21.3	106	9.4	94	85
86	774	860	344	430	200.4	287	129.0	215	86	172	57.3	143	38.2	124	21.5	108	9.6	96	86
87	783	870	348	435	202.7	290	130.5	217	87	174	57.9	144	38.6	125	21.8	109	9.7	97	87
88	792	880	352	440	205.0	293	132.0	220	88	176	58.6	146	39.1	127	22.0	110	9.8	98	88
89	801	890	356	445	207.4	297	133.5	222	89	178	59.3	148	39.5	128	22.3	111	9.9	99	89
90	810	900	360	450	209.7	300	135.0	225	90	180	59.9	149	40.0	130	22.5	113	10.1	100	90
91	819	910	364	455	212.0	303	136.5	227	91	182	60.6	151	40.4	131	22.8	114	10.2	101	91
92	828	920	368	460	214.4	307	138.0	230	92	184	61.3	153	40.8	132	23.0	115	10.3	102	92
93	837	930	372	465	216.7	310	139.5	232	93	186	61.9	154	41.3	134	23.3	116	10.4	103	93
94	846	940	376	470	219.0	313	141.0	235	94	188	62.6	156	41.7	135	23.5	118	10.5	104	94
95	855	950	380	475	221.4	317	142.5	237	95	190	63.3	158	42.2	137	23.8	119	10.7	105	95
96	864	960	384	480	223.7	320	144.0	240	96	192	63.9	159	42.6	138	24.0	120	10.8	107	96
97	873	970	388	485	226.0	323	145.5	242	97	194	64.6	161	43.1	140	24.3	121	10.9	108	97
98	882	980	392	490	228.3	327	147.0	245	98	196	65.3	163	43.5	141	24.5	123	11.0	109	98
99	891	990	396	495	230.7	330	148.5	247	99	198	65.9	164	44.0	143	24.8	124	11.0	110	99
100	900	1 000	400	500	233.0	333	150.0	250	100	200	66.6	166	44.4	144	25.0	125	11.1	111	100

Bibliography

Selected Literature of Generally Available Sources Useful for Additional Readings

The following list includes references to only those items which are in English, and which are readily available or easily procured. They will be found useful for reference or for further reading in the topics under which they have been included.

General

C. H. Deetz, "Cartography," U.S. Coast and Geodetic Survey *Special Publication 205*, Washington, D. C., 1936.

David Greenhood, *Down to Earth*, Holiday House, New York, 1951.

Erwin Raisz, *General Cartography*, 2nd Ed., McGraw-Hill Book Co., New York, 1948.

World Cartography, Vol. 1, United Nations, New York, 1951 (available from Columbia University Press).

Historical Background

Lloyd A. Brown, *The Story of Maps*, Little, Brown & Co., Boston, 1949.

H. G. Fordham, *Maps, Their History, Characteristics and Uses*, Cambridge University Press, Cambridge, England, 1943.

W. W. Jervis, *The World in Maps*, Oxford University Press, New York, 1938.

M. Proudfoot, "The Measurement of Geographic Area," Bureau of the Census, Washington, D. C., 1946.

Erwin Raisz, *General Cartography*.

John K. Wright, "Highlights in American Cartography, 1939–1949," *Compte rendu du XVIe congrès international de géographie*, Lisbon, 1949.

Coordinate Systems and Projections

W. G. V. Balchin, "The Representation of True to Scale Linear Values on Map Projections," *Geography*, Vol. 36, 1951.

Wellman Chamberlin, *The Round Earth on Flat Paper*, The National Geographic Society, Washington, D. C., 1947.

C. H. Deetz and O. S. Adams, "Elements of Map Projection," U.S. Coast and Geodetic Survey *Special Publication 68*, Washington, D. C. (latest edition available).

Irving Fisher and O. M. Miller, *World Maps and Globes*, Essential Books, New York, 1944.

Wm. Garnett, *A Little Book on Map Projections*, Philip and Son, London, 1921.

A. R. Hinks, *Map Projections*, Cambridge University Press, Cambridge, England (latest edition available).

H. A. Hoffmeister, *Construction of Map Projections*, McKnight & McKnight, Bloomington, Ill., 1946.

G. P. Kellaway, *Map Projections*, 2nd Ed., Meuthen & Co., London, and E. P. Dutton & Co., New York, 1949.

F. J. Marschner, "Structural Properties of Medium and Small Scale Maps," *Annals of the Association of American Geographers*, Vol. XXXIV, 1944.

O. M. Miller, "Notes on Cylindrical Map Projections," *The Geographical Review*, Vol. 32, 1942.

Erwin Raisz, *General Cartography*.

Arthur H. Robinson, "An Analytical Approach to Map Projections," *Annals of the Association of American Geographers*, Vol. XXXIX, 1949.

Arthur H. Robinson, "The Use of Deformational Data in Evaluating Map Projections," *Annals of the Association of American Geographers*, Vol. XLI, 1951.

J. A. Steers, *An Introduction to the Study of Map Projections*, University of London Press, London, 1937.

J. Q. Stewart, "The Use and Abuse of Map Projections," *The Geographical Review*, Vol. 33, 1943.

Techniques and Design

Faber Birren, *The Story of Color*, The Crimson Press, Westport, Conn., 1941.

S. W. Boggs, "Cartohypnosis," *Scientific Monthly,* Vol. 64, 1947.

E. De Lopatecki, *Advertising Layout and Typography,* The Ronald Press, New York, 1935.

Max Eckert, "On the Nature of Maps and Map Logic," *Bulletin of the American Geographical Society,* Vol. 40, 1908 (translated by W. L. G. Joerg).

Ralph M. Evans, *An Introduction to Color,* John Wiley & Sons, New York, 1948.

Higgins Ink Company, *Techniques,* 5th Ed., Brooklyn, N. Y., 1948.

International Printing Ink Corporation, *Three Monographs on Color,* New York, 1935.

L. H. Joachim (editor), *Seventh Production Yearbook, The Reference Manual of the Graphic Arts,* Colton Press, New York, 1941.

L. O. Quam, "The Use of Maps in Propaganda," *Journal of Geography,* Vol. 42, 1943.

Arthur H. Robinson, *The Look of Maps, An Examination of Cartographic Design,* University of Wisconsin Press, Madison, Wisc., 1952.

Walter Sargent, *The Enjoyment and Use of Color,* Charles Scribner's Sons, Chicago, 1923.

Hans Soffner, "War on the Visual Front; Use of Maps, Charts, and Diagrams for Purposes of Propaganda," *American Scholar,* Vol. 11, 1942.

U.S. Government Printing Office, *Typography and Design,* Washington, D. C., 1951.

John K. Wright, "Map Makers Are Human. Comments on the Subjective in Maps," *The Geographical Review,* Vol. 32, 1942.

Lettering and Type

Merideth F. Burrill, "U.S. Board on Geographical Names," *Surveying and Mapping,* Vol. 6, 1946.

Ross F. George, *Speedball Text Book,* Hunt Pen Co., Camden, N. J., 1948.

Higgins Ink Company, *Lettering,* 2nd Ed., Brooklyn, N. Y., 1949.

U.S. Government Printing Office, *Typography and Design.*

Daniel B. Updike, *Printing Types, Their History, Forms, and Use; a Study in Survivals,* Harvard University Press, Cambridge, Mass., 1922.

J. G. Withycombe, "Lettering on Maps," *Geographical Journal,* Vol. 73, 1929.

Kinds of Maps and Distribution Mapping

John W. Alexander and George A. Zahorchak, "Population Density Maps of the United States: Techniques and Patterns," *The Geographical Review,* Vol. 33, 1943.

H. J. Allcock and J. R. Jones, *The Nomogram,* Pitman & Sons, London, 1938.

J. A. Barnes and A. H. Robinson, "A New Method for the Representation of Dispersed Rural Population," *The Geographical Review,* Vol. 30, 1940.

T. W. Birch, *Maps, Topographical and Statistical,* Oxford University Press, London, 1949.

S. W. Boggs, "Mapping the Changing World: Suggested Developments in Maps," *Annals of the Association of American Geographers,* Vol. XXXI, 1941.

Sten DeGeer, "A Map of the Distribution of Population in Sweden: Method of Preparation and General Results," *The Geographical Review,* Vol. 12, 1922.

Wellington D. Jones, "Ratios and Isopleth Maps in Regional Investigation of Agricultural Land Occupance," *Annals of the Association of American Geographers,* Vol. XX, 1930.

R. R. Lutz, *Graphic Presentation Simplified,* Funk and Wagnalls Co., New York, 1949.

J. Ross Mackay, "Dotting the Dot Map," *Surveying and Mapping,* Vol. 9, 1949.

J. Ross Mackay, "Some Problems and Techniques in Isopleth Mapping," *Economic Geography,* Vol. 27, 1951.

F. J. Marschner, "Maps and a Mapping Program for the United States," *Annals of the Association of American Geographers,* Vol. XXXIII, 1943.

E. Mather, "A Linear Distance Map of Farm Population in the United States," *Annals of the Association of American Geographers,* Vol. XXXIV, 1944.

Erwin Raisz, "The Rectangular Statistical Diagram," *The Geographical Review,* Vol. 24, 1934.

Erwin Raisz, "Landform, Landscape, Land-Use and Land-Type Maps," *Journal of Geography,* 1946.

Erwin Raisz, *General Cartography.*

E. C. Wilcox and W. H. Ebling, "Presentation of Agricultural Data in the States," *Journal of Farm Economics,* Vol. 31, 1949.

John K. Wright, "A Method of Mapping Densities of Population with Cape Cod as an Example," *The Geographical Review,* Vol. 26, 1936.

John K. Wright, "A Proposed Atlas of Diseases, Appendix I, Cartographic Considerations," *The Geographical Review,* Vol. 34, 1944.

John K. Wright, "The Terminology of Certain Map Symbols," *The Geographical Review,* Vol. 34, 1944.

Representing the Terrain

R. B. Batchelder, "Application of Two Relative Relief Techniques to an Area of Diverse Landforms: A Comparative Study," *Surveying and Mapping,* Vol. 10, 1950.

Preston E. James, "On the Treatment of Surface Features in Regional Studies," *Annals of the Association of American Geographers,* Vol. XXVII, 1937.

Capt. H. G. Lyons, "Relief in Cartography," *Geographical Journal,* Vol. 43, 1914.

J. E. Mundine and Hal Shelton, "Visual Topography," *Photogrammetric Engineering,* 1945.

Erwin Raisz, "The Physiographic Method of Representing Scenery on Maps," *The Geographical Review,* Vol. 21, 1931.

Erwin Raisz, *General Cartography.*

Arthur H. Robinson, "A Method for Producing Shaded Relief from Areal Slope Data," *Annals of the Association of American Geographers,* Vol. 36, 1946.

Eugene Romer, "Hachure in Recent Cartography," *Report of the Proceedings of the International Geographical Congress of Cambridge, 1928,* Cambridge University Press, Cambridge, England, 1930.

Guy-Harold Smith, "The Relative Relief of Ohio," *The Geographical Review,* Vol. 25, 1935.

K. Tanaka, "The Orthographical Relief Method of Representing Hill Features on a Topographical Map," *Geographical Journal,* Vol. 79, 1932.

K. Tanaka, "The Relief Contour Method of Representing Topography on Maps," *The Geographical Review,* Vol. 40, 1950.

Government Publications

Branches of the government have issued useful publications concerning many aspects of cartography. Particularly helpful are those issued by the U.S. Coast and Geodetic Survey relating to projections and the Department of the Army relating to topographic mapping and drafting, map reading, and map reproduction.

Index